MAYFLIES

THE ANGLER, AND

THE TROUT

MAYFLIES, THE ANGLER, AND THE TROUT

Fred L. Arbona, Jr.

Introduction by Ernest Schwiebert
Foreword by Carl Richards
Photographs and Technical Drawings by the Author
Other Drawings by Jim Marc
Fly Tying Instructions by Mike Lawson

NICK LYONS BOOKS

Lyons & Burford *Publishers*

To my father, Fred L. Arbona, Sr.,
who took me on my first fly fishing trip
on my thirteenth birthday,
and ever since has been my companion
in the pursuit of trout; and to all
fly fishermen dedicated to the
preservation of this most noble sport.

Library of Congress Cataloging-in-Publication Data

Arbona, Fred L.
    Mayflies, the angler, and the trout.

    Bibliography: P.
    Includes index.
    1. Trout fishing. 2. Mayflies. 3. Fly tying.
4. Fly fishing. 5 Mayflies—Identification.
I. Title
SH687.A69   1989   799.1'7   88-37281
ISBN 1-55821-032-6

Designed by Joyce C. Weston

Printed in the United States of America

Preface to the 1989 Edition

The Colorado is a wild and muddy river, at least until it is stopped by the massive walls of Glen Canyon Dam near the Arizona-Utah border. The dam creates Lake Powell, which can be excellent for bass and stripers; and the water that comes out of the bottom of the dam is crystal-clear and cold, supporting one of the best rainbow fisheries in the country. The canyon walls flanking the river are marbled and truly magnificent, and this is one of the few places I know where even if the fishing is slow, that really doesn't matter.

The fishing, however, is never slow. The entire sixteen-mile stretch of the Colorado from Glen Canyon Dam to Lee's Ferry is one of short riffles then mile-long pools. It is filled with *very* large trout.

These trout have three main alternatives for dinner: freshwater shrimp, midges, or such small mayflies as the *Baetis*.

Since the riffles are heavily fished, the best trout often drop down to feed quietly in the mile-long flats. Few fly fishers tangle with the tougher trout found in these smooth waters; most—for some bewildering reason—prefer to be packed like sardines in the short riffles. Thus most of the water is left for me, or for anglers who know how to match the hatch in waters where trout get ample opportunity to look over your offering carefully.

A few weeks ago I found myself fishing to some tough trout at Lee's Ferry, during a sparse *Baetis* hatch. An unusually large fish of perhaps eight pounds was slowly cruising the dead-still backwaters upstream from one of my favorite stretches. I wanted him badly so I approached cautiously and crouched quite low; now that I'm over forty, that hurt. Then I knelt down and waited until he cruised within thirty feet before making the first cast. First casts are rarely perfect; but this one was good enough to catch his interest—and earn a refusal.

What seemed like it would be a quick deal became a drawn-out game of cat and mouse—me trying to understand what he was feeding on and he slowly cruising within an inch of my fly, before continuing his search for safer food. After half an hour of such frustration, I started to get the feeling that I had been in this fishing scenario before—a good fish rising to what appeared as "invisible flies." The cause was usually a *Baetis* hatch, the solution an emerger pattern like a floating nymph.

I really hate to use tiny floating nymphs because, first, I can't see them on the water; second, I still have a hard time accepting the fact that trout are really looking for a minute nymph imitation on the surface film with a little piece of dubbing on top of it, giving them the impression it is an emerging dun. Let's be serious! Yet floating nymphs have saved the day a hundred times for me when nothing else would work. Nearly twenty years ago, Mike Lawson and I couldn't touch a trout one day without a floating nymph. That eight-pound rainbow at Lee's Ferry took the floating nymph, without hesitation, the instant he saw it.

Much has changed since I wrote *Mayflies, the Angler, and the Trout*. I remember those carefree college summers in Montana with Zulu, my black lab, fishing and researching. Those were the days before graphite rods, the new leaders, and before hoards of fly fishermen had even heard of, let alone fished, the Henry's Fork. But though the equipment we use has changed, and we now fish waters we did not know existed then, the insects in our streams have remained the same—and, more importantly, so have the trout and how they depend upon and react to those insects. Trout could care less whether today's anglers are fishing with rods made of graphite or boron, or standing in new neoprene waders. They have their old preoccupations: eating and surviving. To them, nothing is new.

I've always thought of fly fishermen as "interceptors,"

especially during a hatch when they slip their imitation in among the naturals, hoping a trout will take it for the real thing. As long as there are hatches left in our streams, the game of "interception" will continue and the information in a book like this will remain as applicable twenty years from now as it was ten years ago.

Mayflies, the Angler, and the Trout took five years of my life to research and write—and kept me broke for years after I finished college. But researching it took me to all the great rivers in the United States, during their best years; fishing the hatches allowed me to enjoy some great fishing; and writing this book taught me a discipline of mind that has made life a lot easier today. I wrote this book to share knowledge I had gained, that had allowed me to enjoy fly fishing so much more. Thousands of serious fly fishermen have told me it has helped them enjoy their sport more, too—and thus I

am especially happy to see this book go into a new paperback edition, hopefully to make more new friends.

After I hooked that huge trout at Lee's Ferry, off to the races we went! He made it to the fast riffle below without much effort, and made good use of my backing. But I caught up with him in the next big pool, he was somewhat tired by then, and I finally managed to bring him close to shore.

I was grateful for the new leader material—but then the fly slipped off when the great fish was hardly five feet away, leaving me exhausted.

Some things never do change, and in many respects that makes me very glad.

FRED ARBONA
Prescott, Arizona
December 1988

Contents

Acknowledgments

DURING the five years that it took to develop and finally complete this work, I received much needed assistance from many individuals who found it in their unselfish nature to encourage me, assist in the collection of naturals, and even become personally involved in the outcome of *Mayflies, the Angler, and the Trout.*

I remain indebted to Dr. C. O. Berg, Dr. J. Pechuman (Curator of the Cornell University Insect Collection), and Dr. Neil Lamb (Armed Forces Pest Control Board) for their instructions and direction on the scientific classification of mayflies and for providing laboratory facilities during my years at Cornell University. Dr. George Roemhild of the University of Montana gave me valuable data on the distribution of western mayfly fauna, and Dr. Hall Daily and Dr. Vincent Resh of the University of California at Berkeley made their facilities and records available during my research of the western states.

Many personal fishing companions contributed collections from trout streams in different areas of the country and made it possible for me to be in "two places at once" during certain years. I take pleasure in thanking them now. They are listed, with the focus of their research indicated in parentheses, as follows: Brad Jackson (California), Larry Schoenike (Idaho, Colorado, and Wisconsin), Mike Kimball (Armstrong Creek, Montana, and Delaware River, New York), Phelps Laszlo (New Hampshire and Vermont), and lastly, Gary La Fontaine (hatches local to Deer Lodge, Montana).

Technical advice from certain individuals resulted in a marked improvement in the presentation of information. Ernest Schwiebert provided encouragement and useful direction during my search for a publisher; and Lefty Kreh and Dave Whitlock saved me valuable time in the photography and drawing of mayflies. Lastly, Jack Gartside provided all the humor during the most trying periods of the evolution of this book.

Introduction

ALMOST ten years ago, I had the privilege of writing the introduction when Nick Lyons issued a commemorative edition of Preston Jennings' *A Book of Trout Flies*, which had first been published thirty-five years earlier. His book is among the most important works of fly-fishing history, and writing its introduction was an act of personal homage to a writer who had been a boyhood idol.

Writing this introduction to *Mayflies, the Angler, and the Trout* is a privilege of another kind. Jennings needed little introduction from me or anyone else, and *A Book of Trout Flies* was a well-known title in fishing circles. But this new book is the work of a relatively little-known writer, Fred Arbona, and introducing his first book seems like a real introduction, as well as a privilege.

It has been several years in the writing, and its original material demonstrates still more years in the fishing. Arbona also brings to it the obvious disciplines of formal training in aquatic entomology, perhaps more than any other fishing writer with the exception of Moseley in England.

Arbona spent his early fishing years in a gypsy-like existence on trout water, first on the famous rivers of our Eastern mountains, and later on the principal streams of the Rocky Mountains. His fishing and fly-hatch work were known to many of the serious fishermen who make annual pilgrimages to the Yellowstone country. His studies of our Western rivers are often unique, based upon several entire seasons of observation astream, and include a full palette of aquatic species not found elsewhere in our fly-fishing literature.

His work *Mayflies, the Angler, and the Trout* is a fresh book in a richly old tradition. Although many anglers are aware that the concept of matching the hatch has a considerable history, few understand that its roots lie with the *Treatyse of Fysshynge wyth an Angle* in fifteenth-century England.

Those beginnings included twelve fly patterns that were imitations of specific hatches. These same dressings appeared in several subsequent books before they were included in Walton's classic *The Compleat Angler* in 1653. Charles Cotton followed with the original imitative flies in his "Being Instructions How to Angle for Trout and Grayling in a Clear Stream," published with *The Compleat Angler* in 1676. Cotton's observations contained so much fresh material that he is considered the father of fly fishing. Later writers like Chetham, Saunders, and Brookes were also concerned with fly hatches, and with Cotton their works shaped fishing in the seventeenth century.

Charles Bowlker emerged during the fifty years that followed, when his classic *The Art of Angling* first appeared in 1747, and his writings dominated his entire century through the editions published later by his son, the famous Richard Bowlker.

George Scotcher and his slim little *Flyfisher's Legacy* included the first color plates of aquatic insects at the threshold of the nineteenth century. William Carroll covered the fly-hatches of the Scottish lowlands in his *Angler's Vade-Mecum*, published at Edinburgh in 1818. G.C. Bainbridge completed his *Fly-Fisher's Guide* in those same years, and these books are clearly important wellsprings of fly-fishing entomology.

Alfred Ronalds was a unique milestone with his *Fly-Fisher's Entomology* in 1836, and his work was the genesis of scientific taxonomy and precise color illustration in fishing books. Ronalds was a logical heir to more than 2,000 years of fly-fishing sport, and his discipline became the yardstick by which all subsequent books on aquatic hatches would be measured in the future.

Frederic Halford followed with a virtual shelf of fishing books, and his *Dry-Fly Entomology* extended our knowledge of British aquatic hatches in 1897. Halford was the historian and philosopher of the dry-fly method. Martin Moseley contributed his handbook entitled *The Dry-Fly Fisherman's Entomology* in 1920, and the unique J.W. Dunne added *Sunshine and the Dry Fly* four years later. These books were important facets of our entire theory and tradition, and their heritage has continued among recent writers, too.

J.R. Harris and his fine *Angler's Entomology* covered both British and Irish fly hatches, and offered excellent color photographs of the European species. His gallery of fly-hatch photography was completed in his comprehensive British book *Trout-Fly Recognition*, which John Goddard published in 1966.

Our American studies in stream entomology had their genesis in Louis Rhead's early work *American Trout-Stream Insects*, which described Catskill fishing in 1920. His work unfortunately made no attempt to identify his insect collections, and his illustrations of naturals and their imitations are little help, either. Our first serious book on stream entomology was Jennings' *Book of Trout Flies* fifteen years later, and its chapters covered our hatches from northern New Jersey to the swift rivers of the Adirondacks in New York.

Since its publication in 1935, its lexicon of fly hatches has steadily been augmented by a series of other American books on stream entomology. Charles Wetzel completed *Practical Fly Fishing* in 1943, and its chapters treated the aquatic insects of Pennsylvania. Arthur Flick first published his *Streamside Guide to Naturals and Their Imitations* only four years later, covering the hatches of the Catskills with the first color photographs of the naturals. Vincent Marinaro added his remarkable *Modern Dry-Fly Code* at midcentury, and although it did not expand our knowledge of fresh aquatic hatches, it was the beginning of a revolution in imitating them.

My own book *Matching the Hatch* first appeared in 1955, and its coverage of our American hatches included new species from the Middle West and Rocky Mountains. Doug Swisher and Carl Richards greatly expanded our knowledge of those regions when their *Selective Trout* was completed in 1971. Alfred Caucci and Robert Nastasi contributed an extensive catalogue of superb color photography on American aquatic insects in their book *Hatches*, which was published in 1975, and included a few species not encountered earlier in our fly-fishing literature.

The new book *Mayflies, the Angler, and the Trout* is a fresh benchmark in this remarkable tradition, and its author has included both fine color photography and a surprising cornucopia of fly hatches that will prove new even to expert fishermen.

Our American tradition is continuing to grow. British fishing circles took almost six centuries to codify the stream entomology in the British Isles, while our colleagues have busily identified and imitated many of the important hatches of an entire continent in the past fifty years. When my book *Nymphs* was published in 1973, I observed that our trout waters still held many secrets, and that our fly-fishing entomology remained far from complete. Those observations included a prediction that our young fishing writers would continue to identify and imitate our principal aquatic species, building an edifice of fresh knowledge brick-by-brick with their books.

Lee Wulff recently commented during a brief conversation in the Yellowstone that a revolution in American trout fishing has taken place since midcentury, and that we have evolved a generation of remarkable young anglers, thoroughly schooled in flies and fishing techniques and casting, and armed with a comprehensive knowledge of aquatic fly-life, all of which makes them better fishermen than we have seen before.

Our knowledge continues to expand with books of the discipline and importance of *Mayflies, the Angler, and the Trout*. Both Fred Arbona and his collaborator in the fly-dressing chapters, Michael Lawson, are unmistakably of that fresh generation.

Ernest Schwiebert
Princeton, New Jersey

Foreword

A BOOK like *Mayflies, the Angler, and the Trout* appears once in a decade, if we're lucky. Every ten years or so, a fly fishing book is written that is so important, it not only becomes an instant classic, but a standard reference to be kept at hand and used repeatedly. This one, by Fred L. Arbona, Jr., is destined to become such a book.

This book contains just about every scrap of knowledge relating to the trout's most important food source—mayflies. It takes the fisherman from the most basic knowledge of the hatch, through all the ramifications of fishing the hatches and spinner falls, to identifying mayflies *down to the species level.* Thus, it is a must for all levels of fishing expertise: from the complete beginner to the most polished expert.

The author is one of those rare individuals who is not only a very fine fisherman but is also an adept writer and an excellent scientist. He has learned the discipline of the science of entomology at Cornell University and has spent many summers camped on the banks of scores of North American trout streams throughout the country collecting and identifying their mayfly fauna.

I know Fred is an excellent fisherman because I remember an action-packed week spent with him on Henrys Fork of the Snake River in Idaho, fishing to very picky trout. I know he is a good writer because I remember spending an afternoon in The Last Chance Cafe looking over a great manuscript. I know Fred is a first-rate entomologist because I remember a whole series of days spent with him at the microscope keying out species of insects, when we could have been out casting to rising trout. This author does not rely on other entomologists to do his work for him; he does it himself, and he knows what he is doing. Only in that way can the fishing writer/entomologist really know what he is writing about at the deepest, most informative level.

This book has hundreds of illustrations, which are both beautiful and extremely useful. The color plates of insects have been taken in the field and are illuminated with *natural* lighting. These plates were photographed by the author and are especially helpful to the reader for identification purposes. Moreover, *Mayflies, the Angler, and the Trout* contains approximately 50 black and white photographs to show the type of waters where certain hatches are found, plus literally hundreds of painstakingly lined drawings to demonstrate the correlation among mayflies, the consequential need for comparatively few artificial patterns, and, at the same time, to offer the reader the option of determining naturals down to the species level!

Mayflies, the Angler, and the Trout opens with an explanation of the reasons why it really is necessary for the angler to become acquainted with the mayfly types found in our trout waters. This knowledge will enable him to become more successful at his chosen sport. Once the reader is aware of this important fact, the book explains how an angler only needs a handful of artificials that exactly imitates the vast majority of all mayfly species, thus reducing the number of fly patterns he must carry to effectively deceive selective trout. The author, working in connection with Mike Lawson (whom I consider one of the best professional fly tyers in the world), has come up with some new and innovative applications and imitations that are extremely successful.

The author then compares mayflies to other important aquatic insects that trout feed upon and explains the differences among them. The mayflies are also separated into their appropriate family or "type" level in the same sequence as they will be treated in the chapters that follow. This part of the book is for the neophyte fisherman who knows absolutely nothing about aquatic insects. It continues through more involved stages, until the latter part of the book can be designated for the "experts" expert. There is something in this tightly written book for everyone.

Chapter 3 explains the determining factors of seasonal and daily emergence and answers some questions that have long puzzled fly fishermen and entomologists alike. Why do mayflies get lighter in color as the summer progresses and then darker again as fall approaches? Why do mayflies of even the same species get smaller in size as the season progresses? These are questions long asked and, at long last, we have the answers to the phenomenon of seasonal variability among mayflies.

In Chapter 4, Fred takes us through the mechanics of presentation. The book could not have been considered complete without this vital section. Chapters 5 through 11 now introduce us to the major insect hatches at the family and then the species level. These are explained in easy-to-understand terms such as: the Sulphurs, Blue-Winged Olives, etc. The hatches are, of course, accompanied by their scientific names for accuracy for those who are, and wish to become, more aware of the precise language of entomology.

Appendix I contains the fly tying instructions for the most practical designs to be employed in tying the artificials for each specific type of mayfly. New designs are included based on streamside observations, and options are given for the tying of certain types. In all, five designs are included for the nymphal stage, five for the dry, and one for the spinner form. This section is done in association with master flytier, Mike Lawson.

Appendix II is the part of *Mayflies* that really excites me. It deals with insect identification, down to the species level, and even the beginner can perform the often simple mechanics of identifying the stages and species of mayflies. This section also includes suggestions for the best methods of collecting and preserving specimens, so that anyone is enabled to do his *own* research. More and more fly fishermen are delving deeper into this fascinating aspect of our sport. Therefore, this is a very important and much needed addition to the literature.

Many years of hard work and basic research have gone into this volume and it shows! It promises to be one of those "once in every ten years" works that is vital to trout fishermen. This is going to be a great one and a must for every angler's library.

Carl Richards
Grand Rapids, Michigan

Author's Preface

THE main objective of this book is the simplification of the mayfly fauna found in our North American trout waters, thus enabling the reader to be prepared with *only* the imitations that he will need to match the hatches he will encounter throughout an entire season. Often in the quest for simplicity and brevity, incompleteness and faulty coverage will result. Such pitfalls are common in books trying to cover too much with too little time and space. From the beginning, I had to make a decision, and that was to deal exclusively with one type of aquatic insect—mayflies—and then proceed to cover them thoroughly from top to bottom. Consequently, this singularity of purpose has allowed me to provide the reader with all aspects of their nature that are significant to his sport; from the rationale of their geographical distribution to their recognition at the species level. If this work could make any claims of uniqueness, it is that no shortcuts have been taken along the way in its treatment.

How any fly fisher goes about his sport is something personal. One may consider it purely for physical relaxation, while another will approach it intently, with the objective of subjecting his expertise to the scrutiny of the largest and wisest trout rising in a pool. He views it as a challenge. If any generality can be made about all fly fishers within these two parameters, it is that all derive the greatest pleasure from catching trout, any trout. Moreover, all have chosen to do so through the imitation of the behavior and physical properties of the natural insects which trout depend on for their very existence. It would then follow that the more a fly fisher understands the natural fauna of the water he likes to fish and the naturals he needs to duplicate, the more successful he will be at attaining his principal objective. In essence, every effort made to get the trout on the hook will be returned in dividends of enjoyment by catching them in the first place.

A second objective of this work is to make anglers aware of the merits of mayfly recognition. Other writers have tried to convey their belief that to recognize a fly is to know how to use its imitation. Unfortunately they have neglected to show, not tell, the reader why this is so. Nor have they provided the reader with a *practical* tool to be able to make the distinctions among the mayfly order.

Since not all insects look alike, emerge similarly, and inhabit the same waters, it becomes apparent that it will not suffice to treat an emerging insect as just a fly or even to think of it as just a mayfly. To think in broad generalities is to approach it indiscriminately and without specificity of purpose. Historically, anglers have refused to treat the hatches of mayflies with an attitude lacking divisability. Thus, they have derived their own system of recognition and applied a series of common names to the hatches, such as the Blue-Winged Olives, Drakes, Quills, etc. Unfortunately, the common-name system is dependent on the descriptions of the dun stage of mayflies, since it is the most obvious and easily capturable stage at streamside. Secondly, the system has had many contributors throughout the years, independent of one another, and it shows in the lack of coordination and consistency of contributions. It now turns out that not all Quills or Drakes are common names intended to describe specific types of mayflies, or those that prefer certain types of waters, or those that emerge at a specific time of year. The common-name system then is an arbitrary one, exhibiting little consistency of purpose and now, in the majority of cases, will not suffice to make any useful distinction and correlation among the hatches of mayflies. This is not to say that it should be discarded overnight, but perhaps fly fishermen in general should begin to let another system gradually take its place.

Scientific language, such as that employed by entomologists for their classification, unfortunately is not concerned with the description of the color of the mayfly dun, as in the common-name system of anglers. It is also, at first, harder to become acquainted with and to remember. However, it does have its merits and very important implications for the fly fisher. To begin with, mayflies in general are classified by scientists into major groups (families), and further broken down into subgroups (genera). The fact that any two species belong to the same division or subdivision immediately tells the angler one thing, that those two species have something in common. It could be in physical structure, preference for the same water type, emergence, and, in the majority of cases and most interesting to note, resemblance in general appearance! The implications to the fly fishing fraternity employing such a system in their language and streamside approach has many immediate and practical applications.

Although the principal concern of this work is to immediately put the angler in the know regarding the hatches he will encounter next season and how to fish them and imitate them, its purpose is also to teach him how to recognize them by both their common *and* scientific classification. It is an option, one better available than not. The reader is not referred to scientific publications that are hard to understand (for an individual lacking the time to become acquainted with its terminology), difficult to find, and often very expensive. All the tools are provided in this volume which the reader has paid for, and the options and opportunities it offers concerning the many facets of mayflies are herewith included in this book.

Historically, angling books identified the species of mayflies by the coloration exhibited by its dun. This method of recognition is helpful when it comes to identifying the largest mayflies, but, in the great majority of cases, identification of the subadult stage or dun of a mayfly is a physical impossibility. Structures such as wing venation, genitalia, and other characteristics needed for positive identification are yet not fully developed and thus unreliable for species determination. The spinner stage, which all duns will transform into approximately 24 hours after the hatch, is the stage used by entomologists and myself for the classification of all species covered in this book. However, determination as to species of a spinner is a painstaking exercise accomplished with high-power microscopes and with a stage that is not as readily available as either the nymphs or duns.

Nymphs, which are most available for study year-round in streams (their discarded exoskeletons are always found floating on the surface of the water during a hatch), are focused here for streamside recognition and identification. From a scientific point of view, not all of the nymphal characteristics have yet been found to separate the species of certain types of mayflies. However, during the five years that it took to conduct the research for this book, I had to raise at streamside many species from the nymphal stage to the spinner. Consequently, I have discovered many reliable characteristics useful to the angler to make distinctions among nymphs. Some of the information in Appendix II (Advanced Entomology and Research) is not part of the scientific community to date.

Not all scientific information is applicable to the fly fisher, and it then becomes necessary for an author to make certain decisions as to what he considers relevant to the angler and of concern only to the scientist. The fly fisher is only concerned with the recognition of certain types of mayflies, their manner of emergence, their imitations, and how to fish their hatches. These angling concepts, on the other hand, are outside the sphere of concern of the entomologists.

For the sake of simplification, the super family and subfamily classifications employed by entomologists have been entirely omitted, and only the principal family divisions are given in this book. A second deviation from scientific information is the placement of genus *Potamanthus* with the burrowing mayflies in Chapter 9. *Potamanthus* nymphs are not true burrowers, at least in their more mature phases; however, they do emerge as burrowers do, inhabit similar waters, and parallel them in size and in general appearance.

In Chapter 8, the family of *Ephemerellas*—the group concept as originated by Dr. Jay R Traver of Cornell in *Biology of Mayflies* and followed by past angling authors—is replaced here by the original Needham subgeneric classification system, reproposed in the revision of that family by Dr. George Edmunds and Dr. Richard Allen in the early 60's. Many *Ephemerella* species have been synonymized and thus are no longer recognized as distinct entities in their own right. Unfortunately, some of these now-obsolete classifications have appeared in angling texts as distinct hatch-producing species in recent years. The changes and synonymies are included in Chapter 8.

As will be seen in Chapter 3, the seasonal emergence of mayflies exhibits a near-predictable order in the emergence of the species, and it barely changes in its sequence despite the deviation in climate from year to year. When this entire emergence sequence will take place during the year is, however, dependent on the average latitude and altitude of a given area. In the pages that follow all reference to seasonal emergence concerning western species is applicable to Idaho and Montana. For the emergence times for other western sections, the deviations given in the map should be kept in mind. When it's an eastern

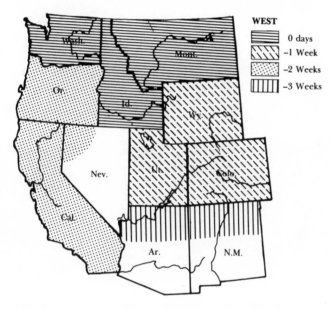

Footnote to Western Map: Due to the thermal influences within Yellowstone National Park, hatches will take place approximately 2-3 weeks earlier in parkwaters than in nearby trout streams in Idaho, Montana or Wyoming.

species, emergence time would apply for the Catskill and northern Michigan hatches; again, the time differences given in the eastern map should be noted. These maps are intended to be only rough guides and are not substitutes for first-hand information obtained in the streams.

It is my hope that the angler will find the need to use and re-use this book constantly. Perhaps nothing will please me more than if one day he approaches me in the stream and asks me to autograph a well-worn volume that has been carefully explored for all its benefits.

Good luck.

Fred L. Arbona, Jr.
Boulder, Colorado

CHAPTER 1: Mayfly Recognition and Imitation

MANY accomplishments have a proudful beginning; this book, however, started as a direct result of a humbling experience—an evening of angling failure on the West Branch of the Delaware some years ago. The stream was as peaceful as ever, the serenity of impending nightfall only interrupted by the reverberating sounds of trout feeding gently on delicate Pale Evening Duns. It is the memory of two big browns that rose for over an hour that caused that evening to remain so fixed in my mind. Steadily those two old-timers seized every unfolding-winged adult as they barely slipped out of their nymphal cases, while they remained unmindful of my created "hatches" of artificial nymphs and dries of many sorts. They remain the biggest fish I have ever fished to during a hatch in an eastern trout stream. Even including the haste of the excited imagination, I still insist (now wisely only to myself) that they approached eight or nine pounds in weight.

Many seasons have run their courses since that evening. Yet even now as I write this from Montana, isolated from that alluring pool on the Delaware River, I still long for a second encounter with those magnificent trout. Even though they do not know it, the credit for this work finally getting started must go to them.

I consider that evening a lost opportunity to hook a trout of a lifetime. Unbelievable as it seemed to me, none of my imitations warranted even a superficial inspection on their part. Nor had I ever noticed, nor possessed, a single pattern that imitated what they were taking. Consider what it would have been like had I been prepared before that hatch, ready with the proper imitation and the knowledge of how to use it. Such, of course, was not the case, even though I had probably encountered the same hatch many times before. I realized that evening that I was unable to rec-

ognize it and, consequently, derived no benefit from past experiences with it. Perhaps this was due to the belief, at the time, that trout behave differently during every hatch, that it would have been a waste of time to recognize individual hatches; and that it would be virtually impossible to ever be prepared with a truly exact imitation to match the stage that the trout were feeding on at the time. I felt there were simply too many species and far too many stages to worry about.

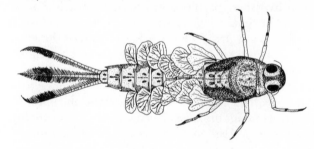

FIG. 1-1 *Siphlonurus occidentalis* nymph (top view)

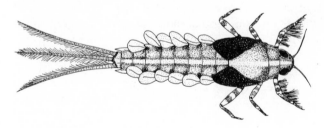

FIG. 1-2 *Isonychia sadleri* nymph (top view)

Following that experience, I embarked on a project of collecting, identifying, and experimenting with hatches in order to improve my fishing—and as it turned out, my research provided the material that many years later became this book. Among my most notable and important realizations is that the great

1

majority of mayfly hatches are brought about by only a handful of dominant species in our eastern and western trout streams. Second, these hatches fall into distinct types which exhibit specific characteristics in seasonal and actual emergence; they are best imitated with an artificial pattern that duplicates that state of emergence most vulnerable to the trout. Third, and as a direct consequence, anglers need not carry boxes of artificial patterns in a futile effort to match every mayfly species and stage. They should carry only those specific patterns that will be required to match the hatches they are likely to encounter, and of the stages of emergence consistently selected by trout to feed upon. Much of the pages that follow will not only illustrate how such a simplified approach to mayfly hatches is possible, but will also make a case for the exact reproduction and use of at least the most common mayfly species and specific stages.

Hatch periods are favorite times for the fly fisher to be on a trout stream. A blank and calm stretch of water, devoid of any surface activity, will abruptly change into an arena of lively action filled with splashing, rolling, hungry trout bent on consuming as many naturals as possible before the emergence is over. So exciting are these streamside events that most fly fishers prefer to fish during a hatch than at any other time.

Historically, mayfly hatches have received the most attention and enjoyed the greatest popularity among anglers. The beauty and delicacy of mayflies are probably contributing factors but there is more to it than just that. Mayflies are a dominant and impressively abundant organism in slow-to-medium running trout waters. Also, in these placid stretches, a mayfly hatch will cause trout to rise to the naturals floating on the surface of the water, enabling them to see and become selective as to what they choose to eat, thereby becoming that much more challenging to the angler.

Another important consideration in the popularity of mayfly hatches is that the majority of mayfly populations emerge at the most comfortable time of the year—the months of April to September, which also coincide with the legal fishing season in most trout states. Moreover, their emergences take place during daylight hours, unlike those of many other aquatic types; thus they constitute approximately 60—70% of all the hatches we encounter in the stream. This presents the streamside angler with the challenge of determining the size, configuration, and even color of the emerging form in order to select an artificial to represent it. This must be done before the hatch

heightens to the point where trout become formidably selective or ends as abruptly as it began. Mayfly hatches, then, make physical as well as mental demands on the angler, and perhaps therein lies their particular fascination.

Today, the amount of water still hospitable to trout has been greatly reduced. Simultaneously, the swelling of the fly fishing ranks has produced such acute pressures on the remaining strongholds that, in extreme cases, we arrive at a stream to find it resembles an event to which too many invitations were sent out. The direct consequence of such crowding is that trout become familiar with as many as a hundred man-made concoctions each day, as opposed to those of yesteryear that rarely saw one artificial per month. Moreover, of late, the "catch-and-release" concept of fishing is becoming more widespread. This means that a trout today that takes an artificial does not inevitably meet its demise, but more likely is returned to the stream with a warier outlook as to what to feed on in the future.

These new developments and findings have led to new demands upon the fly fisher, encouraging that more time and effort be invested in economical approaches to angling, innovations in fly-tying, and improvement of artificial imitations. In order to better take trout we must better understand their behavior, and in order to do that, we must better understand the behavior of the third player in the game of fly fishing—the insects themselves. And in order to understand these insects, it has proved imperative that someone take upon himself the formidable task of making a thorough investigation of the multitude of species comprising the mayfly fauna in eastern, midwestern, and western trout streams to discover the similarities of forms among their numbers and to reveal the consistencies they exhibit in emergence. For the angler, these objectives have important implications: the elimination of needless patterns, the introduction of certain new ones based on new findings, and the simplification of streamside approaches when encountering the hatches they are supposed to imitate.

That a need exists for this material is best illustrated by the most common occurrence in trout streams during mayfly hatches today. How often have you seen a fly fisher surrounded by rising trout wasting precious time exhausting his crammed fly boxes and failing to come up with anything that works. Hatches should not be sessions of frustrations, but the time to get your best catches accomplished. They are certainly not the times to be forced to become a frustrated spectator of the game taking place before you. The genesis of this book lies in just such an experience.

In a sincere attempt to become familiar with the third players in the game of fly fishing, anglers have in the last two decades given great emphasis to the recognition of particular hatches, and to their scientific names. Scientific language has taken such a foothold in the fly fishing fraternity that even professional entomologists are genuinely impressed with our recent, but continuing sophistication. However, many more direct benefits of the actual recognition of an emerging insect remain to be realized by fly fishers. It will not suffice, nor can we derive much advantage from simply knowing the common or scientific name of a hatch. The fact that a hatch is of *Ephemerellas*, *Siphlonurus*, or what have you, can also serve to put us in the know as to the manner of their actual emergence, the customary response and selectivity that trout will exhibit toward the naturals, and the type of artificial that will be most credible to them. *With experience* these relevant facts can be recalled and put to use in the future and where it counts—when trout are rising during the beginning of the multitude of hatches we will encounter in seasons to come. The benefits of determining the classification of the emerging naturals are multipurpose, and can well make the difference between success and failure, or satisfaction and frustration in the stream.

As hatch producers, mayflies are unsurpassed, and their influence on our sport is a most direct one. To take full advantage of the opportunities they have to offer we need to take a closer look at their underwater world. We must then simultaneously investigate the interaction that takes place every day in the stream or river between the concentrated hatches and the trout. The concepts of selectivity, matching the hatch, streamside recognition, and the benefit of scientific language we must now turn to are the very principles upon which the information in the rest of this book will depend. Perhaps by way of apology, the information in this book is not meant to be entertaining, and lacks the amusing fishing stories and big trout episodes that make up a substantial bulk of angling literature. Not that I have none to tell you; I sincerely believe that the true story of success of any book is not the streamside feats of the author, but those of the reader as a direct result of the information he was able to derive from its pages.

MAYFLY HATCHES AND TROUT SELECTIVITY

The world of the trout is no haven of leisure; in fact, the opposite is true, for the trout's survival is entirely dependent upon its keeping strong through constant feeding, which in turn is directly linked to selecting and defending an advantageous position in the stream. Trout in general prefer situations that give the greatest food return for the least output of energy. Concentrated hatches, or flush emergences, of aquatic insects, provide that circumstance when vast numbers of one species leave their protected hiding places at the bottom of the stream. They then become available to the trout in the current and surface of the water in abundant numbers.

FIG. 1-3 A waiting trout.

FIG. 1-4 A rise.

FIG. 1-5 A hatch-activated brown trout.

When a hatch is sparse, the energy required to chase its emerging insects may be more than the energy the food supplies. It will then simply fail to bring about feeding activity. Other factors, most noticeably weather, also determine the trout's course of action. Extremely hot, sunny periods inhibit trout mobility. Moreover, when water temperatures exceed 66°F, trout become lethargic. In general, all species of trout abhor direct sunlight, especially the brown trout, and even in a water-temperature range of 50°F to 66°F, feeding takes place only in shaded areas. Hatches of insects, generally speaking, are not very profuse during such weather (for reasons given in Chapter 3), thus failing to give trout enough of a return of their expenditure of energy and their general discomfort. However, aquatic insects are able to postpone their emergences by as much as three or four days, until better weather, such as a cooler or cloudy day, comes along.

If a hatch is profuse enough to cause trout to feed they will select those positions in a stream with a natural drift that accumulates the naturals and enables them to intercept large numbers of them with little expenditure of energy. A good hatch can provide as many as 25 naturals per minute over a holding fish, though most range more toward 10. The more naturals a given trout consumes, the more he will choose those naturals of given size, configuration, and even color that he finds most satisfying. This may explain why trout are usually never selective at the very beginning and end of a hatch, but only during the peak period when it is in full progress.

This does not mean that during a hatch trout may not take the natural or imitation of another insect,

however. The point is that during a good hatch of a single species, there appears to be a point at which trout tend to ignore naturals (and their imitations) that are different from or unrepresentative of what they prefer at the time. Even during multiple-hatches, when more than one insect is emerging at a given time, we can notice the phenomenon of selection—in this case, for one species over another.

An axiom of the science of biology states that every species occupies a specific niche in the natural order. Consequently, no two species can indefinitely occur together without accommodating to each other eventually on space or in time. Even when two species of mayflies are forced by irregular climate to emerge simultaneously, one will be more profuse than the other within a given period. The time slot really "belongs" to only one; the other is an intruder. The two species will not emerge in similar densities and trout will still have the choice to select that which is most common. A classic example of such trout selectivity occurs during the hatches of member species of Family *Baetidae*, which produce the thick hatches of Little Brown Quills and Tiny Olives during the entire season and throughout the country. Why trout should become so selective on such minute flies (No. 18 to 22 hook sizes) will forever remain a mystery to anglers, but they do, as demonstrated by the chart below.

During these *Baetidae* hatches, the little nymphs float quite a while on the surface film before the duns begin to emerge from the nymphal exoskeletons. Such a lengthy nymph-to-dun transition results in hundreds of the little nymphs being collected along the natural drift lanes of a stream. As a result, the trout are offered an otherwise rare opportunity to ingest them in great numbers while barely moving from their preselected stations. Even if another hatch of

FIG. 1-6 A profuse mayfly hatch—a time for exact imitation.

much larger insects simultaneously takes place, but does not offer the same opportunities, the trout customarily stay with these little mayflies. In this way, trout will avoid the necessity of foraging about in an effort to seize the bigger naturals.

The best proof of trout selectivity comes from examination of the contents of their stomachs. The information given below was obtained from approximately 1,000 trout, the stomachs of which were carefully siphoned with a pump during hatches I personally witnessed over the past eight years. All trout were then released. The figures serve to demonstrate that anglers, at least during the hatches of the first four types of mayflies, are well advised to duplicate closely what the trout are concentrating on. This is done in order to avoid lessening their possibilities by using an artificial too far removed from the true natural. These types cause extremely thick emergences during the season and, on average, result in allowing trout to become selective approximately 75 percent of the time. By the same token, the low percentage of selectivity for the last three types is certainly a direct reflection that the hatches are not profuse and often take place sporadically throughout a given day.

Nymphs and *emerging* duns, according to the stomach contents examined, do turn out to be the most frequently found and apparently the most vulnerable

stages of emerging mayflies. Consequently, they are given much emphasis in this book. Fortunately for the dry fly purist, artificial imitations of both of these stages are designed to be fished just under or on the surface film during the hatch, and thus will still provide the lover of the dry fly the thrill of seeing the ring of a trout rising to his imitation.

Selectivity on the part of trout during concentrated hatches of certain insects is finally being accepted by anglers. However, the reasons for selection are probably more complex than just being a direct function of availability (abundance of the emerging natural) and consequential short-term conditioning. In the case of the little *Baetidae* it is just as plausible that selectivity is also the trout's best defense against anglers. Since very small artificials (hook sizes No. 18 and smaller) are seldom used by anglers, a trout's negative experiences with artificial imitations of such sizes are rare enough for it to consider feeding on the small mayflies safe, free from the treachery of man. In any event, if the phenomenon of selection still elicits skepticism, the disbeliever should scrutinize carefully a few stomachs of trout after a particularly heavy hatch. In most cases, their stomachs will be stuffed as tightly as sausages with literally hundreds of one species of insect, and in the most extreme cases, with that insect in a particular stage of its emergence!

FAMILY OR TYPE	COMMON NAMES OF HATCHES	NUMBER OF HATCHES OBSERVED	SELECTIVITY*	
Family Baetidae (tiny swimmers)	Little Brown Quills Tiny Olives	154	83%	
Family Ephemerellidae (sprawlers)	Hendricksons Sulphurs Blue-Winged Olives	243	78%	
Family Ephemeridae (burrowers)	Eastern Green Drake Great Lead-Winged Drake Brown Drake Yellow Drake	88	75%	High
Family Tricorythidae (tiny spaawlers)	Tiny White-Winged Black; *Caenis*	112	71%	
Family Heptageniidae (clingers)	Gordon Quill American March Brown Gray Fox Light Cahill	187	52%	
Family Leptophlebiidae (sprawlers)	Slate-Winged Mahogany Dun	62	37%	Low
Family Siphlonuridae (large swimmers)	Gray Drake Great Lead-Winged Coachman	71	28%	

Table 1-1

* Percentage of observed hatches in which the stomach content of trout caught during the hatch contained only specimens of the emerging insect (nymph and/or dun stages).

MATCHING THE HATCH

The concept of exact imitation of natural insects, or matching the hatch, relies on the assumptions that trout do get selective in varying degrees during hatches, and that anglers will be better off using an artificial pattern that duplicates the emerging species as faithfully as is humanly possible. As we have seen, not all hatches are so profuse that trout will feed with a "selective defense." In such cases, fly fishermen have no need to employ true-to-life duplications. However, the effect of a given hatch upon trout is so paradoxical, and the point during a flush emergence at which they may become selective so unpredictable, that it is well beyond the control or power of prediction of anglers. Therefore, it may behoove anglers to develop the habit of matching the hatch at the start of any hatch, and then concentrating fully on proper presentation. In essence, uncertainty of representation is eliminated and the emphasis is shifted to presentation, the demanding and intriguing art (covered in Chapter 4) of simulating the behavior of the natural.

In the search for more effective patterns, however, it is often easy to become so imitation conscious that we neglect the important role of proper presentation in fly fishing. Many anglers, on the other hand, stubbornly refuse to use anything but general, nondescriptive patterns during hatches and place all their hopes on presentation. The correct placing and drift or action of an artificial is the most important factor involved in getting the interest of a trout; the selection of an exact imitation in conjunction with proper delivery is the key to make him take it. The two fly fishing principles go hand in hand and are not meant to be divorced from each other. When an angler is confident of his pattern, of its realistic representation of the emerging natural, he is then free to concentrate fully on the delivery of his artificial, which remains, regardless of what he is using, integral to successfully fishing hatches of mayflies.

Each fishing season presents anglers with numerous mayfly hatches brought about by a myriad of species that follow each other throughout the season in a nearly predictable order. The seasonal occurrence of even the most common ones, like the Pale Evening Duns, lasts but a few weeks. It would then be impractical for fly fishermen to adopt a hatch-by-hatch (or species-by-species) approach and to expect to benefit from memorizing and imitating them all. It is unfortunate that this is precisely what has been demanded by some angling authors. These authors treat each species separately, as if each had a distinct biology and a different emergence sequence. Consider the mobile nature of our present society, the different types of trout waters that anglers will visit in a given year, and the fact that many of these streams will contain different species of insects. In this context, the hatch-by-hatch approach would require anglers to go astream armed with a trunkful of artificial patterns and then invest valuable time during a hatch to deducing when and how to use them. The duration of most hatches is at most an hour or two, and since they are accompanied by the excitement of rising trout, they leave little room and patience for experimentation with artificial patterns and fishing applications. Surely what most fly fishermen would prefer would be to carry only those imitations essential for the mayfly hatches they will encounter 99 percent of the time, to know when and where they will in all likelihood encounter them, and what stage of emergence will merit duplication. Such a specific method to the treatment of mayfly hatches has taken years to develop and to prove with workable artificial patterns. It is, however, conveyed here to the reader.

The multitude of mayfly species that exist among the weeds, rocks, and silt of the bottom substrate of a trout stream will surprise most anglers. It would be utterly impractical to imitate each and every species exactly. However, the trout streams whether in the eastern or western half of the country support a separate handful of dominant species that constitute the majority of the most profuse and longest hatches anglers will encounter. These "super species" are not only the most common, but serve as excellent representatives for other closely related, almost identical ones. Thus the exact imitations of them and an understanding of their emergence will prepare the fly fisherman to successfully fish not only their hatches, but those of comparatively less general importance.

It would perhaps help to give a few examples. An informal survey of a four-square-foot section of the Beaverkill River, just below the town of Roscoe, New York, reveals a total of 35 different mayfly species. The exceptional richness of aquatic life in this river makes it practically impossible for anglers to adopt a species-by-species approach to its hatches; however, once simple correlations are made among the related and nearly identical mayflies, imitation of all of them becomes possible. For example, the common and important Blue-Winged Olive hatches in this river and most eastern waters are caused by no less than 6 of these 35 mayfly species. They resemble each other closely in configuration, color, and general biology,

SPECIES	DENSITY	COMMON NAME	ARTIFICIAL PATTERN RECOMMENDED
Family Baetidae (tiny swimmers)			
*Baetis vagans**	147 —Little Iron-Blue Quill		
*Baetis intercalaris**	139		Floating Nymph
Pseudocloeon carolina	76 } Little Slate-Winged Brown Quill		
Pseudocloeon dubium	53 }		
	415		
Family Heptageniidae (clingers)			
*Epeorus pleuralis**	61 } Gordon Quill		
Cinygmula subequalis	17 }		Flat-Body Nymph
*Epeorus vitreus**	38 } Gray-Winged Yellow Quill		
Heptagenia hebe	9 }		
*Stenonema vicarium**	37 —American March Brown		Emerging Wet Fly
*Stenonema fuscum**	32		
Stenacron interpunctatum	7 } Gray Fox		Hen-Winged Dun
Stenonema rubrum	4 }		
Stenonema pulchellum	1 }		
	206		
Family Leptophlebiidae (sprawlers)			
*Paraleptophlebia adoptiva**	26 }		Conventional Nymph
Paraleptophlebia mollis	9 } Slate-Winged Mahogany Dun		No-Hackle Fly
Paraleptophlebia debilis	11 }		
	46		
Family Ephemerellidae (sprawlers)			
*Ephemerella subvaria**	93 —Dark Hendrickson		
*Ephemerella rotunda**	104 } Light Hendrickson		Conventional Nymph
*Ephemerella invaria**	81 }		
*Ephemerella dorothea**	61 —Pale Evening Dun		
*Ephemerella cornuta**	56 }		No-Hackle or Emerging Dun
Ephemerella walkeri	7		
*Ephemerella cornutella**	69 } Blue-Winged Olive		
Ephemerella lata	21		
Ephemerella simplex	31 }		Hen-Winged Spinner
Ephemerella attenuata	6 }		
Ephemerella deficiens	29 } Little Dark Hendrickson		
Ephemerella needhami	4 }		
	562		
Family Ephemeridae (burrowers)			
Hexagenia limbata	0 —Great Lead-Winged Drake		Wiggle Nymph
*Ephemera guttulata**	37 —Eastern Green Drake		Paradrake Dun
*Ephemera varia**	31 } Yellow Drake		Double-Winged Spinner
Potamanthus distinctus	12 }		
	80		
Family Siphlonuridae (large swimmers)			
*Isonychia bicolor**	23 }		Streamlined Nymph
		Great Lead-Winged Coachman	
Isonychia sadleri	9 }		Hen-Winged Spinner
	32		
Family Tricorythidae (tiny sprawlers)			
*Tricorythodes stygiatus**	41	Tiny White-Winged Black	No-Hackle Dun Poly Spinner

Table 1-2
An informal survey of four square-foot sections of the Beaverkill River just below the town of Roscoe, New York, revealed the following mayfly fauna. The left column includes the species which were found, the middle column reveals individual density, the third and last columns list the common names and artificial patterns that should be employed to fish their hatches.

Asterisk signifies what may be considered an eastern and midwestern super species.

though they come in two sizes, and thus can be imitated by a single pattern (No. 12 and No. 18 hook sizes). When we make simple associations like this (which are given more fully in chapters 5–11), we discover that the formidable task of imitating so many species is reduced to preparing only 15 artificial patterns yet still accomplishing the objective and benefit of exact imitation.

Most interesting to note is that the six species that cause the Blue-Winged Olive hatches in eastern waters exhibit common morphological and biological traits, and thus are classified by entomologists as *Ephemerellas*. What implications that has for the angler we will come back to, but it should now be noted that these 6 species (*E. cornuta, E. walkeri, E. cornutella, E. lata, E. simplex,* and *E. attenuata*) are nearly identical in appearance and biology, all choosing mornings in which to emerge; this is no mere coincidence, but an interesting aspect of the consistency of aquatic nature of significance to the fly fisherman.

Upon seining a local stream, the western angler will also find a diversity of mayfly types in his waters. No other river can probably be found that would yield as true a representative sample of the mayfly fauna in western trout streams as the Henry's Fork of the Snake River. It varies drastically in general character throughout its 80-mile length and consequently offers the kind of microhabitat for the subsistence of all kinds of mayflies. The river reveals the existence of a total of 27 mayfly species, but with the elimination of those species not common enough in this particular river to constitute a fishable hatch and making appropriate associations among the remaining species, the patterns needed to exactly imitate every one of the hatches is reduced to only 10 in number.

I have purposely taken two very divergent rivers in mayfly aquatic biota to illustrate that the exact imitation of their mayfly hatches is possible and within the realm of practicality. Most trout streams throughout the country, however, exhibit on the average only five or six dominant species that cause good mayfly hatches throughout the season. Those species that are most abundant in our North American trout streams are, logically, the only ones that can produce heavy hatches that cause trout to become selective. They warrant our efforts to match them as exactly as possible. It is these "super species" that are given specific treatment in this work. The less prevalent mayflies that are related and are close in size and color are also included, but only to allow the reader to become acquainted with them. No artificial patterns are given for them since anglers will find little occasion to use them, and the differences in artificial patterns would undoubtedly prove superfluous.

THE BENEFITS OF STREAMSIDE RECOGNITION

One important aspect of mayflies is that they can be separated into certain groups, or types, whose members exhibit a natural association in general appearance, manner of emergence, and even time of the season of emergence. It is both necessary and in the long run convenient to refer to these groups by their scientific classification. This is not done to make this book appear scholarly or scientific, since its object is to help the reader catch trout. The family concept of the entomologist is adopted for what it can do to help the reader succeed during the hatches of mayflies.

From a biological point of view, mayflies (Order *Ephemeroptera*) are divided into families by entomologists, seven of which are of principal concern to the fly fisherman. This division into families is based on physical characteristics in the mayfly nymphal and adult stages as well as on biological traits common to all the species. From the fly fisher's point of view this implies that since the species within each family exhibit similar living and emergence habits, they can be imitated by a similar artificial pattern (varying only in hook size and color to match the representative ones) and be fished in a similar fashion!

Let's take two examples to show what important ramifications this has for the fly fisher. The Pale Evening Dun is a member of Family *Ephemerellidae*. It is just one of the species of that family that produces exceptional hatches throughout the country during the angling season. All *Ephemerellas* have a common manner of emergence and thus all should be imitated by the same artificial type of pattern resembling the most vulnerable stage to the trout during the hatch. A similar type of pattern can thus be employed during all *Ephemerella* hatches. These include Dark Hendricksons (*E. subvaria*), Light Hendricksons (*E. rotunda*), and the Blue-Winged Olives (*E. cornuta, E. cornutella,* and *E. lata*) of the East and Midwest, as well as the Western Green Drake (*E. grandis*), Small Western Green Drake (*E. flavilinea*), and Pale Morning Duns (*E. infrequens* and *E. inermis*) so important in all western waters.

Understanding the biology of the group of member species constituting each family is invaluable for the development of effective artificial patterns. Following

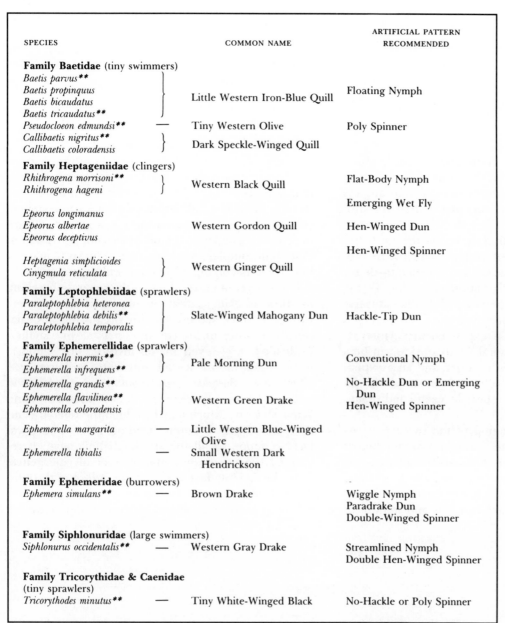

SPECIES	COMMON NAME	ARTIFICIAL PATTERN RECOMMENDED
Family Baetidae (tiny swimmers)		
*Baetis parvus***		
Baetis propinquus	Little Western Iron-Blue Quill	Floating Nymph
Baetis bicaudatus		
*Baetis tricaudatus***		
*Pseudocloeon edmundsi*** —	Tiny Western Olive	Poly Spinner
*Callibaetis nigritus***	Dark Speckle-Winged Quill	
Callibaetis coloradensis		
Family Heptageniidae (clingers)		
*Rhithrogena morrisoni***	Western Black Quill	Flat-Body Nymph
Rhithrogena hageni		
		Emerging Wet Fly
Epeorus longimanus		
Epeorus albertae	Western Gordon Quill	Hen-Winged Dun
Epeorus deceptivus		
		Hen-Winged Spinner
Heptagenia simplicioides	Western Ginger Quill	
Cinygmula reticulata		
Family Leptophlebiidae (sprawlers)		
Paraleptophlebia heteronea		
*Paraleptophlebia debilis***	Slate-Winged Mahogany Dun	Hackle-Tip Dun
Paraleptophlebia temporalis		
Family Ephemerellidae (sprawlers)		
*Ephemerella inermis***	Pale Morning Dun	Conventional Nymph
*Ephemerella infrequens***		
*Ephemerella grandis***		No-Hackle Dun or Emerging Dun
*Ephemerella flavilinea***	Western Green Drake	
Ephemerella coloradensis		Hen-Winged Spinner
Ephemerella margarita —	Little Western Blue-Winged Olive	
Ephemerella tibialis —	Small Western Dark Hendrickson	
Family Ephemeridae (burrowers)		
*Ephemera simulans*** —	Brown Drake	Wiggle Nymph
		Paradrake Dun
		Double-Winged Spinner
Family Siphlonuridae (large swimmers)		
*Siphlonurus occidentalis*** —	Western Gray Drake	Streamlined Nymph
		Double Hen-Winged Spinner
Family Tricorythidae & Caenidae (tiny sprawlers)		
*Tricorythodes minutus*** —	Tiny White-Winged Black	No-Hackle or Poly Spinner

Table 1-3
Double asterisks denote species constituting the "super hatches" in Henry's Fork of the Snake River in Idaho.

our present example, all *Ephemerellas*, including Pale Evening Duns, emerge the same way (see fig. 1–7), with nymphs rising to the surface film during the hatch (1), where the enveloped duns will quickly escape the nymphal exoskeletons or shucks (2). The newly emerged duns are not the perfectly upright-winged dry flies depicted in most drawings or photographs in books. They are crumbled-winged insects struggling to get their wings in an upright position through the use of their thoracic muscles (3). This stage of emergence actually lasts about ten seconds, but apparently this is enough time to give trout their opportunity. (The emerging dun pattern that we pro-

pose for all *Ephemerella* hatches in the fly tying section of this book is so lethal during the hatch that friends who have field-tested it conclude that the pattern should be outlawed!) Though anglers may not see a single trout take an upright, a stomach autopsy will divulge hundreds of duns all with yet-unfolded wings.

Among other types of mayflies, as a second example, are the tiny swimmers of Family *Baetidae* (genera *Baetis*, *Pseudocloen*, and *Callibaetis*). Unlike *Ephemerellas*, they swim swiftly—like small minnows—to the surface during their hatching, then momentarily hover at the surface film while the little duns slowly appear out of the *front* of the nymphal cases in the shape of a

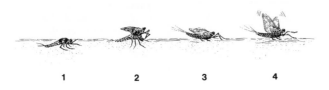

FIG. 1-7 Emergence sequence of *Ephemerellas.*

ball. Thus, the inherent credibility of the floating-nymph artificial recommended in this book. Its effectiveness is well proved by the excellent results anglers attain when employing it during these otherwise-difficult hatches.

One of the most worthwhile habits the fly fisher should get into when confronting a hatch is to capture a natural right at the outset in order to determine its overall size, configuration, and color. Trying to determine these characteristics while the natural is in flight or floating on the surface of the waters is much more difficult, as is explained in Chapter 4. However, capturing a natural at streamside can be a major task without the aid of a net, and an inexpensive aquarium net, available in any pet shop, will undoubtedly turn out to be especially useful and practical.

The streamside recognition of the two types just discussed is really routine, once the angler knows what features to look for. *Ephemerellas* are instantly recognizable by their three tails and the large hind wing which has a slight angle in its fore margin. Members of Family *Baetidae* have two tails and minute or

no hind wings at all, which makes them unlike any other type of mayfly. For the characteristics of all the seven families, see Chapter 2. Moreover, each of the seven families is given a separate chapter, organized according to their seasonal emergence.

TAKING SOME OF THE MYSTERY OUT OF SCIENTIFIC LANGUAGE

By the same manner in which we are borrowing the family concept from the entomologist so, if we were to look into his subdivisions of families into genera (plural of genus), and even species, we stand to learn even more. The language of the entomologist may at first seem complex, but it has consistencies that are of help when becoming acquainted with it.

For an overall grasp, think of the separation among mayflies as akin to that of an index-filing system, where divisions are erected for organizing information. The order of insects *Ephemeroptera*, or Mayflies, is divided into seven major divisions, or families, whose scientific names all end with the letters *dae.* They are *Baetidae, Heptageniidae, Leptophlebiidae, Ephemerellidae, Ephemeridae, Siphlonuridae,* and *Tricorythidae* (to which may be added the related Family *Caenidae*). Each family heading gives us general facts common to all the species belonging to it regarding their taxonomy and manner of emergence. Take the *Siphlonuridae,* for example. A look at the family card will show that all species of this classification are large and streamlined in configuration in the

FIG. 1-8 Daily migration of nymphs of Family *Siphlonuridae (Siphlonurus* and *Isonychia)* are found most enticing by trout.

nymph stage, and two-tailed as either duns or spinners. Besides common taxonomic characteristics, they also share a similar biology, having a long seasonal duration; they are found in trout streams from June until September. Furthermore, unlike any others, their nymphs migrate en masse to the margins of streams prior to emergence. When their hatches take place, they will actually crawl out of the water, like stoneflies, before the duns emerge out of the nymphs. Customarily they are late-afternoon-to-evening emergers, and the spinner forms of the duns that hatched the day before return to the stream every evening. This would all tend to suggest to the angler that these mayflies are important to him when the guide-darting nymphs are migrating toward the banks, for trout would then have the opportunity to attack them as they would a school of minnows. The angler would also benefit from the spinner stage, when the large imagoes return to the stream in great concentrations.

Once again we can appreciate how much benefit we can derive from streamside recognition, in this case of the empty nymphal shucks left behind along the banks of the stream by members of this family. Taking our present example a bit further, the family is subdivided into groups, or genera. Finer morphological characteristics are employed by entomologists to make the distinction. Family *Siphlonuridae* is composed of two genera: *Siphlonurus* and *Isonychia*. *Siphlonurus* nymphs are recognizable by the presence of leaf-like gills and *Isonychias* by a bushy clump of spines on their forelegs. The adult stages of both types can also be specifically identified. The subdivisions to the generic level are especially relevant to the fly fisherman, for they will give the general size and color of the species belonging to each group. *Siphlonurus*, in all stages, average a No. 8 hook size and are grayish in general color; thus they are commonly known as Gray Drakes. *Isonychias* are one hook smaller and often are referred to as Great Lead-Winged Coachmen; most species are reddish-brown.

As we can see, when an angler is informed that a hatch is *Siphlonurus*, for example, he is given much valuable and pertinent information for his sport: the time of year he can expect to meet its hatches, the time of daily emergence, what stage of hatching is important to him, and the expectation of experiencing the exciting spinner falls in the evening. The nymph, dun, and spinner stages will approximate a No. 8 hook size and should be minnow-like in configuration and of a gray coloration. What more could he ask or need?

The last possible distinction to be made in the mayfly filing system would be to determine specimens or hatches as to species. This last exercise is in most cases unnecessary, such as in the case of *Siphlonurus* or *Isonychias*, whose member species are virtually indistinguishable from each other in general appearance and biology. Only the members of the Family *Ephemerellidae* need be determined to the species level, for *Ephemerellas* vary greatly in general size and color from each other and, most importantly, in seasonal and daily emergence. They happen to be, fortunately, the easiest mayflies to determine to the species level. Species determination, however, is in all cases the most exacting definition possible.

Thus far our entomological tree looks like this:

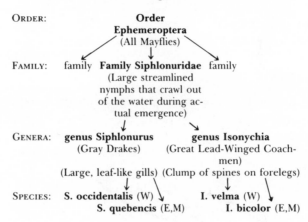

Historically speaking, in an effort to describe the dun stage and refrain from scientific jargon, fly fishermen have evolved their own common names for many of the mayflies. It is unfortunate that the loose application and utilization of these common names still persist in the fly fishing fraternity and, as a direct result, ambiguity of language continues among fly fishers. While there is only one mayfly scientifically designated as *Ephemerella cornuta*—a size No. 12 Blue-Winged Olive that emerges every morning during the month of June in eastern and midwestern trout waters—there are no less than 11 other hatches labeled with this overly used common name. They are much different in appearance, emerge at other times of the day and of the season and even on opposite sides of the country!

Some of the flaws of the common-name system so widespread in angling literature were discussed in the Foreword of this book. Its most serious deficiency is that it tells us little about the hatch itself, how the natural behaves, what stage of emergence the trout will prefer, or what types of artificial would best be employed to fish the hatch. For precisely that reason, I have included an Advanced Entomology section (Appendix II) in this book. This is also in recognition that a good percentage of fly fishermen are ready to delve into such disciplines as determining an emerging mayfly as to species. Although many angling texts dictate which mayfly species should be of importance, it is clear that many of us want to determine for ourselves which species we need to know, based on our own experiences in the streams we frequent.

One of the most direct benefits from being able to make family or generic determination of a mayfly hatch is that we can then derive benefit even from our failures. When we do miserably in the stream—which is inevitable at times—we need only make a simple collection of a nymph or dun of the natural and put it in a little vial filled with alcohol. We then have the chance to take our streamside experience home and classify it and derive any help we can from fishing books we may own. That is, of course, if the books have been specific enough to include the scientific name of the hatch the authors are writing about. Perhaps in printed pages we may find some plausible reason for our failure and points to remember next time we meet the same hatch.

FIG. 1-9 The aquatic community of a trout stream.

1. Mayflies (Ephemerellas - sprawlers)
2. Caddies (Glossoma)
3. Stonefly (Acroneuria)
4. Stonefly (Pteronarcys)
5. Mayfly (Rhithrogena - clingers)
6. Backswimmer (Notonecta)
7. Mayflies (Ephemerella)
8. Caddies (Brachycentrus)
9. Caddies (Dicosmoecus)
10. Mayflies (Rithrogena - clingers)
11. Damselfly (Zygoptera)
12. Dragonfly (Anisoptera)

CHAPTER 2: The Aquatic Fauna of a Trout Stream

MAYFLIES by no means possess an absolute monopoly among the aquatic fauna found in our North American trout streams, even though they do constitute a substantial part. Other orders of aquatic organisms can also be found in running-water environments and offer additional concentrated hatches to the fly fisherman during the season. A microview of the bottom of a trout stream would reveal all the aquatic forms going about their everyday functions: mayfly nymphs actively scraping minute organisms and plankton from the rocks and vegetation, stoneflies scurrying on smooth-faced boulders, caddises' larvas constructing little houses of wood and stones, and so on. The microscenario is one of a busy community full of activity, resembling the hustle and bustle of our own man-made cities.

The main concern in this book is, of course, the mayflies found in trout streams, their biology, recognition, and imitation as well as fishing the hatches. However, imperative to the reader's understanding and utilization of the information given in the chapters that follow is the ability, on his part, to make certain basic differentiations between the members belonging to the mayfly order and the other aquatic groups that he will encounter while fishing in a stream. Furthermore, the present chapter goes one step further and breaks down the order of mayflies into types or families, into which chapters 5 through 11 are divided, and as the reader already has seen, the family division is an invaluable aid to understanding and fishing the hatches.

Mayflies are the most important aquatic order to the fly fisherman. This is due not to their abundant numbers found in every stream but also to their general biology. For one thing, they appear over a period of six to eight months out of the year, thus encom-

passing the entire fishing season in most states. Secondly, mayflies (like caddises) demonstrate a near-predictable chronological sequence in their seasonal emergence, and thus, their hatches can be encountered by design and not only by sheer accident. Furthermore and unlike many types of caddises, they are, with very few exceptions, daytime emergers and ovipositors, adding to their frequency in our trout streams when we can indeed fish them most comfortably. Lastly, they are not explosive but relatively slow emergers and therefore consistently entice the feeding activity of trout and often present the challenges of solving the selective behavior of trout. The realities of their aquatic nature cause them to produce the majority of fishing action for anglers even where they may not exceed, in absolute numbers, those of caddises or other orders.

Contrary to popular belief, mayflies are very hardy insects and are even found in running-water environments unable to support populations of trout. Their adaptability allows them to survive in a wide variety of habitats. Mayflies are one of the first aquatic forms found in the very beginnings of mountain streams. Their wide range of tolerance for pollution and high water temperatures allows them to also exist in environments inhospitable to most other aquatic types. Many of the mayfly species that we will discuss in this book, the dominant ones of trout streams, can also be found for hundreds of miles downstream from the point in a given river where trout no longer can survive. In fact, some species that produce great hatches in trout waters will peak in numbers and hatching density in warm nontrout areas.

All of the aquatic orders included in this chapter collectively constitute the total biota present in a clean, pure-water environment, similar to that which

Table 2-1

COMMON NAME	ORDER	IMPORTANCE	ENVIRONMENTS WHERE FOUND
Mayflies	Ephemeroptera	widespread	Streams, rivers, lakes, and ponds
Caddises	Trichoptera	widespread	Streams, rivers, lakes, and ponds
Stoneflies	Plecoptera	locally	Cold streams and rivers
Craneflies and Midges	Diptera	locally	Cold rivers, lakes, and ponds
Alderflies, Hellgrammites, Dobsonflies, Fishflies	Megaloptera	limited	Cold streams and lakes
Dragonflies and Damselflies	Odonata { Anizoptera Zygoptera	limited	low to fast streams and rivers; lakes and ponds
Water Boatman Backswimmers	Hemiptera	limited	Lakes and ponds; margins of trout streams

supports all species of trout. They are listed in Table 2-1.

Scientific language is not only very useful for effective communication among anglers, but also aids in recognizing the level of division among aquatic orders. Class Insecta encompasses all the aforementioned aquatic insects, and it is divided into orders whose scientific names end with the four letters *tera*, from the Greek word meaning wing. Orders are in turn further divided into families, which end with the three letters *dae*, and finally they are themselves separated into genera (or subgenera in the case of Family *Ephemerellidae*) and species. Thus a mayfly, such as the common Dark Hendrickson of the East (*Ephemerella subvaria*), is classified in the following manner:

Ephemerella subvaria:
  CLASS INSECTA (Mayflies, Caddises, Stoneflies, Dragonflies, etc.)
  Order Ephemeroptera (Mayflies); aquatic insects with upright wings
  Family Ephemerellidae (Those nymphs with platelike gills on the dorsal side [ternites] of their abdomen: adults have three tails and a pronounced angulation on the fore margin of their hind wing)
  Subgenus Ephemerella (Nymphs with feeble legs and lateral spines on segments 3–7)
  Species subvaria (Nymphs with black, well-developed spines on abdominal segments 2–8)

Often the species is written in its short form *E. subvaria* instead of *Ephemerella subvaria*.

CLASS INSECTA

Mayflies *(Order Ephemeroptera)*

Nymph: visible gills of varied structure; usually with three tails. Adult: upright wings.

An order of insects which produces concentrated hatches in most waters that support trout, though of principal importance in slow to medium flowing habitats. Constitutes the bulk of aquatic biomass in many streams. Nymphs and adults shown in Fig. 2–1 are twice their actual size.

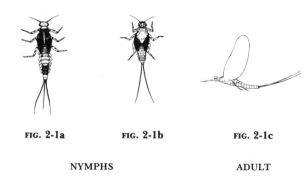

FIG. 2-1a	FIG. 2-1b	FIG. 2-1c
NYMPHS		ADULT

FAMILY BAETIDAE *(tiny swimmers)*
  (Chapter 5)

IDENTIFYING CHARACTERISTICS: Nymph: small, 4–9mm; streamlined. Adult: two tails; minute hind wings

BIOLOGY: found in all waters
SEASONAL EMERGENCE: February to November
DAILY EMERGENCE: midday to late afternoon
IMPORTANCE: second only to *Ephemerellas*; principal hatches of early spring and late fall

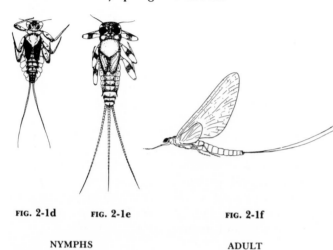

FIG. 2-1d   FIG. 2-1e   FIG. 2-1f

NYMPHS   ADULT

FAMILY HEPTAGENIIDAE *(clingers)*
(Chapter 6)

IDENTIFYING CHARACTERISTICS: Nymph: medium to large, 8–16mm; flat head; eyes on top. Adult: two tails; wings usually barred; hind tarsi 5 segments
BIOLOGY: medium to fast waters
SEASONAL EMERGENCE: March to September
DAILY EMERGENCE: midday to evening
IMPORTANCE: most important in fast waters and in spinner stages

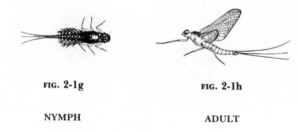

FIG. 2-1g   FIG. 2-1h

NYMPH   ADULT

FAMILY LEPTOPHLEBIIDAE *(sprawlers)*
(Chapter 7)

IDENTIFYING CHARACTERISTICS: Nymph: medium, 7–12mm; forked gills. Adult: three tails; hind wing rounded on fore margin
BIOLOGY: all waters
SEASONAL EMERGENCE: April to September
DAILY EMERGENCE: morning to noon
IMPORTANCE: locally abundant though major importance is in the very beginning and end of fishing season

FIG. 2-1i   FIG. 2-1j
NYMPH   ADULT

FAMILY EPHEMERELLIDAE *(sprawlers)*
(Chapter 8)

IDENTIFYING CHARACTERISTICS: Nymph: medium size, 5–15mm; small platelike gills on top (dorsal) side of abdomen. Adult: three tails; hind wings pointed on fore margin
BIOLOGY: found in all waters
SEASONAL EMERGENCE: April to August
DAILY EMERGENCE: morning, midday, evening
IMPORTANCE: produces the majority and most important hatches of the season

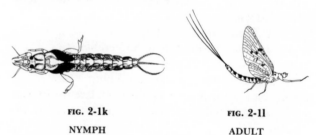

FIG. 2-1k   FIG. 2-1l
NYMPH   ADULT

FAMILY EPHEMERIDAE *(burrowers)*
(Chapter 9)

IDENTIFYING CHARACTERISTICS: Nymph: large, 13–35mm; branched flummed gills; frontal tusks. Adult: two or three tails; extremely large flies
BIOLOGY: best in slow, silted streams
SEASONAL EMERGENCE: June to August
DAILY EMERGENCE: evening
IMPORTANCE: extremely important where found because of its size and concentrated hatches

FIG. 2-1m   FIG. 2-1n
NYMPH   ADULT

FAMILY SIPHLONURIDAE *(large swimmers)*
(Chapter 10)

IDENTIFYING CHARACTERISTICS: Nymph: large, 12–18mm; streamlined. Adult: two tails; hind tarsi with four segments

BIOLOGY: cold waters of varied character
SEASONAL EMERGENCE: June to September
DAILY EMERGENCE: afternoon or evening
IMPORTANCE: nymphs crawl out of water during emergence; thus dun stage of limited significance; nymph and spinner stages are very important

FIG. 2-1o   **FIG. 2-1p**

NYMPH   ADULT

FAMILIES TRICORYTHIDAE AND CAENIDAE
(tiny   sprawlers)
    (Chapter 11)

IDENTIFYING CHARACTERISTICS: Nymph: small, 3–8mm; enlarged platelike first gill. Adult: three tails; no hind wing
BIOLOGY: found in slow waters
SEASONAL EMERGENCE: July to September
DAILY EMERGENCE: *Tricorythodes* usually in the morning, 9 a.m. to noon; *Caenis* in evening
IMPORTANCE: of principal significance late in the season; spinner falls exceed the importance of the hatch itself

---

Caddises *(Order Trichoptera)*

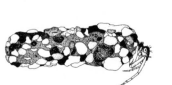

LARVA   LARVA
FAMILY LIMNEPHILIDAE   FAMILY HYDROPSYCHIDAE
(CASE MAKER)   (FREE-LIVING FORM)

PUPA   ADULT

BIOLOGY: A very diverse group of aquatic insects which occurs in almost all types of freshwater habitats from cold trout streams to stagnant marshes. They are known as the "engineers" of aquatic nature because of their complex and ingenious con-

structions of nets and houses of sticks, rocks, and vegetable matter.
EMERGENCE: Caddises, unlike mayflies, dragonflies, and stoneflies, have a complete life cycle, meaning that they have an egg, larva, pupa, and adult stage. Upon emergence, the pupa will escape the larva in the bottom of the stream and rise quickly to the surface of the water. The adult then appears out of the pupa almost instantaneously. Adults will not molt into spinners and will preserve their basic appearance when they return to the stream for as much as two weeks after they emerged.
IMPORTANCE: Extremely important to fly fishermen, especially in faster waters, and second in importance only to mayflies, though they surpass them in numbers in certain waters. Free-living forms (*Hydropsyches*) are by far the most common and significant to anglers, with other larger types, such as the Orange Sedges (*Limnephilus*) producing good hatches in cold streams, lakes, and ponds.

Stoneflies *(Order Plecoptera)*

LARVA   LARVA
FAMILY PERLIDAE   FAMILY PERLODIDAE
(GENUS ACRONEURIA)   (GENUS ISOGENUS)

ADULT

BIOLOGY: Principally an inhabitant of cold running-water environments though also found in still-water environments. Upon emergence nymphs will crawl clear out of the water before adults escape the nymphal shucks. Adults will return to the stream to oviposit and complete the life cycle as much as two to four weeks after they emerged.
EMERGENCE: Emerges during the months of April to August, though some types will emerge throughout the first three months of the year and are thus referred to as "winter flies."

IMPORTANCE: In general, stoneflies are the third most important group in the aquatic natural order. Anglers know them as Salmon Flies, Big Goldens, and Yellow Sallies.

Craneflies and Midges (*Order Diptera*)

LARVA   ADULT
FAMILY TIPULIDAE
(CRANEFLIES)

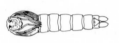 

PUPA   ADULT
FAMILY CHIRONOMIDAE
(MIDGES)

BIOLOGY: Found virtually in all cold waters, though their best numbers are found in the shallow margins of streams, lakes, and ponds, which are rich in aquatic vegetation and of a soft muddy character.

EMERGENCE: Entire year. Upon emerging, the pupa floats helplessly to the surface in dense numbers, and adults slowly escape out of the pupa exoskeleton.

IMPORTANCE: Even though they are found in all trout streams, those types indigenous to cold lakes (*Chironomous*) are the ones of principal importance to anglers. In these waters, trout of all sizes slowly cruise along the surface and "gulp" thousands of the helpless pupa in a single session. Most species found in trout lakes are olive green in color and approximate No. 18 to No. 22 hooks sizes. The floating nymph and stillborn patterns are very effective for fishing the morning and evening emergences of *Chironomous*.

Alderflies, Hellgrammites, Dobsonflies, Fishflies (*Order Megaloptera*)

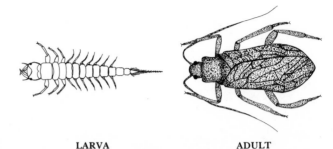

LARVA   ADULT
FAMILY SIALIDAE
(ALDERFLIES)

BIOLOGY: Well-aerated, running water supports fair populations of these critters. Their geographical range includes the entire country; however, the majority of species of *Megalopteras* are found in the eastern part of the country.

EMERGENCE: Adults are really not aquatic and deposit their eggs at midday on objects overhanging the water. When the eggs hatch, the newly hatched larvas drop into the water. They remain there until full maturity occurs when they will then migrate to the margins of the stream to burrow into the soft banks and make dens for final pupation.

IMPORTANCE: Flies of this order are weak fliers and generally inactive near aquatic environments. The immature to mature larval stages, on the other hand, are available to the trout near the banks of streams and cold lakes. The larval form is best imitated with the Wiggle Nymph imitation given for burrowing mayflies with which *Sialis* are often found.

Dragonflies and Damselflies (*Order Odonata*)

ADULT
DRAGONFLY

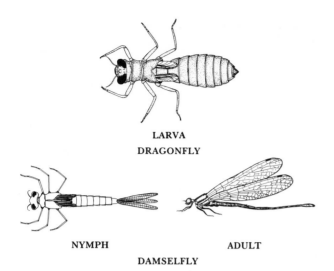

LARVA
DRAGONFLY

NYMPH
DAMSELFLY
ADULT

Water Boatmen and Backswimmers (*Order Hemiptera*)

NYMPH
FAMILY NOTONECTIDAE
(BACKSWIMMERS)

BIOLOGY: Found in lakes, ponds, and streams since many types prefer cool, fresh waters rich in aquatic vegetation. Growth to maturity may take up to five years. Consequently, nymphal forms of *Odonata* can be found in varied sizes at any time of the year.

EMERGENCE: Nymphs (or naiads) crawl out of the water like stoneflies when actual emergence takes place, and they exhibit the similar tendency of schooling and migration to shallows before their hatches.

IMPORTANCE: Damselflies have concentrated migrations during the summer months, thus they are of importance in certain localities. Dragonflies are sometimes important when the females are ovipositing their eggs on the surface of the water.

BIOLOGY: Found in a wide variety of habitats ranging from lakes and ponds to streams of various sizes and composition. Their tolerance of water temperature covers an extremely wide range, and thus, they can be found from sea-level areas to areas as high as 15,000 feet. Backswimmers, in particular, prefer large pools of streams and medium-sized pools.

EMERGENCE: Mostly summer during the months of August and September.

IMPORTANCE: Water boatmen and backswimmers are both of only local importance.

CHAPTER 3: The Rationale of Mayfly Existence and Emergence

OURS is the great fortune of living in an expansive country, traversed by thousands of accessible trout streams and rivers varying in outlook anywhere between limestone and chalk streams, small freestone, and ample, silted rivers. In current tempo they range from the fast and turbulent to the smooth-running flows comfortable for wading and conducive to the surface feeding of trout. Mayflies, those seemingly delicate aquatic insects, occupy every one of these ecological niches and, fortunately for fly fishermen, commonly occur and will emerge profusely in many of them.

Our focus must be confined to those waters that can support permanent populations of trout. The water temperature must vary within the limits of 32 to 77 degrees throughout the year, and there must be sufficient insect biota to help support the trout's numbers. However, trout become most active during those periods of the year when water temperatures hover between 44 to 68 degrees. This happens to be the same temperature zone needed by mayflies to accomplish their annual growth, migration, and actual emergence. The direct dependency of trout upon the mayflies it shares its environment with parallels the dependency of the fly fisherman who must make his casts at the right time and place when the natural exchanges between trout and mayflies are taking place in nature.

ANCESTRY

Mayflies are among the oldest orders of aquatic insects, breaking away from the primitive ancestor common to all aquatic insects over 300 million years ago. Geologists named this the Permian epoch in earth's history. The forms present in established trout streams of the world, however, are known to have been in existence for only the last 200 million years. This still places them in time long before the advent of dinosaurs that inhabited and trampled the earth many years later. Modern-day mayflies not only appeared before the dinosaurs but also before the permanent splitting of the single land mass called Pangaea, which covered half of the globe and was surrounded by the primeval Pacific Ocean. This mass underwent a definite breakup, and its decomposed parts eventually took the position and shape of our existing continents.

With a common ancestor and the mayflies' preference for a comparatively nonchanging, running-water environment it is little wonder why, to this day, they exhibit a remarkable similarity of form throughout the world. Present-day mayflies still exhibit much resemblance in morphological structure and general biology whether they inhabit the mountain ranges of South Africa, Australia, New Zealand, or South America or the Holarctic regions of Europe, Asia, or North America.

A running-water environment, such as the one preferred and dominated by mayflies, caddises, stoneflies, and midges, is permanent and continuous in nature, changing relatively little throughout the ages. Conversely an impounded aquatic environment, as a lake or a pond, in time could only ensure its oblivion through perpetual deposition and shallowing with age. Running-water environments on the other hand are not evolutionary traps and, consequently, have preserved much of their original forms for eons of time. However, this is not to imply that similar families, genera, and species of mayflies are found in all parts of the globe, simply because they occupy like continuing environments. Despite the existing parallelism of mayfly fauna, climatic and environmental forces unique to each area have brought about distinct pressures for separate lines of evolution. As a result, new forms and species evolved in separate areas of the world. Though a running-water environment is continuous, it is not static. It is in a constant state of flux simply because it is a function of the climatic and geographical realities unique to each area. Furthermore, mayflies are specialized not diversified eaters (most preferring plankton and a few being carnivores) that live in a crowded environment also inhabited by other aquatic insects. They have felt the pressures of time more than any other aquatic types. Consequently, today they exhibit divergent forms, at least on the generic and species level, in different continents and even regions of a given continent.

NORTH AMERICAN MAYFLIES

Just as no two continents of the world exhibit exactly the same mayfly fauna, neither do the separate halves of our own country. The continental United States can be divided into two major trout regions—the West and Midwest-East. The Great Plains Region bisected our country when the last Ice Age dried up enough land, which is unable to support cool, running-water environments today. In essence, it has become an aquatic barrier for the intermingling of the mayflies "trapped" on each side of the country, and therefore, two different groups of species classified under each genera (of each family) have evolved. The differences in climate and geography are distinct enough to even suppress some genera from occupying the same niche of importance in both areas; some genera that dominate and are well represented on one side are practically devoid on the other (*Stenonema, Rhithrogena, Potamanthus*). We can speculate that the evolution of the separate groups of species has taken place only in the last 10,000 years, since the last ice age, and though it is a short time, as far as evolutionary history is concerned, apparently it has been sufficient enough for the rise of separate species.

By the same token, only those mayflies that are also able to tolerate warm, low-oxygen waters can still inhabit the marginal trout rivers of central Canada and preserve the link between their original western and midwestern/eastern distributions. To date they maintain their original species status and are found in both eastern and western regions of the country

(*Ephemerella margarita, Rhithrogena undulata, Ephemera simulans* or Brown Drake, *Hexagenia limbata* or Great Lead-winged Drake, *Ephoron album* or White Drake, and *Leptophlebia nebulosa* or Black Quill).

TROUT STREAMS

In the world of the trout, oxygen and food are prerequisites for survival. Both aspects determine its existence or nonexistence in an aquatic environment. In general, oxygen is a function of water temperature, oxygen-producing plants, and the aeration of the moving current, the latter being the most important source of oxygen in most running-water environments that support trout. Trout lakes are characterized by having a high-oxygen content due either to the water-cooling effects of altitude or latitude, vegetation, and cold, spring-like beginnings. The types of organic food in trout waters, however, are dependent on the physical composition of the substrate (bottom) exhibited by a given body of water.

Current is the most significant characteristic of trout waters, which are environments exemplified by moving or constantly replenished water. The typical trout stream has its genesis from the cold springs high in the mountains with currents as fast as 200cm/second. Within either a few miles or hundreds of miles, it will eventually transform into a barely moving body of water crawling as slow as 20cm/second. Between these two extremes in current, a myriad of microhabitats (or ecological niches) is created.

A stream that flows in a straight path and maintains a uniform depth and width, descending gradually in slope, will exhibit a gradual change in its bottom ranging from the coarsest to the finest particles the farther it courses downstream. Boulders, which can be found at the very beginning of the flow, will be replaced by small rocks, then pebbles, gravel, and vegetation, and eventually silt and rich marl. Consequently, the smallest and lightest particles are always the last to be deposited along the bottom of an unvarying stream.

However, if there is one generality that can be made regarding the result of the forces of nature, it is that they do not lend themselves to simple examples. No better example can be offered than that of geographical variations. Most trout streams will experience dramatic rises and falls throughout their course. Many descend in stepladder fashion, while others are forced to take great current-slowing bends around uncarvable rock formations. As is often the case, most will acquire infusions of water along their course, thus, once again, increasing their force and bedload-carrying capacity. High-altitude lakes and spring creeks, on the other hand, have plateau-like beginnings, flow for miles smoothly, and then drop abruptly in altitude; theirs is a placid origin with a fast ending, almost the reverse of the preceding example.

In conclusion, it could be said that waters that support trout are, in actuality, extremely diverse habitats which vary dramatically in general character. Therefore, no single example will suffice for a general description.

Since trout waters have to conform to the topography over which they traverse throughout their course, a multitude of microhabitats is created along their bottom in any given area. These microhabitats have given rise to divergent types of mayflies that can be found in the majority of trout waters that vary in configuration from fishlike appearances to outlines of extremely flat, slim forms. However, although aquatic organisms (including mayflies) are not subjected to the intensity of the forces of adaptation as are terrestrial dwellers, they are still compelled to yield to the rigors of natural selection—the biological process by which advantage is conferred to those organisms that have the structures and functions enabling them to cope successfully with the conditions of their immediate environment. The adaptive process of nature is of significance to anglers for it has resulted in certain types of mayflies abundantly occupying only certain trout streams or specific stretches of them.

THE MAYFLY TYPES

Adaptation is a prerequisite to survival in the treacherous, competitive world of the mayflies. As a result, some specific forms have evolved to take full advantage of specific microecological niches available along the bottom of trout streams.

The Swimmers (*Families Baetidae and Siphlonuridae*)

FIG. 3-1 *Isonychia* nymph (side view)—see also Fig. 1-2.

These nymphs have a fusiform body which offers the least resistance in a fluid environment. Their body structure is widest approximately one-third along their length and is tapered at the ends, an optimal configuration for an insect (or fish) that has to continually face the swiftest current or swim efficiently about in search of food. In a turbulent environment they also have to regain their lost footing and in a tranquil one, perpetually escape the predation of trout.

The three principal genera belonging in these two families are: 1. *Siphlonurus*—a moderate-current dweller that has to elude its enemies continually. As a consequence, its numbers are uppermost in waters, such as those with submerged beds of vegetation, which afford them natural protection. 2. *Isonychias*—a closely related genus. However, unlike *Siphlonurus* nymphs, they are food strainers and are in the habit of facing the faster current to intercept and catch passing particles of food with the basket-shaped hairs on their forelegs. 3. *Baetis* (and *Pseudocloeon*)—little mayflies that continually have to regain their footholds in the bottom substrate of a stream because of their small size and light weight.

All three of these streamliners are among the most common mayflies found in running waters. Members of other aquatic orders exhibit a similar configuration and consequential adaptation to the same type of waters. For example, the majority of stoneflies and free-living forms of caddises, such as the extremely common wormlike *Hydropsyches*, are most notably among these.

Clingers (*Family Heptageniidae*)

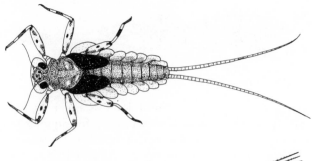

FIG. 3-2 *Epeorus pleuralis* nymph (top view)

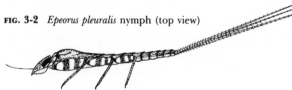

FIG. 3-3 *Epeorus* nymph (side view)

The clingers are strictly feeders among the smooth surfaces of a trout stream's exposed sections of boulders, pebbles, or gravel. Their squashed configuration permits them to scrape their food rather than catch it in the nearly dead-calm one-inch "boundary layer" of current that encircles permanent objects in a stream. For protection, their pencil-thin side or lateral configuration allows them to slip into the crevices among the rocks to escape their natural enemies. A further adaptation for survival in a treacherous, white-water environment is the enlargement of their gills which serves to increase marginal contact and prevent water from getting underneath their abdomen and prying them loose from their holds. Genera *Epeorus* and *Rhithrogenas* are the neotypical mayflies of a fast-water environment and, contrary to popular belief, their gills *do not* act as "suction cups."

By no means is flatness a prerequisite to fast-running waters. Two genera in this family, *Stenonemas* and *Heptagenias*, are well suited to survive in nearly dead-calm habitats. Their survival again depends on their ability to slip into the gravel when an enemy approaches and on the difficulty trout have picking them off the surface of roughly faced rocks.

Burrowers (*Family Ephemeridae*)

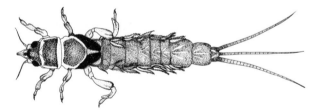

FIG. 3-4 *Hexagenia limbata nymph (top view)*

FIG. 3-5 *Hexagenia nymph (side view)*

Nymphs of this type exhibit long, slender bodies and shovel-like frontal processes used for digging U-shaped burrows in the soft bottom substrate of streams. They are completely unconcerned about the speed of the current, for their survival depends entirely on remaining buried. As long as the bottom substrate is penetrable, their numbers will thrive often with impressive density. Customarily, slow-moving sections of rivers, where the reduced bedload-carrying capacity of the current allows silt to accumulate along the bottom, support their best num-

bers—as many as 500 nymphs in just one square-foot section. Few mayflies (and trout) can exist in some of the low-altitude portions of rivers where some burrowers are found because of the dangerously low content of oxygen in such waters.

Sprawlers (*Family Ephemerellidae and Families Caenidae and Tricorythidae*)

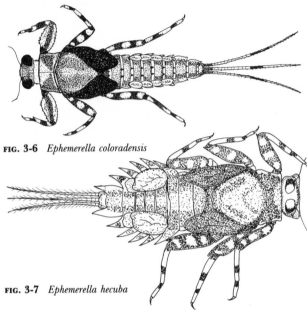

FIG. 3-6 *Ephemerella coloradensis*

FIG. 3-7 *Ephemerella hecuba*

These types are the most varied in form and general appearance, being the product of adaptations to a wide diversity of ecological niches. As a result, they are the most geographically widespread and abundant of all the aquatic forms found in trout streams. *Ephemerella* hatches are also the most predictable and consistent and, in general, the most important mayfly hatches to anglers.

Some *Ephemerella* forms closely resemble those of the swimmers, while others resemble the flat, clinging types. This is most obvious in *E. coloradensis*, which occupies the faster rocky sections of the headwaters of western trout streams. On the other hand *E. hecuba* (and *Caenidae* members) gravitate to the slow silted areas and depend entirely for their survival on lying flat on the stream bottom to allow the hairs on their bodies to collect particles of silt, serving to camouflage them from enemies. Moreover, their enlarged first gill serves to cover the rest and prevent them from suffocating with the minute silt particles that constantly settle to the bottom in their microhabitat.

Mayflies are particular feeders and are specialized in form as a direct result of adaptation to certain specific underwater habitats. The swimmers, members of families *Baetidae* and *Siphlonuridae*, are well equipped to forage about in search of food and are especially important to fly fishermen in weedy streams, though they can also thrive in other types of waters. Free-stone streams are made to order for the clinging types (Family *Heptageniidae*). Rivers that flow at a crawl, allowing silt to build up along the bottom, create optimal microhabitats for the burrowers and may even be devoid of other types of mayflies. Every environment is perfectly suited for one and limited for another. Consequently, the importance of each type is also dependent on the personal preference of anglers themselves. *Ephemerellas*, on the other hand, are significant to all, for the sole reason that they are found in all habitats. Their exceptional adaptation ensures their wide geographical spread and consequently their importance.

FIG. 3-8 Optimal habitat for members of Family *Baetidae*: *Baetis, Pseudocloeon*, and *Callibaetis*

In conclusion, North American trout streams, in general, that have similar biological properties will have similar types of mayfly fauna, whether they are located in Pennsylvania, Michigan, or Montana. Furthermore, the manner of emergence of the members belonging to each type will also duplicate itself in all waters.

The family concept in the treatment of our North American mayflies not only helps us to understand the different groups and their biology but also facilitates the making of correlations among their member species found on opposite sides of the continent. Each mayfly family contains members in the western and eastern regions which resemble each other closely in general appearance and general biology. However, because of morphological differences, they are not taxonomically classified as the same species. Thus the counterpart of the eastern Pale Evening Dun (*Ephemerella dorothea*) is the western species *Ephemerella inermis*, which, because of its physical similarity from the angler's point of view, is commonly re-

ferred to as the Pale Morning Dun. The Gordon Quill (*Epeorus pleuralis*), so common in eastern trout streams during the month of May, is represented in the West by the species *Epeorus longimanus* or the Western Gordon Quill. As a general rule, western counterparts emerge about a month later in the season.

SEASONAL EMERGENCE

Most mayfly species found in our trout streams emerge during a seven-month period during the year, normally between the months of April to September. The observant angler will also notice that the species will emerge for the season in a nearly predictable chronological sequence. Though the entire order may be advanced or delayed by deviations in climate from one year to another, it never undergoes major alterations in its basic progression. With a remarkable stability, every species is immediately preceded and succeeded by the same two species year in and year out. This phenomenon of aquatic nature depends upon the fact that most mayflies require the same amount of annual days to achieve full maturity (and to hatch). Thus, deviations in seasonal climate will influence all species similarly, preserving the uniformity of their emergence order for every season.

Accepted as an article of faith among animal ecologists is the axiom that no two species which occupy the same ecological niche can occur together indefinitely in the same habitat. This would imply that all mayflies, even closely related ones which belong to the same genera, will have to exhibit differences either in space or in time. In a crowded trout-stream environment, spatial accommodations among the species are basically impossible; however, cooperation, when it is time to emerge, is most clearly evident. Every species has a time slot in which to emerge or hatch, and only during unusual circumstances, such as extremely cold or stormy weather, does more than one species emerge during a given time. Such occasions are multiple-hatch situations that are exceptions rather than the rule. "Cooperation" to reduce direct competition in the natural order is not out of altruistic or economic reasons, but results from the occupation and domination by one species of every spatial and/or time opening that is available in nature.

To further ensure the survival of the species, aquatic insects, including mayflies, will appear in great concentrations when they emerge. Concentrated emergences will ensure the meeting of large numbers of males and females approximately 24 hours after the hatch, thus guaranteeing the copulation and ovipositing of fertilized eggs which will be deposited back into the stream. Though females will mate more or less at the same section of the stream in which they emerged from, they will head *upstream* for as much as one or two miles during ovipositing. They travel this distance to compensate for the washing-down effect of the current which they underwent during their long growth to full nymphal maturity!

The nymphs of most mayfly species require approximately 364 days of aquatic growth to accomplish full maturity, and only then are they capable to emerge or hatch. Yet, after emerging, they barely live more than 24 hours as a terrestrial, thus the name *Ephemeroptera*, order of the short-lived winged insects.

Though growth to maturity takes place over hundreds of days, it does not take place uniformly during that time simply because it is a function of the prevailing water temperature which undergoes a very dramatic general cycle from one season to another. Actually, the growth of nymphs occurs when the temperature of the water exceeds the 45-degree mark, and this will take place in a trout stream for only about seven months of the year. Full maturity, then, must be accomplished in approximately 210 days out of 365.

Species like the Dark Hendrickson (*Ephemerella subvaria*), that emerges in the early part of May in eastern and midwestern streams, will attain almost 11mm in size by mid-October, remain nearly the same size until the following April, and then will grow the final millimeter for full maturity (now 12mm), hatching soon after. Similarly, other species that hatch in spring will exhibit the same seasonal growth pattern. Those species that appear at midseason will attain only half their full growth by fall (*Ephemerella grandis*—7mm), which will not again commence until the spring (7.5mm), and yet will be finished by late June (15mm).

Unseasonably cold winters can delay the water temperature from reaching the 45-degree mark by as much as one, two, or even three weeks in the spring, leaving less time for growth to occur. This will cause all hatches to take place that much later during the fishing season.

The reader should bear in mind that water temperature in a given trout stream is also a function of its latitude, altitude, seasonal climate, and distance from its source. Streams in the lower longitudinal zones will experience warmer climates earlier than more northern regions, and their entire chronological order of emergence will be ahead of that of the colder area. The hatch of Light Hendricksons (*Ephemerella rotunda*) takes place as early as March in the states of Tennessee, North Carolina, and lower Virginia, yet will not make its seasonal appearance until late May in New York and Michigan.

The altitude of a general area is also a determining factor in seasonal emergences. All the western hatches are delayed as much as one month behind those in the East and Midwest. It also influences, in a very general way, emergences within a *given* river where the seasonal appearance of a species "moves" upstream because of the colder waters caused by the higher altitude. However, the more we go upstream the closer we get to the river's cold, spring-like source which also is influential in causing its hatches to be delayed, and always to be moving in an upstream direction.

The approximate 210 days of growth is simply not enough for a few large mayfly species, such as the big, burrowing mayflies. In their case, growth to maturity may take two or even three years, similar to the length of time required by the larger stoneflies and caddises. Consistent with our previous comments, a species like *Hexagania limbata* or Great Lead-winged Drake, which requires two years to be ready to hatch in a trout stream in Michigan, may achieve full maturity within one year in a more southerly latitude.

Once each species has had the necessary amount of

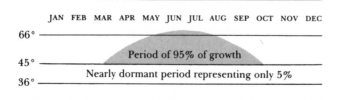

Table 3-1 Example given is for a typical eastern stream.

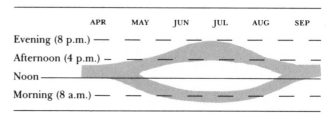

Table 3-2 Seasonal adjustment of mayfly hatches.

days for full maturity, it is ready to hatch, and it will do so for approximately a two- to three-week period during the season. Spring and fall emergers customarily appear at midday, while midseason mayflies hatch in the mornings and evenings during the summer months. In a broad sense the seasonal occurrence of all mayflies, when graphed against the periods of the day, can be represented as in Table 3-2.

Each mayfly family contains a number of species that will follow each other quickly in seasonal succession. They will, as a group, adopt an evening or morning timetable. The six families of mayflies (excluding *Ephemerellidae*) will adjust as follows:

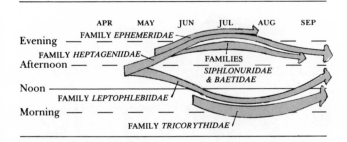

Table 3-3 Daily adjustment of mayfly families.

Family *Ephemerellidae*, which contains the extremely common *Ephemerellas*, is a notable exception in the sense that not all of its species will adjust in the same direction in the daily timetable (only eastern species are shown):

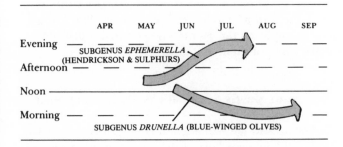

Table 3-4 Daily adjustment of eastern members of Family *Ephemerellidae*.

As the reader can see, even though Family *Ephemerellidae* species will not appear or move at the same time of day throughout the season, the species within each of its subgroups will. *All* Hendricksons and Sulphurs (*E. subvaria*, *E. rotunda/E. invaria*, and *E. dorothea*) move in one direction, while Blue-Winged Olives (*E. cornuta/E. walkeri*, *E. cornutella/E. lata*) prefer the morning hours of the day in which to make their seasonal appearance.

DETERMINANTS OF DAILY EMERGENCE

While water temperature plays its role in accomplishing full maturity of the nymphs of each species and determining *when* they could emerge during the season, the time of day they choose to do so is solely dependent on the solar radiation of the sun. Mayflies, in particular, are extremely sensitive to direct sunlight. The variation of the sun's heat from spring to summer to fall causes them to *biologically* adjust to the cooler times of the days—evenings and mornings—during the summer months, as we have just seen. So, regardless of the time of day the nymphs of a given species reach full maturity, when they will emerge depends entirely on when they can do so without reducing their chances for survival. For a better understanding of this important reality of mayfly survival, we should look into their life cycle, which happens to be a common one to all its species.

The mayfly cycle (see page 26) has two stages: an aquatic one of approximately 364 days for most species (A), and a terrestrial phase lasting but a day or two in duration (B). Once the nymphs are matured, exhibiting black wing pads, they are ready to leave their aquatic environment and be transformed into terrestrial, winged forms. The mechanics of this conversion from one habitat to another is accomplished by the nymphs either floating (1) to the surface of the water or actually migrating to the margins of the stream and crawling out of the stream (as is the case with members of Family *Siphlonuridae*). The first winged stage, known to scientists as subimagoes and to anglers as duns, will quickly slip out of the nymphs (2), flutter momentarily to dry their wings (3), and be off quickly to the streamside flora (4).

The mayfly cycle cannot be completed until a second metamorphosis is experienced when the duns shuck their exoskeletons and are therefore transformed into spinners (or imagoes) (5). This last phase is imperative for the survival of the species, since mating of males and females, and the fertilization and ovipositing of the female eggs back into the stream, can only be accomplished in the imago stage (with the exception of female duns of genus *Ephoron*). However, the change from dun to spinner depends in nature on a very precarious balance of *moisture preservation*, and *cannot* occur if the dun exoskeleton is not maintained pliable and breakable. This important need for the preservation of body moisture is most obviously exemplified when mayflies are raised in a controlled environment, such as a home aquarium. Under these circumstances, those individuals left to

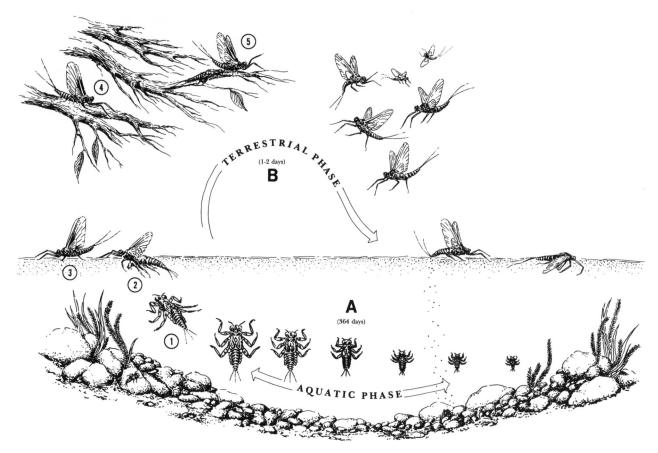

FIG. 3-9 The mayfly life cycle.

cling to the glass just above the water, after they emerge, will molt into spinners, those removed to a drier room temperature will be unable to do so and soon perish. Perhaps the reader can recall a time astream when he captured a few duns and placed them in one of his plastic fly boxes, only to discover later that they shriveled up like prunes within a few hours. Or perhaps he has held one up to the sun and found that within minutes it began to flutter and, when held too long, would not even be able to fly. Such is the fine line between surviving and perishing in the world of the mayfly.

It is little wonder why hatches never take place during hot, sunny days, and yet are at their best during cool and/or cloudy weather, as is usually the case with spring and fall days. The forces for survival are so intense that some species that are customarily *midday* emergers will refuse to appear during bright, sunny periods and will even wait until a more favorable day for emergence. This may delay their scheduled emergence by as much as five days, though the nymphs have reached full maturity 80 to 100 hours before!

To give the reader a chance to mentally digest the points I have made in the preceding pages, I will now state them in a more referable manner. The foregoing example of the Henry's Fork will be utilized to make some of them that much clearer.

Axioms of Mayfly Seasonal and Daily Emergence

1. Spring and fall hatches will customarily take place at midday, regardless of the water temperature and the weather, in most circumstances; those that occur during summer will be either in the morning or evening.
2. Water temperature is the principal *long-run* determiner for when the entire chronological order of mayflies will take place in the season. It will not determine *when* a hatch will take place in a given day. (Compare the water temperature when the Pale Morning Duns [*E. infrequens*] emerged on June 21st and June 25th in the above example.)
3. Cloudy days will, on the average, experience the most profuse and longest hatches and, most impor-

tantly, will be the most conducive periods for the feeding of trout.

4. Sunny summer days will exhibit the opposite of cloudy days. Sparser and shorter hatches will take place very early and late in the day. They will have a similar effect on the formulation of spinner swarms.

5. Midday emergers are those "scheduled" by nature to appear between 11 a.m. and 3 p.m. during the day either because of the *time of year* or because they occupy a *midday ecological niche* during summer. They will postpone their daily emergence altogether during hot, sunny periods only to reappear when a more favorable day for emergence arrives. Consider the case of the Western Green Drake in the chart.

6. Evening and morning emergers will emerge earlier and later in the day, respectively, on cool, semicloudy, or cloudy days. A good example is the emergence "movement" of the Pale Morning Duns, as well as that of the Small Western Green Drake (see chart).

7. Chronological order of daily emergence will be preserved regardless of weather as exemplified by the times that the Pale Morning Duns and Western Green Drake appeared on June 21st and June 28th. On cool, semi-cloudy, or cloudy days, however, overlaps in emergence will occur.

PHYSICAL ADAPTATIONS DURING THE SEASON

We have thus far covered the general biology of mayflies, the determiners of seasonal and daily emergence, and have pointed out that, as a group, mayflies must make certain adjustments in time to conform to the climatic changes that take place during the fishing season. We have found out that the preservation of body moisture must be accomplished for the duns to molt into spinners approximately 24 hours later and to complete their life cycles. So far we know they make *biological* adaptations in time to ensure their survival; however, it is also apparent that they make some *morphological* or physical accommodations to achieve the same objective. This is the last issue in our present discussion, which we will now turn to.

We said before that each family (or type) contains a few genera (or groups), and, in turn, each genera is composed of a small quantity of species that will emerge during the season in a predictable sequence. We also saw in this chapter that more than one species in some genera of families may be of importance to anglers. We will only use one of these families, *Ephemerellidae*, to illustrate perhaps the most interesting aspect of the *physical* adaptations of mayflies as the season progresses. Not only do the species move to earlier and later times of the day for the preserva-

Table 3-5

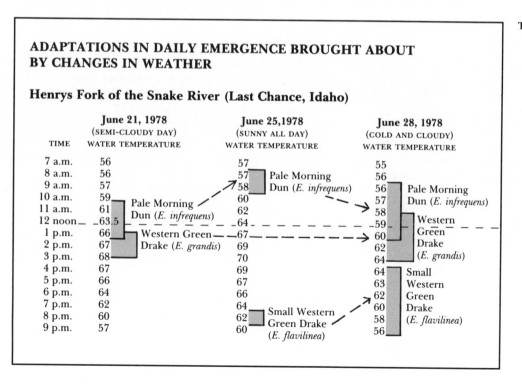

ADAPTATIONS IN DAILY EMERGENCE BROUGHT ABOUT BY CHANGES IN WEATHER

Henrys Fork of the Snake River (Last Chance, Idaho)

tion of moisture, but they will also get *smaller in size* and *lighter in color.* Both of these physical body changes will ensure lower heat absorption during warm weather in cold-blooded animals and will help mayflies remain internally cooler during the summer months. Let's look at an example—subgenus *Ephemerella* and *Drunella*, which belong to Family Ephemerellidae and are two very important groups for anglers.

Eastern and Midwestern Ephemerellas:

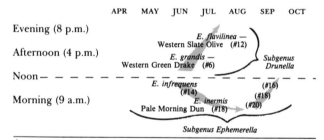

Table 3-6

Western Ephemerellas:

Table 3-7 Emergence times are for the temperature zone of the United States; hook type 94833 3X Fine.

The first concept the reader should realize, by studying the preceding example, is the difference in the time of seasonal emergence between eastern and western *Ephemerellas.* This is neotypical of the approximately one-month delay of western hatches behind those that take place on the opposite side of the country. Second, note the obvious adjustment of even related species to move in unison toward an evening or morning timetable. Third—the point of our immediate purpose—the chart indicates that the species *within* each subgenera (genera for any other family) will get smaller in size (and also lighter in color) as the season progresses; the latter adaptation is most obvious among those that move toward an evening timetable.

The size range can be very volatile, as exemplified by the Pale Morning Dun (*E. inermis*). This can occur to such an extent that past angling authors recommend a different hook size for the imitation of the same hatch. Ernest Schwiebert in *Nymphs* gives a size No. 12 to a size No. 14 for *E. inermis*, while Doug Swisher and Carl Richards in *Selective Trout* call for sizes No. 20 to No. 22 for the same species. Yet Al Caucci and Bob Nastasi in *Hatches* recommend hook sizes No. 16 to No. 18.

Actually, all three recommendations are correct; however, the reader should keep in mind that the excellent Pale Morning Dun hatches of the West are caused by two species: the first is *E. infrequens* of a No. 14 hook size, and it appears in June; it is then followed by *E. inermis*, which emerges from the middle of July to the middle of August. Within a period of just one month, this species will drop from a size No. 18 to No. 20 during the last two weeks of July, and then will start reversing itself back to size No. 18 and even No. 16 by the middle of August. *E. inermis* is a classic and rare case of drastic size adaptation to changes in temperature. Its smallest size is reached at the hottest time of the year, the last days of July.

In mayflies, size and coloration changes during the season are functions that primarily regulate the absorption of sun energy, which in their case, tend to decrease the thermal budget in their body. They do not appear to be adaptations for the purpose of camouflage as with other animals in nature. However, it is also possible that their size and coloration adaptions are the result of compromise between various *complementary* selective pressures. Though when viewed within the full context of seasonal emergence in general, both of these *physical* changes appear to be consistent with the *biological* changes of emergence time that they also exhibit. All three adjustments are, in all probability, for the same purpose—the preservation of body moisture so that the duns can molt into the spinner phase and complete their life cycle. Their very survival in nature depends on it.

Hatches—the phenomena when flotillas of duns appear on the surface of trout waters—were historically the original impetus for the birth and consequential development of the sport of fly fishing. Regardless of the many other applications we have invented for the fly rod, to date the majority of fly fishermen still depend on the hatches of mayflies to offer them the same sportive pleasures as they did to the founders of the sport many years ago. The challenges for success have never waned: cautious approach, precise delivery, naturalistic presentation,

FIG. 3-10 A hatch of mayflies.

and the ever-present demands for more effective artificial imitations as a result of increasingly sophisticated trout. As in the past, mayfly hatches today continue to breathe life into an otherwise silent stream, and demand the best of those anglers who insist on success in place of failure at the hands of a most cagey opponent.

In this chapter we have covered the plausible reasons that have caused the present distribution of mayflies and the realities involved that will determine their seasonal and daily emergence. Its sole purpose has been to explain why some forms exist only in certain environments and why hatches take place as they do during the season. The author has found it necessary to speculate on their evolutionary development and ventured forth in selecting the controlling aspect of nature (moisture preservation) to explain the biological and morphological adaptations that mayflies exhibit during the year. Needless to say, exceptions to the rules will occur for no other reason than that the forces of nature are neither predictable nor yet

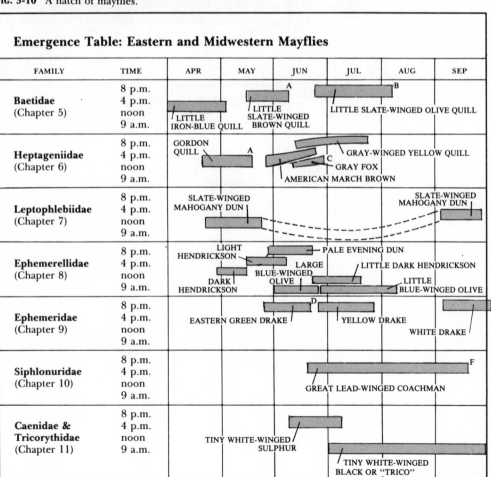

Emergence Table: Eastern and Midwestern Mayflies

Table 3-8

Emergence dates are applicable to the southern zones of midwestern, New York, and New England states. Subtract approximately 30 days for lower Appalachian states, 20 for the states of Virginia and Maryland, and 10 for Pennsylvania. Add 10 days for northern regions of the midwest, New York, and New England.

A—Strictly an eastern hatch.
B—Strictly a midwestern hatch.
C—Gray Fox seasonal emergence is sporadically continued by other *Stenonema* species until the middle of August.
D—Replaced by *Hexagenia limbata* in the Midwest.
E—Of importance only where *Ephorons* are known to exist (see Chapter 9).
F—Sporadic hatches, best on cloudy days.

fully explainable. However, the angler would agree that it is better to walk within guidelines than to lack rhyme or reason. With some thought as to why hatches occur during certain times of the day, he will find that a sixth sense, indicating when to meet them, will develop. With the information given in Chapter 4 pertaining to presentation, he will become aware of the best ways to fish them.

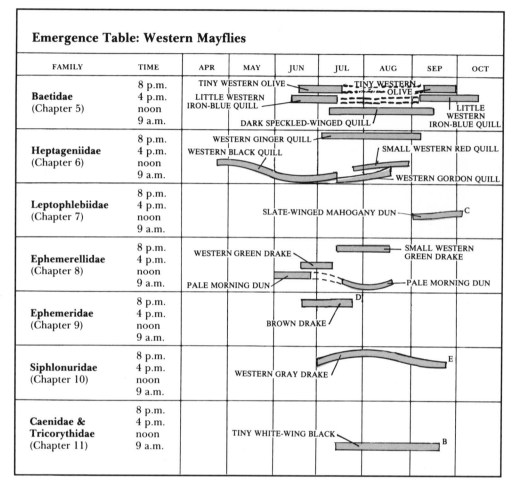

Emergence Table: Western Mayflies

FAMILY	TIME	APR	MAY	JUN	JUL	AUG	SEP	OCT
Baetidae (Chapter 5)	8 p.m. / 4 p.m. / noon / 9 a.m.	TINY WESTERN OLIVE / LITTLE WESTERN IRON-BLUE QUILL / DARK SPECKLED-WINGED QUILL			TINY WESTERN OLIVE		LITTLE WESTERN IRON-BLUE QUILL	
Heptageniidae (Chapter 6)	8 p.m. / 4 p.m. / noon / 9 a.m.	WESTERN GINGER QUILL / WESTERN BLACK QUILL				SMALL WESTERN RED QUILL / WESTERN GORDON QUILL		
Leptophlebiidae (Chapter 7)	8 p.m. / 4 p.m. / noon / 9 a.m.			SLATE-WINGED MAHOGANY DUN			C	
Ephemerellidae (Chapter 8)	8 p.m. / 4 p.m. / noon / 9 a.m.	WESTERN GREEN DRAKE / PALE MORNING DUN			SMALL WESTERN GREEN DRAKE / PALE MORNING DUN			
Ephemeridae (Chapter 9)	8 p.m. / 4 p.m. / noon / 9 a.m.			BROWN DRAKE	D			
Siphlonuridae (Chapter 10)	8 p.m. / 4 p.m. / noon / 9 a.m.		WESTERN GRAY DRAKE			E		
Caenidae & Tricorythidae (Chapter 11)	8 p.m. / 4 p.m. / noon / 9 a.m.		TINY WHITE-WING BLACK			B		

Table 3-9

Emergence times given are for the states of Montana and Idaho. Subtract 14 days for California and Oregon, 7 days for the states of Colorado and Wyoming (including Yellowstone National Park).

A—followed in October and November and again in February-March by *Baetis tricaudatus*, a very prolific mayfly.

B—Of principal importance to anglers in the spinner stage.

C—Will appear sporadically earlier in the season, hatches caused by *Paraleptophlebia heteronea*.

D—Replaced by *Hexagenia limbata* in California, where the species is found.

E—Time of day given is for spinner falls, actual emergence occurs at 11 o'clock in the morning.

CHAPTER 4: The Mechanics of Good Presentation

MOST circles of life manifest different philosophies of approach to accomplish a certain task or to attain a specific level of expertise. Analogously, the fly fishing fraternity also demonstrates distinct schools of thought as to how to succeed in the taking of trout. For lack of a better terminology, the two camps will be referred to as the presentationists vs. the imitators, or hatch masters. The difference rests on how their group members perceive the manner in which trout make the separation between a natural and an artificial imitation.

The presentation-oriented angler, in the strictest sense, believes that emphasis need only be given to the credible manner in which a pattern is offered, the degree in which it duplicates the behavior or motion of the natural. He insists on using nondescriptive imitations during all hatches. The match-the-hatch purist tends, on the other hand, to place all his hopes on the imitative virtues of his artificial. I doubt any one individual in the real fly fishing world would fit either of these two models exactly, but most anglers naturally gravitate toward one philosophy at the expense of the other. As may be suspected, when considering the lessons of reason from other quarters of life, the most beneficial and rational approach is, in all likelihood, a compromise between the two.

Unfortunately, too many anglers place excessive trust on their favorite patterns, failing to appreciate that no single or mere handful of artificial imitations can possibly duplicate, even remotely, the wide spectrum of mayfly types exhibited in nature. It would behoove them to imitate closely, in a most practical manner, the emerging insect.

As we saw in Chapter 1, trout will be selective three-fourths of the time during the emergence of the principal types. Occasional marginal successes tend to reinforce the presentationists' philosophy that insects need not be imitated closely to catch trout. Yet, periods of total failure, usually during good hatches when trout develop a strong sense of comparison between natural and artificial, are dismissed as being the results of the noncooperation of nature. A common excuse is "there are just too many naturals and no one can take those trout." Perhaps, but it is doubtful that such cause and effect transitions are based on strong links of logic. After all, the path of least mental resistance in the stream is to throw the blame on those damn mayflies!

On the other hand, the strict imitation extremist is often caught in the stream with as many as 20 trout feeding frantically about him. He is desperately scrambling through his fly boxes and trying pattern after pattern, casting each only a few times and moving from one to another too hastily. He usually fails to fish each thoroughly and *correctly* before moving on to his next experiment. He is convinced, however, that once he hits upon the "right fly," and only then, will he succeed and proceed to clean house.

During the research necessary for this book, I have been most fortunate to encounter and fish hundreds of mayfly hatches that have varied greatly in overall density. Some were so mediocre that the trout's hunger remained so insatiable that they would have taken anything cast to them. The great majority caused them to become selective only three-fourths of the time. Some, encountered by design and not sheer accident, were so thick that the wing tips of the floating naturals would literally touch each other, and their collective density would practically change the color of the water. A good example of the latter phenomenon is the hatches of the Tiny Western Olives (*Pseudocloeon edmundsi*) that take place in the early summer and again during the fall months in western trout streams.

In all frankness, I never encountered a hatch that produced trout that could not be taken with a marked degree of regularity. I will spend the rest of the pages in this chapter to explain and demonstrate how such a degree of success is possible. The mechanics involved in being successful during all hatches, regardless of their density, are dependent on: the right equipment, the proper positioning to rising trout, precise and economical delivery, and an exact imitation that will cause trout to take the artificial with an equivalent confidence exhibited for a recently consumed natural. These four concepts are really borrowing from both hypothetical types discussed previously—the strict presentationists and the imitators. As the reader can already detect, the answer to success during any hatch is to adopt the most rational and advantageous approach—that which incorporates the best of these two worlds.

THE NONHATCH SITUATION

If a survey could ever be conducted among fly fishermen as to whether they would rather fish during a hatch and, presumably, to rising trout, or cast at a blank stretch of water devoid of any surface activity, surely the great majority would choose the first option. It is a pity, though, that on many occasions anglers will not have the benefit of a hatch in

progress when arriving at a stream. During such periods, all they can do is make the best of it. The best possible recourse would be to use a nymph to reach trout holding deep in the bottom of the stream. The decision then would concern the selection of a nymph pattern, hoping to find one that represents the nymphal stage of an aquatic insect available to the trout in the waters to be fished. Some decisions are better than others, since certain types of nymphs have the advantage of already being familiar and more credible to the trout that are habitually feeding on them.

For example, in the smooth-flowing sections of streams and rivers where burrowing mayflies can thrive, a large wiggle-nymph artificial is often extremely effective during the two hours before hatching. Imitations of the big *Isonychias* (Great Lead-Winged Coachman) and *Siphlonurus* (Western Gray Drake) are good producers at midday during summer months. Their nymphs, at this time, are perpetually migrating to the shallows of streams so they may crawl out of the water when actual emergence finally takes place. In fast waters, the imitations of *Heptageniidae*, clinging mayfly nymphs, or the larvas of the olive worm-like *Hydropsyches*, members of the caddis complex, are often impressive producers between mayfly and caddis hatches.

An hour before a mayfly hatch is to take place, its nymphs will become quite active along the bottom of

FIG. 4-1 Trout holding deep during nonhatch periods; the moment of the nymph.

a stream. Consequently, they will be swept into the main currents where they are made available to the trout in comparatively greater numbers than those of an inactive species.

A good example of this phenomenon was made very clear one day when a group of friends and I were fishing the Madison River in Montana. We had all started using streamers, Muddler minnows, and other heavy hardware since no hatch was taking place. As if by accident, I detected a single Pale Morning Dun (*E. inermis*) emerging near the margin of a pool, and since we were doing so terribly with the bigger flies, I decided to give a size 16 nymph a try. For the next hour, until the hatch began in earnest, we proceeded to take seven fish, the best an unexpected four-pound rainbow whose stomach was full of Pale Morning Dun nymphs. The angler should keep in mind, however, that nymphs during nonhatch times are rarely available to trout in sufficient quantities to warrant their moving into the natural feeding underwater lanes in a stream. They usually stay in their protected lairs, foraging out only to intercept a natural that is drifting very close by. For such reasons, working a nymph version of the hatch-to-be should be done deep and as close to holding places along the bottom where trout can take them with a minimal amount of effort.

Unfortunately, much too often we find ourselves in the stream without any indications as to what hatches will be shortly taking place nor of their prevalent aquatic types whose imitations we should put to use. In such situations, I do one of two things. First, I hold a small seine net, which I always carry in the back pocket of my vest, against the bottom of the stream with one hand for about a minute. Frequently, it is a good way to intercept the free drift of those types of nymphs or larvae presently active and available to the trout. If nothing turns up, my alternative is to *gently* tip over a few small boulders just upstream from where I am holding the little net. This dislodges a few nymphs and causes them to drift into my net. Examples of the size and shape of the most prevalent types can be determined with a quick glance. The nymphs can then be gently released back into the water. By the way, those with black wing pads are near to or have fully reached maturity. Imitations of them are usually the most credible to the trout, and the most effective before their actual emergence that same day.

Interesting to note, selectivity (admittedly to a lesser degree than in hatch periods) can and does take place during nonhatch periods. The scientist calls this the "available factor," which mathematically demonstrates the preference or selectivity of trout for a certain type of highly available insect; for example, mayflies when they become exceedingly active along the stream bottom an hour or two prior to their hatching, or when they undergo their underwater migrations (*Strenomenas* toward shore for the week before the appearance of their species; *Paraleptophlebias* and *Leptophlebias* during their swims upstream in schools before their seasonal occurrences). Selectivity during nonhatch periods can occur for any type of aquatic insect which fulfills the requirements of availability and size.

Fishing a nymph properly is in one way more difficult than fishing an artificial near the surface, since the angler will have no indication as to the relative speed of his artificial in comparison to that of the current in which it is drifting. Unlike surface fishing, no feedback is offered by the trout while a false take or roll gives some clues as to the effectiveness of presentation or duplicative qualities of an artificial. No such messages are visually transmitted by a trout holding deep, and they either take the nymph pattern or ignore it. The reasons for their outright refusals are not always obvious.

The most important concept to remember in fishing a nymph "blindly" along the bottom of a stream is that, for inherent credibility to a waiting trout, it must be drifting at the same speed as that of the current. Mayflies, regardless of their size or type, are unable to streak through the water more than a few inches per second, even when frantically swimming away from a natural enemy. Moreover, it should be remembered that the speed of the current near the bottom of a stream, due to the friction encountered when flowing around fixed underwater objects, moves approximately one-third as slow as that on the surface current. The first prerequisite to making your imitation appear to be drifting as a natural would is to prevent it from crossing wildly across natural drifts or from moving erratically. It should be slowed down by fishing it *with* the natural current of a stream. As in dry fly fishing, cast the imitation upstream or fish downstream, paying out plenty of slack as you would if you had to minimize the effects of current-producing *drag* on a dry fly. When fished across currents, it should be slowed down by the constant mending and remending of the fly line, upstream from the presumed position of the imitation, to the point that it appears as if the leader is holding it back.

The position of the angler in relation to where he chooses to place his nymph is important, something that becomes more apparent when fishing a dry fly. A 90-degree position, when casting across a multitude of crosscurrents, will undoubtedly cause an artificial to be instantly swept too rapidly and immediately serve to warn the trout that what just streaked by is another one of those anglers' concoctions.

The concepts discussed in the pages that follow concerning the mechanics of the presentation of a dry fly or near-surface imitation will undoubtedly help the angler to become aware of how to compensate for the natural sweeping effects of current. They will also make the angler doubly aware of the important need for line control through better positioning to a specific objective point, which minimizes the serious disadvantages of drag.

Just like dry imitations, nymphs should be constructed out of soft artificial materials. As is most obvious with artificials fished on the surface, trout can take and release a natural faster than a human can blink his eye. In this book, careful attention has been paid to the materials recommended for nymph construction. None are called for that would make a nymph look exquisite on the vise but prove disastrous in the stream. This is an important point not emphasized enough in angling texts. True naturals of mayflies, caddises, stoneflies, and other aquatic insects are soft-bodied insects and not nearly as hard in structure as many of the artificials oftentimes offered by commercial enterprises. A lifeless, steel-hard imitation is meant to hook the buying impulse of the angler not the trout who will reject it the instant they close their mouths on it, if they take it in the first place.

A HATCH SITUATION

In fly fishing, the definition of presentation means either how faithfully an artificial resembles the motion of the natural or how successfully an angler can make it appear *more* vulnerable than the natural. Generally speaking, during the great majority of mayfly hatches, the streamside behavior of the emerging species, whether speaking of the nymph just under the surface film or dun on the surface, falls into two types of action: floating immobile or fluttering momentarily. Mayflies, in general, are exemplified by an emergence cycle in which the nymphal form swims clear to the surface film and, after hovering there for a few seconds, the dun will escape out of it. The dry form then proceeds to float immobile for a distance to dry its wings before it suddenly leaves the water. Larger mayflies, like the majority of caddises, exhibit no dif-

ficulty in escaping out of the nymphal exoskeleton, but they do have a tough time getting airborne. Whatever the case, the object would then be to imitate the motion of the natural exhibited at streamside during the hatches. This happens to be at times when trout have a strong opportunity to compare any discrepancies between the behavior of the numerous naturals and the occasional passing artificials. The quickest way they can make the distinction is by visible behavior; those objects that move freakishly and *unnaturally* require no further inspection on their part. It matters little whether they conform closely in size, configuration, and even color to the others.

In general, there are many concepts involved in achieving good presentation or the duplication of the natural's movement or nonmovement. The proper equipment, careful wading to attain an advantageous casting position, precise delivery of an artificial with a marked degree of efficiency and consistency, and the attainment of either a drag-free float or slight controllable motion are prerequisites for success during hatches. All are meant to work in unison toward a common goal. These are the mechanics that are essential for the controlled and precise placement of a credible imitation.

It would literally be impossible to do justice to every one of these broad subjects in just one chapter in a book. A complete work would be required to cover each thoroughly. There would be no better example than the subject of equipment which is characterized by many variables and is largely a matter of personal choice and budget. It could then be discussed here only within the realm of generality. Since the obvious thing that an angler is trying to do when casting to a rising trout is not to spook him, the most beneficial choice an angler can make is to use the lightest possible line that he can get away with for any given situation. The lighter the line the less disturbance it will make on the water, and the less the angler will have to resort to excessively long, uncontrollable leaders. The time of the year is also a determining factor in the selection of line weight. For rivers that change in current tempo from spring to fall, appropriate lines for the early season will have to be replaced during summer and fall months with much lighter ones, in the four to five weight class. As with lines, rod lengths are also a matter of personal choice. Since casting control is one of the principal prerequisites of good presentation, the longer graphite and boron rods now available in the 8-foot-plus sizes offer more option for distance, accuracy, and line handling than the shorter ones that are too short to maneuver comfort-

FIG. 4-2 Natural drift lanes in a meadow stream.

ably. In conclusion, it must be said that what the reader owns, feels confident with, and can handle properly is exactly what he will need regardless of its length, weight, and action.

Casting should be refined to the point where an artificial is able to be placed exactly where it is intended to land. Placement should not be a matter of chance but within the control of the angler. During mayfly hatches, the accurate and consistent placement of an artificial, with the right amount of *slack* on the line, leader, and tippet, is imperative, since the angler will be facing situations in which trout will be rising in place, namely in the same position in a stream. Thus the need for exact delivery in a particular point just upstream from a rising fish is essential for success.

Of all the styles of casting I have observed in the stream, the straight overhand method is the most advantageous to fish the hatches; it meets the prerogatives for exact and consistent delivery more effortlessly than other forms. In this type of casting, the rod is held perpendicular to the body, not at a pronounced angle. When making the cast, the angler will utilize the *entire* forearm and hand, moving them in a perfectly even plane. This arm motion will also cause the rod tip to move in a parallel plane and make the line travel smoothly *over* the tip of the rod in each stop position. The size of the arc should be between the ten and one o'clock position, which will develop a forward slant to the entire cast and keep the line close over the surface of the water. The close proximity of the cast to the rising fish will not spook him, however, since it will be maintained within his blind area of vision. Besides, false casting will *never* be done over a fish, but short of him. For those who are used to the common sidearm method, I strongly recommend de-

veloping this type of cast. Though it may feel a bit awkward at first, the angler will be pleasantly surprised with the better results attained in precision and control with a minimal amount of effort. Eventually, the hand and forearm will become sensitive to the amount of power required to turn over the fly line and leader smoothly. The angler will learn to refrain from applying too much force and line speed, which will cause the cast to develop a tail loop. This type of cast, however, is not for the lover of the long, impressive cast, who cannot pick up a rod without instantly double hauling his way to the opposite side of the river. It is for the individual who wants to master comfortable, efficient casting in order to have the necessary line control to succeed when encountering rising trout.

DRAG-FREE FLOATS

Perfectly straight casts are advantageous during certain circumstances, for example, in smooth-as-glass waters such as lakes. But in most real-life situations they are at best unnecessary and at worst seriously detrimental for the attainment of drag-free floats. (A drag-free float occurs when an artificial is moving exactly at the same speed as the current in which it is riding, just like a free-floating natural.)

Most trout streams are not the perfectly smooth scenarios often depicted in pictures, at least during most of the season. In actuality, their surfaces are a complex and unpredictable maze of eddies, swirls, and mini-crosscurrents. The angler then might as well resign himself to the fact that the beautiful perfect-picture cast is not the one he needs; in fact, it should immediately warn him that he is going to have *undetectable* drag on his artificial. He will certainly be better off with the type of cast in which part of his line, leader, and tippet, depending on the uniformity of the surface, will fall in a near bundle so that the natural motion of the current will slowly straighten it out, preferably not before his fly floats past the trout!

The angler will find that casts with slack are the most useful approaches in the real world of fly fishing, and that the leader is also an extremely important aspect for the attainment of drag-free floats. The leader's construction and balance are very instru-

FIG. 4-3 A good example of the Reach Cast, so useful in slow-moving waters. With this cast the leader and fly line are laid out upstream of the fly, resulting in a drag-free float.

mental in either helping or hindering the angler preserve the slack that he is purposely trying to achieve. For this type of float, the long midsection leader is optimal. It begins to collapse or pile at midlength and is the greatest insurance that anglers have to prevent *imperceptible* or undetectable drag unlike a natural. This is the type of drag which is almost impossible to detect, and it can hurt their success dramatically.

The limitation of the naked eye to see this drag was made quite clear to me while I was shooting a super-eight movie with a friend out West. We had taken our time in carefully wading toward three good-sized trout rising in a placid pool of the Gibbon in Yellowstone National Park. I went ahead and, by crawling on my stomach on the tall buffalo grass, managed to get within ten feet of their positions. When I had set up my telephoto lens, my friend started to make his casts. However, no sooner had his fly landed, than it began to move slightly faster than the smooth current. We wasted 50 feet of film before getting back together, still without the sequel of a trout taking an artificial. He could not believe that he was getting drag on his float, but, after a moment's thought, he realized that was the very reason the trout had kept on rising yet had never bothered to even inspect his imitation. After returning to my position, he forced himself to develop deliberate slack on his line which made a great difference in the results.

The short butt, long midsection leader optimal for slack is constructed as shown in Table 4-1.

So, in reality, what the angler wants to achieve for the important and most useful drag-free float is slack in his line, leader, and tippet. In most cases, the more he has the better. There are many types of casts which will achieve such slack in an angler's line and leader. The most appropriate for pocket fishing is the pile cast, where the entire leader has to practically drop into a small area. This cast is brought about by making a conventional cast, but before the line straightens out in front of the angler, the rod tip is

.020 Round Monofilament	3 feet
.015 "	18 inches
.013 "	12 inches
.011 "	12 inches
.009 "	12 inches
Tippet (.007 = 4X)	4 feet
(.006 = 5X)	
(.005 = 6X)	
(.004 = 7X)	

Table 4-1 Construction details for a leader for slack-line casting.

brought down to the nine o'clock position taking the turnover power out of the cast so the leader does *not* straighten out at all. The S-curve cast achieves an accordion-like configuration on the complete line and is again accomplished by making a regular cast. Once it straightens out, three or four feet above the surface of the water, the rod tip is quivered horizontally to cause the line to form curves before it lands on the water. A very similar type of cast is the stop cast. This cast is begun as the previous cast, but instead of quivering the rod tip, it is brought back sharply to force the line to develop bends. This cast is a bit tougher to master than the S-curve. The selection between the two is a matter of personal choice and style. Both of these latter types of casts are practical when fishing waters that have a broken surface. The pile cast, on the other hand, is optimal for pocket waters, such as fast-flowing freestone streams.

For waters that do not move fast enough to warrant the amount of slack produced by these three types of casts, the drop cast is applicable. It attains the least amount of slack and will not suffice in waters with a multitude of crosscurrents. It is made to order for those barely moving waters in which a perfectly straight cast will cause an artificial to start skittering the instant it is made. Drop casts are executed by forcing a belly or mend of line to be made upstream from the artificial before it reaches the target. Whether the line is dropped to the right or left is, of course, dependent on the direction of the current.

Every one of these casts is well suited to specific situations and conditions, and therefore, all have their place and merit. However, all are easiest to master when the initial cast is made overhand, causing the line to be already in the straight-away position. The line can then be dropped (pile cast), the rod end can be quivered (S-curve cast), pulled back (stop cast), or dropped to the right or left (drop cast). Also remember that regardless of the cast and of the direction of the current, immediately after the cast is made the rod tip is brought down to *follow* the floating line. This move is just as important as the cast itself.

On the opposite side of the scale, the perfectly straight cast is the one required in flat, smooth-surfaced waters. In most cases, it is needed when fishing lakes or during the latter part of the season. Under such situations, there is little current to produce drag on your artificial. However, it is important to be aware of the spookiness of fish, since there is little surface defraction to break the outline of a falling line or little current to defuse its sound when it drops. The flat cast helps to keep a safe distance between

FIG. 4-4 The S-Curve Cast will provide a longer drag-free float than the Reach Cast.

where the line lands and a trout. The best leader for this type of fishing is designed to accomplish exactly the opposite effect as the previous suggested one, and its dimensions are quite different.

Leader butts have traditionally been in the .020 thickness class to match the thickness of the end of the average fly line. But, unfortunately, *round* monofilament in such a thickness is much stiffer than that of the fly line. It will cause casts, regardless of how they are made, to end in disadvantageous wider loops and with less flatness than is oftentimes desired. To avoid this detrimental effect when fishing very placid waters, the regular round monofilament should be replaced with .020 *flat* section. The new material, in conjunction with a longer butt section and shorter middle piece, will cause the power of the cast to be delivered to a farther point down the leader and result in a flatter, more controllable and exacting cast. Many flat-mono leader tapers are now offered by manufacturers, but if the reader chooses to construct his own, the following formula is recommended.

.020 Flat Monofilament	5 feet	
.015 Round Monofilament	6 inches	
.013 "	6 inches	
.011 "	6 inches	
.009 "	6 inches	
Tippet (.006=4X)		
(.006=5X)	4-5 feet	
(.005=6X)		
(.004=7X)		

Table 4-2 Leader construction for straight-line casts.

Both types of leaders have their own separate merits and place. The utilization of the correct one, according to specific circumstances, leads to more controllable casting and a better delivery and presentation, which, in essence, will mean more success in the stream. However, oftentimes the difference between success and failure will depend on *just* the leader, as Mike Lawson and I found out one evening when fishing a high-altitude lake in the Gravelly Range of Montana. Since we had been fishing the waters of the Henry's Fork the previous week, we had both of our outfits fitted with leaders that collapsed quickly, which helped us attain drag-free floats in the eddied currents. We barely arrived when we detected the first signs of surface activity, and a quick look at the water informed us that the game was going to involve the hatching of the little White-Winged Blacks or Tricos. Mike beat me to the first cast, and no sooner did his line hit the water than the first brown stopped rising. I also received a similar welcome from the first fish I cast to. It took us a few more downed fish before we realized that something was wrong. We signalled to each other and held conference. After examining our imitations and recreating our approach, we narrowed the trouble down to our casting. We took a few practice casts and realized our leader turnover was just too short. Those browns were not accustomed to having fly lines, even of a four weight, plopped so close to them. We thought of increasing the leader length, but upon giving it some thought, we concluded that it would have sacrificed exact and timely delivery, so important when fishing to gulping, cruising trout. We switched to the flatter tapers discussed previously, and finally achieved the distance

and control that we needed for this particular situation. The reader may expect me to tell him that we then proceeded to pick off every fish within casting distance in quick succession, but such was not the case. Those browns proved extremely tough, and that is probably the very reason why they are still there. However, we did get a chance to cast to many without instantly putting them down by our casts alone, and though we could have done better (you always can), we did manage to defend ourselves. The best fish was a colorful 17-inch brown—better than none at all.

The reader may have noticed that an approximately four-foot tippet length was recommended for both types of leaders. There are many advantages for an exceptionally long tippet. For one, it minimizes drag drastically since it will give easier around micro-eddies that are present on the surface of most trout waters. It will also land with more slack than a shorter one. Long length is also instrumental in protecting ultra-fine tippets, and when a trout first strikes and dashes, it will stretch to prevent it from breaking. This is especially important when fishing over good-sized trout with small flies in relatively shallow waters of say four feet or less.

Tippets should be as fine as is practical under a given situation, for they will inevitably lead to more fish caught. Probably the main reason for the better results attained by tippets in the 4X to 7X class is their weight relation to the artificial. The artificial tends to pull the fine tippet around rather than vice versa, consequently, less imperceptible drag will occur.

The attainment of drag-free floats is the most useful type of presentation during mayfly hatches. However, oftentimes the angler will have to put some movements on his imitation *in the event* that the naturals are "sudden inching" their way across the surface. In such cases, tighter, flatter casts are better since they will make it easier to transmit the action of the rod tip to the artificial nymph or dry. It should be remembered that mayflies cannot scurry across the surface film like caddises, and movements of one inch are undoubtedly sufficient to convey the aliveness of an artificial to the trout. However, this type of fishing requires a warning, for few times is movement beneficial on an artificial during a hatch, and it should *never* be given before a few, perfectly drag-free floats are made first over a specific fish.

At what point movement is imparted to an artificial is very important. Stationary trout rising during a hatch will be accustomed to the conduct of the true naturals. Exact duplication of the true naturals' movement by the angler is really quite difficult to achieve, and at best very chancy. Nonetheless, giving your imitation some life is beneficial at times, but it should be done when *outside* of the trout's immediate area of sharp focus or *cone of vision* (from his eye to the surface of the water straight above him). Movement can then be given to an artificial, giving the trout the *illusion* that it is indeed a restless mayfly which is about to become airborne. This movement should be stopped when the imitation is about to enter his circumference of sharp vision, so as not to allow him to detect the fraud, and appealing to his greedy nature not to let any flies escape his day's menu. A twitch when the fly is approximately four feet upstream from his position, and then allowed to drift placidly over him, will achieve the benefits of the tantalizing "sudden inch." In most situations, however, giving a *mayfly* imitation action is like a bluff in a poker game, and once it is tried and is not successful, it should never be attempted again during that particular encounter.

APPROACH

How many times has the reader barely stepped into a pool and all the fish suddenly stopped rising? This occurs quite often in rubble-bottom freestone streams when a carelessly placed step will send every trout within a hundred feet scurrying back to their hiding places. To make good controllable casts, it is certainly important to get as close as possible to a group of fish or to a specific one. It then follows that good wading is also a prerequisite of good presentation, since it will result in shorter casting distances and optimal casting angles. It will simply amaze most anglers to discover just how close they can get to a feeding trout when exercising careful wading by taking each step softly and carefully. In wading toward rising trout it is also helpful to keep the sun *behind* you, if possible. Of course, it should be at an angle that does not cast your shadow where you intend to fish. This position will undoubtedly enable you to have a better vantage point in which to see your artificial and also will put you where the trout will most likely be unable to see you. Their vision is really adjusted to the whole 360 degrees of vision, and thus their retina will invariably be too widely opened when looking toward the source of sunlight illuminating the water. They will, therefore, be limited in their ability to detect shapes of objects, and, as a result, often will not recognize your upright human form,

FIG. 4-5 Keeping a low profile in order to get closer to rising fish for more line control and precise delivery.

which is what would immediately alarm them and put them on guard.

When positioning yourself in a stream, keep in mind that you are going to concentrate on a specific group of fish or, better yet, on a specific fish whose size warrants forgetting about all the others that also happen to be rising. During hatches, when a stretch of water may contain two dozen trout rising all at once, it is very hard to exercise enough discipline to stick to one trout. The tendency is normally to cast at random to as many as possible. In all likelihood, they are all feeding on the same exact emerging insect, and if the first two that were cast to did not take your artificial, the others most likely will not either. It pays to refrain from casting to too many fish at once, which often undermines good presentation and causes panic to set in after too many refusals.

Where the angler places himself in the stream, in relation to a group of rising trout, is extremely important. In general, the best positions are those in which casts will not have to be made over a multitude of drag-producing currents. Generally speaking, casts made 90 degrees to a fish are the most dangerous, since they are instantly subjected to the pulling and pushing of the current on your line and leader which causes drag. The downstream position, straight behind a trout, is a good one, especially if you position yourself within the blind spot of the trout's vision, which is exactly behind him along his back. In fact, it is very easy to slowly and carefully wade so close to him that you can actually see him when he is laying in his feeding position or when he rises. This position to a rising fish, however, demands that every cast be made very carefully in order to line him *only* with the tippet section of your leader. This will not spook him, provided the tippet is fine enough. A second disadvantage with this positioning is that when the trout takes your artificial, the first thing he will encounter is the tippet, and he may "bump" the fly right out of his mouth. For such reasons, it may require more than one take to hook him. Usually he will be hooked on the upper lip.

Probably the optimal angle to a rising trout is *upstream* from him. Casts can now be dropped up to ten feet upstream from his position, and slack line can immediately be paid out to cause the artificial to float peacefully over him. Unlike the downstream position, positioning up from a fish is not exactly in his drift lane, for your wading will stir up the bottom and this will certainly manage to put him down. Besides, if you were exactly above him and if he happened not to take your first cast, you would have no choice but to pull back your line right over his head for the next cast. The upstream position, then, is at a slight angle to a rising trout, and its merit is that it minimizes the amount of currents an angler will have to cross over with his cast. The only disadvantage is that the trout will see a fly fisherman much more easily in front of him. The angler who chooses to fish in this manner must be aware of the visional abilities of trout.

Trout possess a cone of vision up to the surface of the water, and then their sight is defracted at a pronounced angle. The circumference of vision would be almost complete (360 degrees) were it not for the narrow blind spot that they exhibit exactly behind them. Their ability to see high objects in the horizon outside of the stream is best exemplified by trout in lakes who will stop feeding when spotting anglers on the high banks as much as 200 feet away. With this information in mind, the reader may suspect that it may be possible to get within a few feet of trout. The approacher must wade very carefully toward them, in a crouched position, maintaining his silhouette within the boundaries of the blind area of the trout's vision, which is between the surface of the water and their line of sight. In any situation, then, an angler should approach as closely as possible in order to shorten the distance and eliminate the necessity of making long, uncontrollable casts.

All that has been said so far concerning lines, casting, fine tippets, and positioning has been to enable the angler to improve his odds when fishing to a spe-

cific trout during a hatch. Now that these mechanics are out of the way, the angler is ready to make his first cast. He should remember, however, that during hatches trout will feed *in place* in all waters that exhibit natural drift lanes. Regardless of how the water surface may appear, natural drifts are the rule in the majority of moving-water environments. When a trout rises in such waters, he will break the surface downstream from his feeding-position point. The distance in which he would have to drop back to intercept the naturals is mainly dependent on the depth and the speed of the water. Contrary to popular belief, trout do not swim forcibly to a natural but merely tilt their position and let the natural force of the current lift them toward the surface. Once they seize an insect on the surface, they pivot downward and again, through hydrodynamics, are pushed by the force of the current in a downward direction toward the bottom of the stream. By barely flicking their pectoral fins, they can propel themselves through the comparatively dead-calm currents that exist in the very bottom of a stream, easing back to their original position. Thus, they will be holding in the same spot and will go through the same motions every time they rise and break the surface, which will be more or less at the same point. In fast-water environments trout will be dropped back a longer distance because of the greater force of the current, and consequently, they will break the surface a considerable distance from where they are holding. In more placid waters, the ring of the rises will practically be immediately above their stations, where they first spotted the natural or the artificial. This is an important point, for better results can be attained by the placement of an artificial as close as possible upstream to the point on the surface where the angler first saw the rise. Consequently, the period of drag-free float will occur where it counts, immediately over the trout. On the average, the placement of an artificial approximately five feet upstream, in the same drift lane, from a rise will ensure it will float drag-free within the trout's sphere of concern so that the trout will see and take the bait.

Before the angler makes his first cast, his first step would logically be to determine what the trout are taking. Assuming that the angler is as close as possible to his target—on an average of 20 to 40 feet—he can surmise that those naturals floating on the water right by his waders are the same insects that the trout are taking. However, he should certainly take a natural in hand before making his pattern selection. If he were to judge a fly while it is floating on the surface of the water, it would undoubtedly appear smaller in size and darker in color than it truly is. Judging them in the air would reveal just the opposite. For example, the Blue-Winged Olive species (*Ephemerella cornuta*) which is dark olive in coloration and hook size #12 would appear nearly white and gigantic in flight. Consequently, the best way to judge the size and color of a natural would be to hold one up against diffused natural light, which is the way trout see them in their natural state. Eventually the angler will become accustomed to the principal species found in trout streams, and he will be able to identify them at a glance.

At this point a second check would prove beneficial, and I will refer to this as the correlation-check. Correlation is the comparison between the behavior of the trout and what appears on the surface near you. Though in most cases anglers can assume that the insect nearest their waders is identical to what the trout is taking 30 feet away, it does not always hold true. Big flies activate fish but, by their very nature, are never as numerous or as prolific as the hatches of little mayflies. Often a multiple-hatch situation may be occurring, when a big fly is on the water and a second emergence of another species is taking place. Through the use of a little logic you can tell which ones the trout are taking.

If you notice say five or six duns of a large mayfly around a trout, but he is porpoising repeatedly without a noticeable break in his feeding rhythm, then obviously he is not feeding on the mayfly you can see. On the other hand, if the water is covered with little flies (for example, *Baetis*), and the fish are only occa-

FIG. 4-7 The smutting rise.

sionally slashing at something on the water, then obviously they are taking something else besides the little mayflies.

Correlating the action of the fish with what you can see around your waders is important. The preceding examples are certainly the exception rather than the rule, but they should be kept in mind. When in the stream, the best way to double check the *presence* of another emerging insect is by looking, for a few seconds, at an angle toward the direction of sunlight. Flies will stand out against this well-lighted background.

By actually capturing or observing mayflies on the water, you can tell *what* the fish are taking; by observing the trout's rise form you will know what *stage* of that insect they are concentrating on. Rise forms are very intriguing and not often easy to interpret, but as with anything else, practice brings improvement. One of the most common types of rises is the smutting rise where the trout are taking the nymphs, or pupas, just beneath the surface of the water, preferring these stages over surface-floating duns.

This type of rise is most common with insects that are easy for trout to capture just before the insects transform to their winged form. Such insects are: mayflies (*Baetidae, Ephemerellidae,* and *Tricorythidae*), many types of caddises, and midges (*Diptera*). In any type of broken-surfaced waters which provides natural drift lanes, accumulations of these naturals will occur in great numbers and will, therefore, become available to the trout which will consequently prefer to rise in place rather than move about. In placid, dead, or nearly still environments, such as lakes, this is also a common rise form, since great numbers of little mayfly nymphs or insect larvas will hover just

FIG.4-6 A multiple hatch situation; a problem of definition.

below the surface. In these waters, however, the trout will slowly cruise in a nearly straight line back and forth.

The "gulping" rise is one in which the trout will vacuum the flies from the surface of the water in quick succession, often with an audible gulping sound. Again, this is a common type of rise when taking small flies which emerge in great numbers *on the surface*, and also when taking spent mayfly spinners

FIG. 4-8 Fly fisher's view of the smutting rise in a western lake.

or crippled duns of any size insect helplessly floating on the surface with little chance to escape their predator. By far, spinner falls are the hardest to detect when they take place in trout waters, and this type of rise should serve as a warning to the angler that spinners are on the water. During such times, the angler may be able to see the mouths of trout barely clear the surface of the water. The distinction between the last case and this rise is important for it will inform the angler whether the trout are taking the insects *below* the surface or *on* it. This is very important as far as achieving credible presentation and resulting success. When the angler is unsure, it is best to watch a single fish intently for a few minutes, and he will soon be able to detect whether a subsurface or surface stage is being taken.

The splash rise is the most obvious, most common, and, certainly, most exciting rise. In such cases, the trout are violently breaking the surface because they either are moving fast after a nymph swimming rapidly toward the surface (burrowing mayflies, bottom-escaping duns of *Heptageniidae*, caddises' pupas) or they are not letting a large juicy morsel escape their

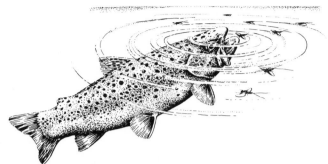

FIG. 4-9 The gulping or sipping rise during a spinner fall.

day's menu. The naturals certainly have to be worth it to warrant such an expenditure of energy. This rise is a representative one during hatches of big mayflies, like the burrowers, big clingers of *Stenonemas* and *Epeorus*, and bigger *Ephemerellas* (Hendricksons, Large Blue-Winged Olives, and Western Green Drakes). It is also a classic type of rise during the emergence of certain types of caddises and stoneflies that, because of their size and enticing flutterings, cause trout to take them with a very deliberate attitude. Again, anglers should make sure that the trout are either after fast-swimming nymphs or large dries; the distinction is easily made by observing a single fish.

Recognizing the type of mayfly that is emerging from the stream often tells you a lot about their underwater behavior, the stage usually most vulnerable to the trout, and the type of artificial that would, in all probability, be most effective. At streamside, this would entail the simple exercise of determining its family classification, something easily mastered with a little practice and with the aid of Table 4-3.

Assuming that the angler has picked his angle to a rising trout, approached as closely as possible, determined what he is taking and what stage it is, he is ready to make his first cast. Before he does so, however, he should just take a minute to observe at least one natural drift over his target fish to determine its direction and movement. Once he determines the spot at which he wants to put his artificial, he should make his first cast, which should be approximately three to six feet upstream in that particular drift. It is hard to generalize on this aspect, since, as discussed earlier, how far the angler should place his artificial ahead of the fish depends on the speed of the current and whether the placidness of the water warrants such a maneuver in the first place. Under most situations, the closer the cast is to the fish the better. An overcast—making the line or the thicker part of the leader land across the drift lane of a rising fish—

FAMILY	STREAMSIDE RECOGNITION	TYPE OF WATER	PRINCIPAL HATCHES	INTENSITY OF HATCH	STAGE USUALLY PREFERRED BY TROUT DURING THE HATCH	RISE FORM	ARTIFICIAL IMITATIONS
Baetidae (Chapter 5)	NYMPH: middle tail slightly shorter or absent DUN: 2 tails; only minute hind wing	All	EAST: Little Iron-Blue Quill WEST: Little Western Iron Blue-Quill; Tiny Western Olive	High	Nymph just below or at surface	Smutting and gulping rise	Floating Nymph No-Hackle Dun
Heptageniidae (Chapter 6)	NYMPH: 3 tails, squashed conf. *Epeorus*—2 tails DUN: 2 tails, many with barred wings	Mod. to Fast	EAST: Gordon Quill; Ame. March Brown; Gray Fox WEST: W. Black Quill; Small Western Red Quill	Med.	*Epeorus* and *Rhithrogena:* dun below surface; wet *Stenonema* and *Heptagenia:* dun on surface	WET FLY: smutting rise DUN: Splash rise SPINNER: gulping rise	Flat-Body Nymph Wet Fly Emerger Hen-Winged Dun
Leptophlebiidae (Chapter 7)	NYMPH: gills as tuning-forks DUN: 3 tails; no point or angle along fore margin in hind wing	All	EAST AND WEST: Slate-Winged Mahogany Dun	Low	Nymph just at the surface, due to the long time in which duns require to emerge out of them	NYMPH AND DUN: gulping rise	Conventional Nymph Hackle-tip Dun
Ephemerellidae (Chapter 8)	NYMPH: 3 tails; plate-like gills on top side of abdomen DUN: 3 tails; angled fore margin in hind wing	All	EAST: Dark Hendrickson; Pale Evening Dun; Blue-Winged Olive WEST: Pale Morning Dun; Western Green Drake; Small Western Green Drake	High	Nymph just below surface; duns, with wings yet folded, on surface	Smutting rise is very common; gulping and splash rise when taking dries (depends on size of species)	Conventional Nymph Emerging Dun or No-Hackle Dun
Ephemeridae (Chapter 9)	NYMPH: Frontal tusks or horns DUN: 2 tails or 3 tails; largest of mayflies	Slow to Mod.	EAST: Hexagenia lim.; Eastern Green Drake; Yellow Drake WEST: Brown Drake	High	Swimming nymphs up to the surface; less commonly, duns	Nymphs taken below the surface produces splash rise; large fluttering duns also produce splash rise	Wiggle-Nymph or Streamlined Nymph Paradrake
Siphlonuridae (Chapter 10)	NYMPH: large, streamlined DUN: 2 tails	Mod. to Fast	EAST: Great Lead-Winged Coachman WEST: Gray Drake	Low	Migrating nymphs to shore; spinners	Smutting rise near margins of streams	Streamlined Nymph Double Hen-Winged Spinner
Tricorythidae (Chapter 11)	NYMPH: 3 tails small in size; appearance of single enlarged gill DUN: 3 tails; no hind wings	Slow to Mod.	EAST, MIDWEST, AND WEST: White-Winged Black, or Trico	High	Nymph just under surface during hatch; spinners	Smutting; Gulping rise	Poly or Hen-Winged Spinner

Table 4-3

FIG. 4-10 The gulping rise as seen from the downstream position.

would be a serious mistake. The first cast will not be harmful if it is too short, but it will kill the whole game if made too long. A common mistake would be to try to hit the right spot the first time, even if the angler feels he would be able to do it on his first attempt. The first cast should purposely be made to be too short, for it will inform the angler if the type of cast he has selected, the leader, and the judgment of drift are correct. When more line is needed, it can be taken out of the reel; the rest should be kept where it belongs, in the reel. In this way, the cast can be *measured* by the amount of free line.

Once an appropriate cast is made and the trout does not take it, it does not mean anything. A rising fish that has many naturals available to him often adopts a rhythm to his feeding cycle, and your artificial might not have passed over him at the right time. Often as many as ten or fifteen casts will be necessary

FIG. 4-11 The splash rise during a Hendrickson hatch.

before he takes it. However, if the trout has stopped rising, *do not* confirm his suspicions by casting again. Rest him a minute. If he has not seen you or your line he will be back on top. (A similar game is played by the archer and the deer; the hunter only moves when the deer is preoccupied with feeding.)

On many occasions trout will repeatedly rise to an artificial and by all appearances appear to want it and have taken it. Yet, upon lifting the rod the angler will find that the trout is simply not there. A trout can change his mind just prior to taking a fly, or after actually taking it, spitting it out in an instant, long before the angler has time to react. The two most common reasons trout change their minds at the last second are: too big a fly and/or too heavy a tippet. The first case is the most common. After receiving more than one false rise the angler should replace his imitation by one or two hook-sizes smaller. The trout will probably stay on next time he rises to the more correct artificial. It is instrumental to keep in mind that size is most important in matching the hatch and trout always prove very particular to the proportions of an imitation in comparison to that of the natural. Moreover, it is not harmful if the angler makes use of an imitation slightly smaller than the naturals during the hatch; on the other hand, a natural markedly larger than the real thing can prove seriously detrimental. Too heavy a tippet has the same effect when it produces drag and causes the trout to reject your imitation.

When the trout takes your offering—and here is a very important point—*do not strike him* with the force you would use to set a hook on a salmon. Remember a light leader is being used and he will set himself when he feels the hook. When the rod is raised to the point where you can barely feel him, if he is not on, he will *not* be spooked. When using small flies, the hook gap is so small that it often fails to hit flesh and thus, the trout will not feel it or even become aware he has lost part of his meal. The angler who takes his time and does not approach the whole matter as if he were about to miss the last train out of town will be rewarded. Above all, take your time and do not feel that you have to try another fish. If that one is worth casting to, he is worth taking. More time is saved doing it all correctly than in a haphazard manner.

The mechanics of good presentation are especially vital when fishing to the more wary fish in good trout waters. These old timers have had a lot of lines cast over them and certainly demand the very best of new challenges. Usually they are found in tough places, like the dead-calm backwaters along banks where many artificials are cast but few with the principles covered here. Though these fish are smart and experienced, they are not infallible. The angler who uses his head in moving as close as possible to them adopts the most appropriate casting angle, and the angler who does not tear the fly when he does take it will land that fish to the disbelief of other anglers nearby. They will swear that he has all the luck! The luck of success in fly fishing is not met, it is made.

AFTER A HATCH

As is usually the case, when a hatch stops, it seems as fast as when someone shuts off a faucet. Oftentimes, though, a few fish will still be seen rising, and in all likelihood, this would be to cripples or "stillborns," results of the imperfections of nature. They are really the ones that emerged imperfectly during the hatch, but, unable to fly, kept on floating downstream until they piled up against a protruding obstruction or were swept into side eddies. These side pockets are not subjected to the regular washing-down effect of the main current and will usually collect cripples in good numbers. They provide food for the fish that prefer these naturals, and they are customarily taken with the gulping type of rise.

Approximately 24 hours after the hatch, the spinner forms of the duns that hatch will return to the

FIG. 4-12 Putting it all together!

stream to mate, oviposit their eggs, and ultimately fall spent on the water. The best way to see them is by detecting their nuptial dances which usually take place just above the banks of the stream, approximately one hour before their mating activity. Spinner falls usually take most anglers by complete surprise, so it behooves them to keep checking the surface of the water for their presence. The spinners will be pasted to the surface so that the trout will have no need, regardless of their size, to take them with splashy rises. Again, trout will pick specific drift lanes in a stream and cruise about only in perfectly still wa-

FIG. 4-13 First warning of the coming spinner fall.

FIG. 4-14 The greatest moment of the whole game—the release!

ters, such as those characterized by impounded bodies of water.

So many precautions have been recommended in this chapter on fishing to rising trout that the reader may feel that following all that is suggested here would require a checklist. By the time all has been properly accomplished, the whole hatch would probably be over. As in mastering any other set of techniques, things appear to proceed in slow motion until they become second nature. The reader should keep in mind, however, that good habits are prerequisites to good presentation, which makes all the difference in the stream. Moreover, good presentation is not to be divorced from the patterns suggested in the chapters that follow.

Little Iron–Blue Quill, *Baetis vagans (male dun)*

Little Slate–Winged Brown Quill, *Baetis intercalaris (male dun)*

Little Slate–Winged Brown Quill, *Baetis intercalaris (male spinner)*

Gordon Quill, *Epeorus pleuralis (male dun)*

Small Gordon Quill, *Cinygmula subequalis (male dun)*

Gray–winged Yellow Quill, *Epeorus vitreus (female dun)*

American March Brown, *Stenonema vicarium (male dun)*

American March Brown, *Stenonema vicarium (male spinner)*

Gray Fox, *Stenonema fuscum (male dun)*

Gray Fox, *Stenacron interpunctatum (male spinner)*

Early Black Quill, *Leptophlebia cupida (male dun)*

Slate–Winged Mahogany Dun, *Paraleptophlebia adoptiva (male dun)*

East/Midwest

Dark Hendrickson, *Ephemerella subvaria (female dun)*

Dark Hendrickson, *Ephemerella subvaria (female spinner)*

Light Hendrickson, *Ephemerella rotunda (male dun)*

Light Hendrickson, *Ephemerella rotunda (male spinner)*

Pale Evening Dun, *Ephemerella dorothea (male dun)*

Pale Evening Dun, *Ephemerella dorothea (male spinner)*

Large Blue–Winged Olive, *Ephemerella cornuta (male dun)*

Little Blue–Winged Olive, *Ephemerella cornutella (female spinner with eggs)*

Little Dark Hendrickson, *Ephemerella deficiens (male dun)*

Great Leadwing Drake, *Hexagenia limbata (male dun)*

Eastern Green Drake, *Ephemera guttulata (male dun)*

Great Leadwing Coachman, *Isonychia sadleri (female dun)*

Gray Drake, *Siphlonurus occidentalis (nymphs)*
Little Western Iron–Blue Quill, *Baetis parvus*
Tiny Western Olive, *Pseudocloeon edmundsi*

Little Western Iron–Blue Quill,
Baetis parvus (male dun)

Tiny Western Olive, *P. edmundsi (female dun)*

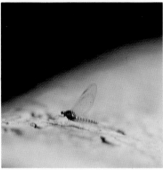

Tiny Western Olive, *P. edmundsi*
(female spinner)

Dark Speckle–Winged Quill,
Callibaetis nigritus (male spinner)

Western Gordon Quill, *Epeorus longimanus*
Small Western Red Quill, *Rithrogena undulata*
(nymphs)

Western Black Quill, *Rithrogena
morrisoni (male dun)*

Western Black Quill, *Rithrogena morrisoni (male
spinner)*

Small Western Red Quill,
Rithrogena undulata (male dun)

Small Western Red Quill, *Rithrogena undulata*
(male spinner)

Western Gordon Quill, *Epeorus
albertae (male dun)*

Western Gordon Quill, *Epeorus albertae (male
spinner)*

West

Western Red Quill, *Heptagenia elegantula (male dun)*

Western Red Quill, *Heptagenia elegantula (male spinner)*

Large Slate–Winged Mahogany Dun, *Paraleptophlebia bicornuta (male dun)*

Western Green Drake, *E. grandis*
Small Western Green Drake, *E. flavilinea*
Pale Morning Dun, *E. inermis (discolored)*
(nymphs)

Pale Morning Dun, *Ephemerella inermis (male dun)*

Pale Morning Dun, *Ephemerella inermis (male spinner)*

Western Green Drake, *Ephemerella grandis (male dun)*

Small Western Green Drake, *Ephemerella flavilinea (male dun)*

Small Western Dark Hendrickson, *Ephemerella tibialis (male dun)*

Brown Drake, *Ephemera simulans (male dun)*

Gray Drake, *Siphlonurus occidentalis (male spinner)*

Tiny White–Winged Black, *Tricorythodes minutus (male spinner)*

CHAPTER 5: The Continuous Emergences of the Little Quills (Family *Baetidae*)

THE species of Family *Baetidae* are probably the second most common mayflies found in our North American trout streams, and all trout fishermen can expect to meet their hatches at one point or another during the fishing season.

The genera or types that belong to this mayfly family produce the majority of small-mayfly hatches that are matched by artificial imitations ranging between No. 18 and No. 22 hook sizes. Species of genus *Callibaetis* are exceptionally larger but are of primary importance only to western anglers who are in the habit of fishing the high-altitude lakes and ponds inhabited by trout.

By far, species of genera *Baetis* and *Pseudocloeon* are the dominant ones in Family *Baetidae*. They are extremely prolific and the mainstay of the continuous hatches of little light brown to olive brown mayflies that occur throughout the entire season. Though they go by a multitude of common names, anglers familiar with these hatches usually refer to them as Iron-Blue Quills and Little Blue-Winged Olives. The latter is a misnomer and a poor description of the natural dun of *Baetis* or *Pseudocloeon*. The title should be reserved to those species of the *Drunella* group of Family *Ephemerellidae*, whose colorations in the subimago stage are precisely characterized by the name Blue-Winged Olive.

One of the inherent problems with these hatches is that their undersized duns are hard to detect when on the surface of the water. As a result, their presence may not become known to the casual onlooker. They are easier to discern during flight when their little wings become crystalline against light-colored backgrounds. The streamside scenario during these hatches usually is one of rising fish to what may first appear as invisible flies, but a closer scrutiny of the water surface will provide the suspicious angler with the clue to the trout's "mysterious" behavior.

Some fishermen who are aware of these hatches simply choose to ignore them altogether or to dismiss them as hatches of "little flies for small fish." In reality, for a number of reasons, the hatches of these little critters can be of great significance to most anglers, and surprising as it may seem, they can preempt the importance of a hatch of much larger flies that may already be in progress.

One reason for the significance of these little flies is that the *Baetidae* hatches begin weeks and sometimes months before the seasonal commencement of other mayflies. In the East and Midwest, they precede the Gordon Quill and Hendrickson hatches of April and May by approximately three weeks. A similar situation exists in western waters, where the appearance of *Baetis tricaudatus* leads the March and April emergence of the Western Black Quill (*Rhithrogena morrisoni*) by a full month. In the fall, at a time when other aquatic insects have completed their seasonal cycles for the year, the little *Baetidae* are once again the only ones found emerging in our trout streams. During these periods, they capture the full attention of the trout and should receive equivalent consideration on the part of anglers.

The hatches of larger mayflies that customarily take place from May until September do not necessarily preclude or lessen the importance of the hatches of *Baetidae*, and the "little mayflies" remain important. In the first place, the species in this family are numerous and extremely abundant in trout streams, and upon emergence, their nymphs and duns can literally carpet the surface of the water. Secondly, they chronologically follow each other without interruption throughout the spring, summer, and fall months. Lastly, each species happens to be multibrooded, meaning that it emerges more than once during the year. For example, a species that appeared in April, in all likelihood, will emerge again in July and even make a third seasonal appearance during the month of October. It is not hard to see why *Baetidae* species can produce extremely concentrated hatches, and, on numerous occasions, surpass the density and importance of another mayfly that may already be emerging.

It seems absurd for trout to feed and even become selective on *small* flies when much larger ones are also available, though not in comparable numbers. As we have discussed in Chapter 1, the selectivity of trout during a hatch is dependent on two principles: the abundance and availability of the hatching . insect. The emergence of many *Baetidae* species, despite their size, often meet both requirements and cause trout to feed on them exclusively. The reader should bear in mind that he may not detect the transition of the trout's preference or even be aware that he is confronted with a multiple-hatch situation. Perhaps when you recollect, the memory of a day in a stream will come to mind when trout ceased to feed on a still-emerging insect and its imitation that had already "cracked the code." They became uncomfortably selective, and all your offerings were met with persistent, point-blank refusals. You certainly should not feel alone, for many fishermen have been in similar frustrating situations and probably more times than they care to remember.

In the East, the Gordon Quills are the first large mayflies to emerge in the fishing season. For years my father and I would schedule our spring trip to the Catskill Mountains to coincide with the seasonal appearance of this mayfly. We would always meet in our favorite pool on the Esopus, an isolated stretch of water that supported good trout and held many lessons in its currents. How well I can remember the trouble we would have with this hatch, for no sooner would it begin than the trout would become impossible to catch. We usually rationalized our failures as part of the "joys" of trout fishing.

It was during one of these skunk sessions that we discovered that the emergence of Gordon Quills is usually accompanied by hatches of the smaller *Baetidae* flies (*Baetis intercalaris* and *Pseudocloeon carolina*), and that the trout will consistently switch to the smaller of the two. Ever since, we have further confirmed that these little critters supplant the importance of many other well-known mayfly hatches, and therefore, it behooves anglers to be on the lookout for their emergence. (See Fig. 4-6.)

The nymphal forms of *Baetidae* members have streamlined, minnow-like configurations that are unmistakable from those of other mayflies. Streams rich in aquatic vegetation will support their populations in

incredible numbers, where they will be found clinging and scurrying about among the web of stems, shoots, and tiny leaves of *charra* or *elodea* plants. When swimming, the nymphs dart with quick, short dashes through the water, deriving their propulsion by the flicking of their filamentous tails.

Duns and spinners are characterized by having only two tails and minute, barely discernible hind wings (*Pseudocloeon* being the exception). The males have curious, large high-seated eyes, unlike those of other mayflies.

FAMILY BAETIDAE

Genus Baetis *(West: abundant; Midwest: abundant; East: abundant)*

The nymphal form of most *Baetis* species has three tails with the center one always conspicuously shorter than the two outer ones. Some species lack a middle tail entirely and, consequently, are often confused with *Pseudocloeon* nymphs. However, *Baetis* nymphs exhibit minute hind-wing pads that are not found in those belonging to its sister genus. (See Fig. 2-1A, *Baetis* diagram on page 14.)

The duns are a light olive brown in color with pale gray wings. The spinners of most species have either light brown or nearly black thoraxes and abdomens, though abdominal segments 2–6 are always conspicuously paler than the rest of their bodies.

Genus Pseudocloeon *(West: abundant; Midwest: abundant; East: abundant)*

Pseudocloeon nymphs have two tails and are usually a distinctive pale olive in color; both these characteristics facilitate streamside identification. Unlike *Baetis* nymphs, those of *Pseudocloeon* lack hind-wing pads. (See Fig. 2-1B, page 14.)

The absence of hind wings differentiates the dun and spinner stages of *Pseudocloeon* from those of *Baetis* or any other genera discussed in this chapter.

Genus Callibaetis *(West: abundant; Midwest: uncommon; East: uncommon)*

Callibaetis hatches are important in the West where they take place in most impounded bodies of water; in particular, those with an abundant growth of vegetation.

Its nymphs are distinctly larger than those of genera *Baetis*, *Pseudocloeon*, or *Centroptilum*. Also, their three tails, heart-shaped gills, and the type of habitat where they are found help to separate them from those of their sister genera.

Callibaetis dry forms have blunt costal angulations on their hind wings and speckled fore wings and abdomens, making them easily recognizable at streamside.

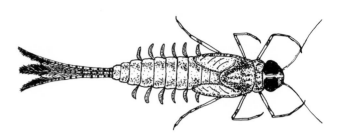

FIG. 5-2 *Centroptilum* nymph

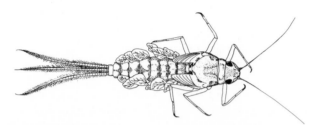

FIG. 5-1 *Callibaetis* nymph

Genus Centroptilum *(West: uncommon; Midwest: rare; East: rare)*

The hatches of this genus are of limited significance to most trout fishermen since they mainly take place in the warmer lower-altitude sections of large rivers that are able to support other species of fish besides trout. *Centroptilum* nymphs occasionally will be found in the back eddies and cutoff pools of cold streams but usually are found in nearly stagnant areas that are avoided by trout. They are also indigenous to many sections of trout streams that become too warm to support trout during the hot summer months when *Centroptilum* emerges.

Upon emergence, the nymphs choose to crawl up the shoots of plants rather than swim to the surface. The duns immediately slip out of them and hide in the vegetation, appearing as spinners within a few hours. Spinner swarms formulate at eye level over the banks of the stream and, after mating occurs, the imagoes of both sexes will fall spent on the water within a foot of the bank.

Centroptilum nymphs are identifiable by their three tails of equal length and the narrow, dark bands at each third segment of their tails.

Duns and spinners are much lighter in color than those of *Baetis* or *Pseudocloeons*, and they have pale cream bodies and almost transparent wings in both stages. Unlike *Pseudocloeons*, *Centroptilums* possess hind wings similar to those found in *Baetis* species.

Few anglers are in the stream early enough to catch these hatches, but they will probably encounter the small clouds of *Centroptilum* spinners that gather in the evening. Their hatches are in the mornings, be-

tween seven and nine o'clock, during the months of June, July, and August. Those that occur during the fall are at midday. I have fished the hatches of *C. elsa* in the Madison River, just outside Yellowstone National Park, and those of *C. conturbatum* in Henry's Fork of the Snake River. Last September, *C. bifurcatum* produced a good hatch in the upper waters of the beautiful Lochsa River in northern Idaho. Mike Kimball, a good friend of mine, informs me that the *Centroptilum* hatch that takes place in the backwaters of Armstrong Creek in Montana is one of his favorites of the whole season. In all these circumstances, the pattern described to imitate *Baetis parvus* in this chapter proved very effective during the hatches of the paler *Centroptilum* flies.

Emergence and Artificial Patterns

When emerging, *Baetidae* nymphs reach the surface of the water rather quickly, and then they float for some distance before the duns start to appear out of them. This state of suspension adds to the normal concentration of these nymphs and results in hundreds of them being funneled between rocks, accumulated against logs, and swirled into side eddies—holding places for trout willing to take full advantage of the little floating naturals. In these places, the trout will adopt a smutting-type of rise, the kind so familiar to anglers who frequently fish smooth, slow-moving streams and creeks. Here, trout have the time to study closely the helpless nymphs and the exactness of the imitation that the angler is offering them as an alternative.

For this type of action, the Floating Nymph pattern and No-Hackle flies are effective and practical and serve to increase the angler's odds in otherwise-difficult hatches.

Spinners

Swarms of *Baetidae* spinners take place at eye level over the banks of streams and margins of lakes. Their rapid, foot-long vertical dance is unmistakable with the nuptial flight of any other mayfly. Duns that hatch in the mornings often come back as spinners later on in the day, otherwise the molting process takes overnight.

EASTERN AND MIDWESTERN HATCHES OF BAETIS AND PSEUDOCLOEONS

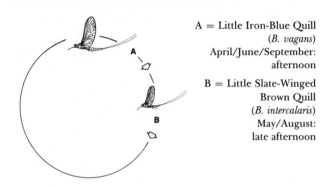

A = Little Iron-Blue Quill
        (*B. vagans*)
   April/June/September:
        afternoon

B = Little Slate-Winged
    Brown Quill
        (*B. intercalaris*)
   May/August:
        late afternoon

FIG. 5-3 Seasonal cycle of eastern & midwestern *Baetis* and *Pseudocloeon* (actual sizes).

Most little-mayfly hatches that take place in eastern and midwestern waters are produced by genera *Baetis* and *Pseudocloeon*. The two types contain no less than eight abundant species that emerge throughout the season. Fortunately for anglers, because of the similarities among them, only two artificial patterns are required to imitate the group and to effectively fish their hatches.

B. vagans, a relatively large species, emerges in the spring, often before the official opening of the fishing season. Its hatches are followed three weeks later by two smaller *Baetidae* members: *B. intercalaris* and *P. carolina*. These two treacherous little creatures emerge in such numbers that they steal the limelight from other insects that may also be hatching. Yet anglers may not even be aware of their presence. As the season progresses other similar species will appear, and their hatches are joined by the second seasonal occurrences of *B. vagans*, *B. intercalaris*, and *P. carolina* (in midwestern waters *P. anoka* is the *Pseudocloeon* species of major importance).

The taxonomy of this family has not been worked out by entomologists to the same extent as other mayfly families, preventing the writer from presenting a simplified and exacting key to the species. The interested reader should compare his specimens in question to the illustrations provided in Appendix II.

Little Iron-Blue Quill *(B. vagans)*

This is the first important mayfly to emerge for the season, and during an unusually warm spring, its hatches might precede Opening Day by weeks. Expect its seasonal emergence to commence when the water temperature reaches the 40-degree mark, normally during the month of April.

B. vagans nymphs prefer the slower portions of freestone rivers, and they may also be found in excellent numbers clinging to the vegetation that grows along the margins of medium-flowing streams.

Like all *Baetis* species, *B. vagans* is multibrooded, emerging for the first time in April, again in the latter part of June, and then in September, suggesting that the species requires only 2½ months for total growth. The spring hatch is at midday, the others occur in the evening; these are the same times of day chosen by the spinners to gather along the banks.

The nymph and dun of *B. vagans* are neotypical of two other *Baetis* species that are also light olive brown in color but emerge much later in the season. *B. levitans* is slightly smaller and found in great numbers in the streams in Pennsylvania and Michigan, producing excellent summer hatches for anglers who wish to stalk working fish in smooth-as-glass waters. Streams like Big Springs, Yellow Breeches, and large shallow rivers, like the West Branch of the Delaware, have excellent hatches. Later in the season, anglers will encounter hatches of *B. pygmaeus* that emerge in the same waters as the previously mentioned species.

Without a doubt, *B. vagans* hatches are important to the fly fisherman because of the abundance of the species and because they take place in the very beginning of the season, when no other hatches are available.

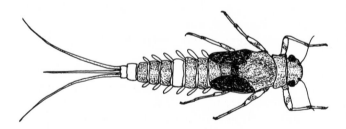

FIG. 5-4 *Baetis vagans*

B. vagans nymphs are easily recognized at streamside by the conspicuous pale markings on their abdomens (segments 5, 9–10) and the lack of bands on their tails. Duns are light olive brown in color and are the first mayflies to appear in the season.

Baetis vagans Imitations

NATURAL	ARTIFICIAL

Conventional Nymph: Light-wire hook Mustad 94840 recommended, to be fished just under the surface during a hatch.

SIZE: 7mm	HOOK: Mustad 3906 #14 or
TAILS: grayish olive	94840 #16
ABDOMEN: olive brown	THREAD: olive prewaxed 6/0
THORAX: dark grayish olive;	TAILS: faintly barred mallard
dark brown wing pads	flank fibers, dyed olive
LEGS: pale cream	ABDOMEN: olive brown
	dubbing blend
	THORAX: dark olive brown
	dubbing blend; mallard quill
	segments dyed blackish
	brown for wing cases
	LEGS: light tan mallard fibers

Floating Nymph*: A very effective alternative pattern to the Conventional Nymph pattern, to be used *during* the actual hatch, and intended to float *on* the surface as a dry fly would.

SIZE: 7mm	HOOK: Mustad 94833 #18
TAILS: grayish olive	THREAD: olive prewaxed 6/0
ABDOMEN: olive brown	TAILS: light dun hackle fibers
THORAX: dark grayish olive;	ABDOMEN: olive brown
medium grayish olive	dubbing blend
unfolding wings	THORAX: dark olive brown
LEGS: pale cream	dubbing; medium grayish
	olive ball of dubbing for
	wing clump
	LEGS: light dun hackle fibers

No-Hackle:

SIZE: 7mm	HOOK: Mustad 94833 #18
	THREAD: olive prewaxed 6/0
TAILS: light slate	TAILS: light dun hackle fibers
ABDOMEN: olive brown	ABDOMEN: medium grayish
THORAX: dark olive brown	olive dubbing blend
WINGS: light slate gray	THORAX: medium grayish olive
	dubbing blend
	WINGS: light gray mallard quill
	segments

*Most recommended

Little Slate-Winged Brown Quill (*B. intercalaris*)

B. intercalaris is the second *Baetis* to emerge in the season, appearing about three weeks after *B. vagans*, and its hatches coincide with those of much larger mayflies. This species is also representative of a group of *Baetis* and *Pseudocloeon* species that will emerge throughout the season. It differs from the *B. vagans* type in size and color in both the nymph and dun stages.

Seasonal emergence usually begins during the middle of May and lasts until early June. The little *B.*

intercalaris duns can literally cover the water during a hatch and can preempt the importance of Gordon Quills (*E. pleuralis*) and even of Hendricksons (*E. subvaria*), two midday species that emerge at the same time.

The little nymphs are much at home in the rocky bottoms of freestone rivers and are equally suited to thrive in good numbers in slow-moving creeks rich

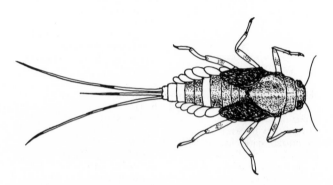

FIG. 5-5 *Baetis intercalaris*

with aquatic vegetation. Over the years, I have witnessed *B. intercalaris* emerging from the Saranac, Beaverkill, and Esopus trout streams of New York and from Penn's Creek in Pennsylvania; however, this hatch can probably be found in most trout waters.

The nuptial flight of spinners occurs in the afternoon and ovipositing is at dusk; the adult habits of *B. intercalaris* are similar to the imagoes of the species that follow.

B. intercalaris is separated from *B. vagans* by the banded tails of its nymphs and the much smaller size and darker color of its duns.

Little Slate-Winged Brown Quill (*B. phoebus*)

Baetis phoebus does not appear to be as common as any of the two species previously described, but it does produce fair hatches for midwestern anglers. It closely resembles *B. intercalaris* as a nymph and dun.

Its nymphs are found in the gravelly runs and riffles of smaller streams, a type of microhabitat it shares with *B. intercalaris*, which it follows in emergence by approximately two weeks.

Good hatches of this little delicate mayfly are found in the trout streams of Michigan and Wisconsin, and they are often thick enough to entice the selective feeding of trout. Anglers have little need to create a special artificial for this species, since the imitation given for *B. intercalaris* will work superbly during the hatches of *B. phoebus* and the species that follow.

Taxonomically, both species are similar, except for the brown abdominal segments of the *B. phoebus*

Baetis intercalaris (and related species) Imitations

NATURAL	ARTIFICIAL

Conventional Nymph: See note for *B. vagans.*

NATURAL	ARTIFICIAL
SIZE: 5–6mm	HOOK: Mustad 3906 #18 or 94840 #20
TAILS: dark brown	THREAD: dark olive prewaxed 6/0
ABDOMEN: dark olive brown	TAILS: dark partridge fibers
THORAX: dark olive brown; black wing pads	ABDOMEN: dark olive brown dubbing blend
LEGS: olive brown	THORAX: dark olive brown blend; black poly or mallard segments for cases
	LEGS: olive brown partridge fibers

Floating Nymph*: An alternative pattern for the above, to be fished *on* the surface during the hatch.

NATURAL	ARTIFICIAL
SIZE: 5mm	HOOK: Mustad 94833 #20
TAILS: dark brown	THREAD: dark olive prewaxed 6/0
ABDOMEN: dark olive brown	TAILS: dark partridge fibers
THORAX: dark olive brown; dark gray unfolding wings	ABDOMEN: dark olive brown dubbing blend
LEGS: olive brown	THORAX: dark olive brown blend; dark gray ball of dubbing for unfolding wings
	LEGS: olive brown hackle fibers

No-Hackle:

NATURAL	ARTIFICIAL
SIZE: 5mm	HOOK: Mustad 94833 #22
TAILS: dark olive brown	THREAD: dark olive prewaxed 6/0
ABDOMEN: dark grayish olive	TAILS: dark dun hackle fibers
THORAX: dark olive brown	ABDOMEN: dark olive or grayish brown blend
WINGS: dark gray	THORAX: dark olive brown blend
	WINGS: dark gray mallard quills

*Most recommended

nymphs which differ from the abdominal color pattern of its sister species.

Little Slate-Winged Brown Quill (B. brunneicolor)

This species is oftentimes found in such numbers in trout streams that its hatches can cause trout to become selective. On those occasions, it probably qualifies as another "angler's curse," as the reader may justly regard the hatches of *B. intercalaris.*

Its hatches chronologically follow those of *B. phoebus*, and once again make it necessary for anglers to be preoccupied with *Baetis* hatches. The months of June and July have the best emergences of *B. brunneicolor*, which take place in the late afternoons or evenings. In mid-July, they are joined and eventually supplanted by the hatches of *P. anoka*, a terrific little mayfly described below.

It has been my good fortune to have fished excellent hatches of this species on the Pere Marquette River in Michigan and on the Macan and Kinnickinnick rivers of Wisconsin.

B. brunneicolor nymphs are easily differentiated from those of other *Baetis* species discussed here by the absence of bands on their tails and by their unicolorous, faintly striped abdominal tergites.

Little Slate-Winged Brown Quill (P. carolina)

This *Pseudocloeon* and the two species of the same genus that follow match the abundance of *B. intercalaris*. *P. anoka* probably approaches the commonest of *B. vagans*. The latter species is considered by most anglers and this author to be of greatest importance to eastern and midwestern anglers. In general, eastern *Pseudocloeon* species emerge during the same time of season (and day) as *Baetis* species and closely resemble them in the different stages of development. As a result, no special patterns are needed to tackle eastern *Pseudocloeon* hatches, only a greater degree of patience, since trout behave very suspiciously during their hatches. (See Fig. 2-1b, Chapter 2.)

P. carolina emerges with *B. intercalaris* and outlasts that species by approximately two weeks, which takes the *P. carolina* seasonal cycle into the month of June. The short, chunky nymphs split their cases swiftly, and the duns are not in the habit of giving the trout much of an opportunity to catch them easily. The nymph pattern for *B. intercalaris* does very well during this hatch.

P. dubium is another *Pseudocloeon* that produces good hatches for the eastern angler, and as far as he is concerned, the two species can be treated as one in all respects. However, this sister species will not begin to appear until July and will make a second showing during the last days of September.

Little Slate-Winged Olive Quill (P. anoka)

Strictly a midwestern species, *P. anoka* emerges in such numbers and regularity that its hatches are gaining a lot of respect from anglers there.

The nymphs are found in the moderate currents of gravelly runs, preferring those sections rich with submerged beds of vegetation. They also occupy the shallow riffles along the margin of streams. In this situation, the little nymphs can easily crawl out of the water during emergence, and therefore, the trout are able to consume them en masse very close to the bank. Fishing this hatch is a close-quarter game of exact delivery, careful wading, and much suspense. The floating-nymph imitation is effective during these hatches and, after a few sessions of success, will give the angler much confidence in dealing with large size trout feeding on such minute mayflies.

P. anoka is primarily a June–July event with a second seasonal occurrence during the month of September. Their nymphs are customarily midday emergers, but they will postpone their hatches until the cooler evening hours during unseasonably hot summer days.

Both *Pseudocloeon* species are separable from *Baetis* members by exhibiting only two tails. *P. anoka* is distinguishable from *P. carolina* by its geographical distribution; it is the only *Pseudocloeon* of significance in midwestern waters.

WESTERN HATCHES OF BAETIS, PSEUDOCLOEONS, AND CALLIBAETIS

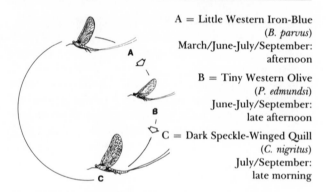

A = Little Western Iron-Blue
(*B. parvus*)
March/June-July/September:
afternoon

B = Tiny Western Olive
(*P. edmundsi*)
June-July/September:
late afternoon

C = Dark Speckle-Winged Quill
(*C. nigritus*)
July/September:
late morning

FIG. 5-6 Seasonal cycle of western *Baetis, Pseudocloeon,* and *Callibaetis* (A,B,C)—actual sizes

The western angler will encounter excellent hatches of the "little mayflies" throughout the fishing season. In his part of the country *Baetidae* nymphs are found in equal abundance in freestone rivers, spring creeks, and meadow streams. *Baetis* and *Pseudocloeons* are again the major types, with the hatches of the beautiful and elegant *Callibaetis* of paramount importance in lakes and ponds. *Callibaetis* are primarily midday emergers during the months of July, August, and September and indigenous to the same type of waters that support good populations of the Tiny White-Winged Black (*Tricorythodes*) that hatch at the same time of year.

Baetis species are the first of these western hatches, commencing as early as February or March and continuing until the fall. Western *Pseudocloeons*, readily recognized by their bright olive color, will appear in concentrated numbers during June and July and again in September with sporadic hatches in between. *Callibaetis* hatches peak in late summer. Each genera contains a number of species that resemble each other very closely, thus making the angler's job of exact imitation simpler. Consequently, only three artificials are needed to match their numbers.

Western members of Family *Baetidae* demonstrate a greater morphological diversity than their eastern and midwestern counterparts. Many of them are easily identifiable by their tail lengths, size, and general color patterns. However, it does appear that many species yet remain to be described. Species of *Callibaetis* are extremely hard to differentiate from one another in both the nymphal and spinner stages. Therefore, no attempt is made here to make unreliable and unnecessary distinctions.

Little Western Iron-Blue Quill (*B. parvus*)

The western angler will find that, regardless of the type of trout waters he chooses to fish, he will always encounter the excellent hatches of this little mayfly. The species is found abundantly in most streams over a wide geographical range that includes all the western states. During our research of western trout waters, we encountered *B. parvus* hatches in such outlying trout streams as Spearfish Creek in South Dakota, the lovely Oak Creek just south of Flagstaff, Arizona, the Kern River that drains part of the Sierras, and the Deschutes River in northern Oregon. Practically every stream and river within this vast area will undoubtedly produce *B. parvus* hatches. (See Fig. 2-1a, Chapter 2.)

The nymphs can thrive in a wide variety of habitats—from the slow-moving spring creeks to the cold and fast waters of freestone rivers of varied sizes. They demonstrate a marked degree of tolerance for warm waters, provided they have higher-oxygen riffled sections available to them.

The months of June and July have the best hatches, though the species does have other seasonal occurrences again in the fall. Its hatches occur in the afternoon. Wave after wave of the little *B. parvus* duns appear for about a three-hour period. Trout relish the nymphs and duns and take both on a fifty-fifty basis.

Spinners gather in the mornings or evenings, and their tight swarms can be observed over the banks of the stream. After mating, the spinners suddenly vanish and reappear spent on the water. Spinner falls that take place during the afternoon may cause them to be on the water with the hatching duns of the same species. Anglers should make sure which one of the two types the trout are indeed taking.

It is possible that two different species are presently being included under *B. parvus*, since all waters contain the species in two distinct sizes: 5mm and 7mm. The two, however, are identical in all other respects. The pattern that follows represents a compromise between their different sizes and colors, and it will imitate the size range of the common *B. parvus* and other important, closely related western members of Family *Baetidae*.

B. parvus nymphs are easily distinguishable from other *Baetis* by their pale abdominal areas (segments 4, 5, and 9–10). Duns are slightly paler than those of other western *Baetis* species.

Baetis parvus (and related species) Imitations

NATURAL	ARTIFICIAL

Conventional Nymph: Recommended to be tied on light-wire hook 94840, for imitation to be fished just under the surface *during* the hatch. Should be tied very slender.

SIZE: 6mm	HOOK: Mustad 3906 #16 or 94840 #18
TAILS: pale cream	THREAD: olive prewaxed 6/0
ABDOMEN: olive tan	TAILS: ginger wood duck fibers
THORAX: olive tan; dark gray wing pads	ABDOMEN: light olive brown dubbing
LEGS: tannish	THORAX: olive brown dubbing; dark mallard fibers for wing cases
	LEGS: ginger wood duck fibers

Floating Nymph*: An alternative to the Conventional Nymph and a very effective pattern to be fished *on the surface* during the hatches of *B. parvus*.

SIZE: 6mm	HOOK: Mustad 94833 #20
TAILS: pale cream	THREAD: olive prewaxed 6/0
ABDOMEN: olive tan	TAILS: pale cream hackle fibers
THORAX: olive tan; light gray unfolding wings	ABDOMEN: light olive brown dubbing
LEGS: tannish	THORAX: olive brown dubbing; light gray ball of dubbing for wing clump
	LEGS: tan hackle fibers

No-Hackle: The most effective *dry fly* pattern during the prolific hatches of *B. parvus*, which are producers of selectivity on the part of trout.

SIZE: 6mm	HOOK: Mustad 94833 #20
TAILS: light tan	THREAD: light olive prewaxed 6/0
ABDOMEN: light olive tan	TAILS: light tan hackle fibers
THORAX: light olive tan	ABDOMEN: light olive tan dubbing blend
WINGS: light bluish gray	THORAX light olive tan dubbing blend
	WINGS: pale slate mallard quill segments

Spinners*: The spinner falls equal the density and selective difficulties for anglers as *B. parvus* hatches, thus the following pattern will prove to be a badly needed one during many excursions in western trout waters. Tie is for the female of *B. parvus*.

SIZE: 5.5mm	HOOK: Mustad 94859 #20 (ring-eye hook)
TAILS: light grayish tan	THREAD: brown prewaxed 6/0
ABDOMEN: medium tan	TAILS: light tan hackle fibers
THORAX: medium tannish brown	ABDOMEN: medium tan dubbing
WINGS: clear (hyaline)	THORAX: medium tannish dubbing
	WINGS: light gray Flyrite fibers or light dun hen hackle tips

NOTE: Hook type Mustad 94833 in size #20 can be substituted with ring-eye style hook 94859 in size #18, which is easier to work with in tying imitations of such small sizes.

IMPORTANT NOTE: For those anglers in the habit of fishing western waters during the months from late October to April, *B. parvus* hatches are replaced by the larger *B. tricaudatus* (94833 #16), which also ranks as one of the most abundant and dense hatch producers of the season. Its duns should be more olive than those of *B. parvus*, and *B. tricaudatus* spinners are conspicuously more brownish.

*Most recommended

Little Western Iron-Blue Quill (B. propinquus)

Like *B. parvus*, this species appears to be very versatile in its adaptation to microhabitats, since it is found in fast to slow waters. However, it exists abundantly only in sluggish, weedy streams and spring creeks, where it is capable of producing excellent hatches for anglers. Trout waters like the Firehole River in Yellowstone National Park, the Big Hole in Montana, and the smooth currents of Hat Creek in northern California contain *B. propinquus* nymphs in good numbers.

Upon emergence, these little *Baetis* can play havoc with anglers because of their minute size (4.5mm) and density. They often manage to eliminate the importance of another emerging insect and undermine the approach of anglers who may be unaware of their presence.

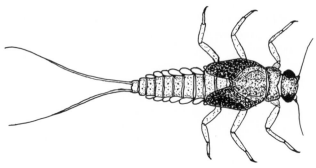

FIG. 5-7 *Baetis propinquus*

B. propinquus is a July and October emerger with sporadic hatches in between. A second two-tailed *Baetis* species found in western waters is *B. bicaudatus*; it is almost identical to *B. propinquus* and emerges at the same time.

Little Western Iron-Blue Quill (B. tricaudatus)

B. tricaudatus is a larger *Baetis* species whose hatches are important to anglers in the very beginning and end of the fishing season. It emerges before spring runoff (late March to May) and again after the first snows in the fall during October and November.

The dark olive nymphs of *B. tricaudatus* are a common sight in deep, meandering streams in the high-altitude meadows of western mountains. Fishing this hatch requires the angler to stalk already rising fish in a hide-and-seek fashion. He should not forget that in tranquil and shallow waters where these hatches take

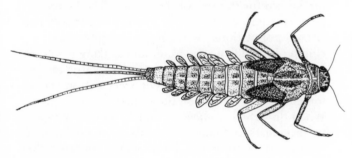

FIG. 5-8 *Baetis tricaudatus*

place, trout have an opportunity to choose between the naturals and his floating nymph imitation, and consequently, the trout's ultimate decision depends largely on his presentation.

Typical of most early- and late-season emergers, *B. tricaudatus* hatches are in the afternoon during the warmest part of the day. They barely last an hour. Spinner flights are also in the afternoon, and their falls occur immediately after the hatches.

B. tricaudatus nymphs are hard to confuse with those of other *Baetis* mainly because of the time of year—late fall and early spring—in which they will be found on the water. They exhibit conspicuous veins on their gills and are considerably larger than other *Baetis* found in western waters.

Tiny Western Olive (*P. edmundsi*)

P. edmundsi is an important little mayfly whose hatches are made to order for those who derive gratification from landing good-sized trout on light tackle and minute flies. At first glance it appears as a tiny Pale Morning Dun.

The species belongs to genus *Pseudocloeon* of Family *Baetidae*, but its biology closely resembles that of the *Baetis* species. *Pseudocloeon* nymphs are indigenous to slow-moving, weedy sections of streams and rivers. Their conspicuous pale olive nymphs can often be observed clinging to and scurrying among the sub-aquatic vegetation that grows along the shallow margins of these waters.

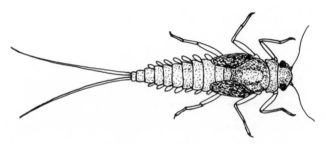

FIG. 5-9 *Pseudocloeon edmundsi*

Seasonal emergence is at its best during the months of June and July with a second seasonal brood appearing in September, the same emergence times for hatches of *B. parvus*. The two usually follow each other in daily emergence, *B. parvus* in the middle of the afternoon, and *P. edmundsi* later in the day.

P. edmundsi is the only *Pseudocloeon* reported in the Northwest by entomologists. Its range encompasses most trout waters from the Black Hills of South Dakota to the Pacific mountain ranges. A second species, *P. turbidum*, dominates the southwest region, and its hatches approach those of its sister species in density and importance to fly fishermen. California waters like Hot Creek, Owens River, and the Merced offer excellent *P. turbidum* hatches as does the Williamson in southern Oregon. Both species are conspicuously pale green in color, making streamside identification simple.

The species also exhibits an inexplicable size range in its mature stages; however, the hook size recommended has proved to be the most effective to meet and fish the hatches of the little *Pseudocloeons*.

P. edmundsi emerges in great numbers, often with other equally prolific species, and always in smooth, flat waters, which are prerequisites for rising and ultra-selective trout. Anglers should not think that any more-or-less pattern will do during these hatches. If they do not believe it, the trout will inevitably make them aware of this reality.

Pseudocloeon edmundsi Imitations

| NATURAL | ARTIFICIAL |

Conventional Nymph: An optional pattern to be fished just under the surface film during the actual hatch. Its configuration should be very slender.

SIZE: 5mm
TAILS: pale olive
ABDOMEN: pale olive or chartreuse
THORAX: pale olive or chartreuse
LEGS: none

HOOK: Mustad 94859 #20
THREAD: light olive prewaxed 6/0
TAILS: hackle fibers dyed pale olive
ABDOMEN: chartreuse or pale olive dubbing
THORAX: chartreuse or pale olive dubbing
LEGS: none

Floating Nymph*: This type of pattern has the advantage of imitating a more vulnerable stage of emergence than either a free-swimming nymph or dun. It is often very needed by the fly fisher during the surface-blanketing of the little *P. edmundsi.*

SIZE: 5mm
ABDOMEN: chartreuse
THORAX: chartreuse; pale gray unfolding wings
LEGS: light gray

HOOK: Mustad 94859 #20
THREAD: light olive prewaxed 6/0
ABDOMEN: chartreuse or pale olive dubbing
THORAX: chartreuse; light gray ball of dubbing for unfolding wings
LEGS: light dun hackle fibers

No-Hackle:

SIZE: 4–5mm
TAILS: light tannish gray
ABDOMEN: chartreuse or pale olive
THORAX: chartreuse or pale olive
WINGS: light bluish gray (almost lacking any coloration)

HOOK: Mustad 94859 #20–#22
THREAD: light olive prewaxed 6/0
TAILS: light dun hackle fibers
ABDOMEN: chartreuse or pale olive dubbing
THORAX: chartreuse or pale olive
WINGS: light gray mallard quill segments

Spinners: This stage of *P. edmundsi* is very similar to the spinner of *B. parvus* (the pattern indicated for its *female*). The spinner fall of *P. edmundsi* is also very important, thus a smaller hook size (Mustad 94859 #22) version tied with its body slightly darker will do very well. It will be the smallest mayfly pattern that the western fly fisher will need to carry in his fly box.

*Most recommended

Dark Speckle-Winged Quill (*Callibaetis nigritus*)

Callibaetis are indigenous to lakes and ponds, the types of water that support few types of insects but are known for the size of their trout. The biomass of lakes choked with aquatic vegetation will mainly consist of populations of *Callibaetis* nymphs. Lifting a clump of weed from the water and shaking it will dislodge hundreds of their numbers. They are very visible in their natural environment, since they are accustomed to cling openly on the stems of aquatic plants. When disturbed, *Callibaetis* nymphs dart away rapidly by flicking their filamentous tails, an action that resembles the darting motions of fleeing minnows. (See Fig. 5-1.)

FIG. 5-10 Typical *Callibaetis* water.

FIG. 5-11 Swarm of *Callibaetis* spinners before mating.

These hatches take place from July to September and oddly enough, *Callibaetis* duns get perpetually smaller as the season progresses, from No. 14 to No. 18 hook sizes. Hatches begin, as do the concentrated falls of spinners, at 11 o'clock in the morning. The trout will invariably focus their attention on the more accessible spinners. Anglers should do likewise instead of becoming preoccupied with matching the actual hatch.

Prior to the time that the spinners return en masse to the water, the angler can usually spot them hovering at eye level over the bushes along the margins of the water. They have distinctive flight patterns consisting of foot-long, fast vertical undulations as if they were suspended on invisible rubber bands. After mating, the females disappear into the brush to give their eggs an opportunity to develop and soon journey to the water to complete their propagative function. The microscopic eggs hatch the instant they touch the surface of the water.

The reader should bear in mind that since *Callibaetis* hatches take place at midday during summer days, he will have to overcome the adverse effects of sunlight and wind. Trout in general abhor direct sunlight, especially in smooth-surfaced waters. Consequently, the only feeding activity of trout during sunny days will take place in shaded areas, normally along the margins of waters. In turn, during partly cloudy days, no sooner is the sun off the surface of the water than it becomes alive with the rises of trout. Wind is also a determining factor during the spinner falls of *Callibaetis*, since it constantly forces the delicate spinners away from the water.

In essence, fishing the spinner falls of *Callibaetis* is characterized by good-sized trout, active when the sun is obstructed by clouds, and rising when the wind allows the spinners to fall spent on the surface of the water. If all prerequisites are met, the fortunate angler stands to do extremely well during these hatches.

CHAPTER 6: Hatches of the Clingers: Gordon Quills, American March Browns, Light Cahills, and Western Red Quills (Family *Heptageniidae*)

AT streamside, inquisitive fly fishermen often lift a boulder out of the stream to determine what type of aquatic insects are attached to it. If the reader himself has indulged in such streamside explorations, perhaps he has noticed the large, flat nymphs that rapidly scurry to its underside; they appear extremely agile and able to move in any direction with equal ease. These are members of Family *Heptageniidae*, commonly found in cold, fast-water streams of a firm-bottom substrate consisting of gravel or rock.

Many well-known hatches, and some that merit more attention, are produced by members of this family. The celebrated Gordon Quill, American March Brown, Gray Fox, and Light Cahill hatches of the East are a few examples. By comparison, western anglers have even better populations of these types, but few are known to anglers and have not yet been covered in angling literature. Consequently, much space in this chapter will be devoted to western members.

In general, these hatches are inconsequential to those anglers who confine their sport to slow-moving, weedy, or silted streams. Except for species of *Stenonema*, midwestern trout waters have poor populations of these critters, and anglers from that area have little reason to concern themselves with their hatches. On the other hand, most river systems that drain the eastern mountain ranges, from the Great Smokies to northern Vermont, are inhabited by good *Heptageniidae* populations. The Rockies, the Sierras, and the Cascade mountains are crisscrossed with trout streams that hold them in excellent numbers.

The nymphs of all types of clingers have flattened heads and bodies well designed to deflect the swift currents of fast-water environments as well as to elude predators in calmer sections. Also, some possess large, circularly arranged gills that collectively look like "suction cups." These gills help them to lie flatly on the smooth surface of the rocks and to further withstand the turbulence of the water.

Besides physical adaptations, these nymphs also demonstrate biological adjustments in their mode of emergence to further guarantee their own survival. Nymphs of other mayflies travel clear to the surface film before the "entrapped" duns proceed to crack the nymphal shucks, but, in the riffled and choppy sections of waters where many *Heptageniidae* are found, such a conventional emergence would prove suicidal. The turbulent motion of the surface would cause the fragile duns to flip on their sides, thus ensuring their destruction by either battering or drowning.

Crucial to their existence, *Heptageniidae* duns escape

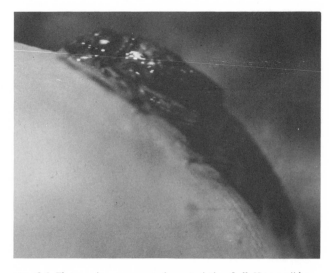

FIG. 6-1 Flatness is a common characteristic of all *Heptageniidae* nymphs.

their nymphal shucks from the bottom of the stream or while ascending toward the surface. This biological adjustment is a response to a basic survival requirement and simultaneously gives rise to the practicability of wet fly imitations used by anglers.

As a general rule, *Heptageniidae* hatches take place at midday, sporadically between 11 a.m. in the morning and late afternoon. Deviations in the time of daily emergence are the result of unusual or adverse weather conditions rather than due to the basic nature of the species. The spinners, in turn, will gather into low-flying squadrons in the evenings and rarely at other times of the day. The imagoes have a distinctive five-foot vertical nuptial dance visible over the banks or riffled sections of streams. On occasion, spinner flights may be as high as 20 feet above the water.

Of the five genera commonly found in trout streams, two are of importance to eastern and, to a lesser extent, midwestern anglers; no less than four are of concern to westerners.

FAMILY HEPTAGENIIDAE

Genus Rhithrogena *(West: abundant; Midwest: uncommon; East: uncommon)*

Rhithrogena nymphs are curious-looking critters that are easily recognized by the conspicuous "suction-cup" arrangement of their abdominal gills and their three tails. They are expertly suited to withstand extremely fast, often unwadable waters where they cling so tightly to the rocks that they look as if they were almost incised in them.

A few species are also found in moderately slow rivers and, surprisingly, appear to be exceptionally tolerant of slow and even warmer waters. A good example is *R. undulata*, an extremely common western species, which inhabits the entire length of the Yellowstone River of Montana from its genesis in Yellowstone National Park to the point where it joins the gargantuan Missouri River in North Dakota, over 350 miles away.

Duns of this genus have reddish brown bodies and medium slate wings, ranging in hook size between No. 14 and No. 16. As a general rule, the evening spinner falls of *Rhithrogenas* are important to anglers and often surpass the influence of the actual hatches.

Few eastern and midwestern trout streams contain good populations of *Rhithrogena*; however, rivers like the Fox, Sturgeon, and Pine in the Upper Peninsula

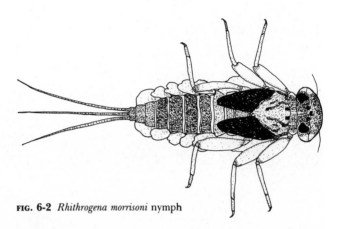

FIG. 6-2 *Rhithrogena morrisoni* nymph

of Michigan have fair populations, as does the uppermost region of the state of Wisconsin. I have found *Rhithrogenas* in certain cold, freestone streams in eastern mountains but never in sufficient quantities to warrant a special artificial imitation to fish their hatches. Anglers will easily recognize *Rhithrogenas* in that part of the country not only by their unique configurations and gill structure but by their striking colors. For example, *R. sanguinea* is a bright red, and *R. jejuna* is an unmistakable pale olive.

From a relative point of view, the West virtually holds a monopoly on *Rhithrogena* populations. Its trout streams hold no less than four extremely abundant species that follow each other in emergence from March through the month of August. They are considered to be one of the most important mayfly groups by those anglers who fish fast western waters. They also are the first large mayflies to appear for the season, with hatches of *R. morrisoni* taking place in March, which is two months before spring runoff has begun in most western mountains. These nymphs are indigenous to either moderate or torrential waters, and the tempo of the surface current dictates the mode of subsurface emergence. In fast waters the subimagoes escape the nymphal shuck from the bottom of the stream, yet in slower or more placid sections they may ascend within a few inches of the surface before the duns slip out of them and make the rest of the journey as wet flies. The angler would do best to use a wet fly imitation in all cases, controlling only the depth of his artificial before starting to retrieve it with an uplifting motion.

Genus Epeorus *(West: abundant; Midwest: fairly common; East: abundant)*

Epeorus nymphs are instantly recognized by the presence of only two tails, a unique characteristic among

all mayfly nymphs with the exception of the tiny two-tailed members of Family *Baetidae* covered in the previous chapter. (See Fig. 2-1d.)

The subimagoes of all *Epeorus* species have grayish brown bodies and slate-color wings. The eastern and western species closely resemble each other.

Unequivocally, *Epeorus* nymphs are found in extremely fast, oxygen-rich waters and will not tolerate sections of streams that slow down to a crawl during the lower-water conditions of summer. The many freestone streams of the entire Appalachian Range support *Epeorus* nymphs in great numbers. The Midwest, however, is practically devoid of them except for one species (*E. vitreus*) that appears to be more tolerant of waters of a low-oxygen content. The cool, spring-fed rivers of the West, from the small to the very large, hold them abundantly.

Epeorus duns escape their nymphal shucks at the bottom of the stream, and trout customarily capture the ascending duns (and ideally your wet fly imitation) midway to the surface.

Genus Cinygmula *(West: common; Midwest: uncommon; East: fairly common)*

These nymphs are identifiable by their emarginated heads which are caused by the mouthparts that protrude from their sides. *Cinygmula* nymphs do not exhibit a "suction-cup" arrangement of their gills; their gills are slender and not circular in fashion. Unlike *Epeorus* nymphs, those of *Cinygmula* have three tails.

The duns of this genus are pretty mayflies ranging

in general colors from pale cream to a reddish brown, and normally averaging a No. 16 hook size.

The nymphs prefer moderate- to fast-current streams that are able to maintain cool-water temperatures during the hottest months of the year. However, they do appear to be more tolerant than *Epeorus* nymphs and are found throughout the entire stream instead of just in its riffled or faster sections. In the West, very good populations are also found in very cold but slow-moving meadow streams.

Only one *Cinygmula* species (*C. subequalis*), from the eastern half of the country, is recognized by entomologists. As far as can be determined, the species has not been covered in any manner in angling texts to date, yet it causes consistent hatches during the months of May and June in eastern trout streams. Many Pennsylvania streams and freestone rivers in the Catskills have good populations, as do those in the Adirondacks and Green Mountains of Vermont.

Western states contain two species of consequence to anglers—*C. reticulata* and *C. ramaleyi*. Their hatches are not as important as those of *Rhithrogena* or *Epeorus*, nonetheless they are productive in meadow

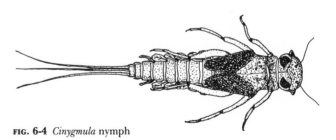

FIG. **6-4** *Cinygmula* nymph

FIG. **6-5** Typical *Cinygmula* waters.

streams of a fine-washed gravel substrate. The upper Gibbon in the Park, the South Fork of the Madison, and Henry's Fork of the Snake River, just below Henry's Lake, are good examples of *Cinygmula* waters. The best populations of these nymphs that I have ever discovered have been in the many fine California trout streams that drain the eastern side of the Sierras. In all western waters, *Cinygmulas* are July emergers.

Emergence in the slower meadow streams is accomplished by the nymphs swimming clear to the surface of the water before the duns escape the nymphal exoskeleton.

Genus Stenonema *(West: rare; Midwest: common; East: abundant)*

Most nymphs of *Stenonema* species are conspicuously large and, as a result, recognizing them is basically a routine matter. When live specimens are observed in the stream or viewed in a saucepan, their tails are held in a natural 90-degree position to each other. However, the slender, threadlike gills on the seventh abdominal segment are what taxonomically differentiate these nymphs from other members of Family *Heptageniidae*.

Duns of *Stenonema* are large and handsome and appear sporadically all day during summer days. As the season progresses, the duns of the species get conspicuously lighter in color and size, changing from the large, reddish brown American March Brown (*S. vicarium*) to the much smaller, nearly white Light

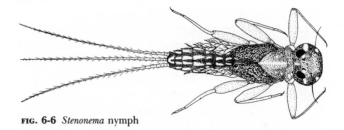

FIG. **6-6** *Stenonema* nymph

Cahills (*S. canadense* and *S. pulchellum*) of late summer.

In direct contrast to genus *Rhithrogena*, the hatches of *Stenonema* are very important to eastern, and to a lesser extent, midwestern anglers; the popular American March Brown, Gray Fox, and Light Cahill patterns were specifically designed to match their hatches. The western angler has no need to even concern himself with *Stenonemas*, for only a few rare and isolated reports are available concerning their existence in western waters.

A few weeks prior to their scheduled seasonal emergence, *Stenonema* nymphs start migrating to the shallower margins of the stream or to quieter eddies and pools. As a result, most of their hatches take place in the shallower waters near the margins of streams. This migratory trait is most evident with species in the beginning of the season, during the emergence of the American March Browns and Gray Fox, than during those that emerge later when lower-water conditions exist in our streams. Light Cahills (*S. canadense*, *S. interpunctatum*, and *S. pulchellum*) do not exhibit the migratory tendencies of their seasonal predecessors.

Genus Heptagenia *(West: abundant; Midwest: fairly common; East: fairly common)*

Heptagenia nymphs may at first glance resemble those of *Stenonema*, but a closer look will reveal that their subequal gills on all seven abdominal segments gradually taper in size. Also, they do not hold their tails in the 90-degree fashion as do the *Stenonemas*.

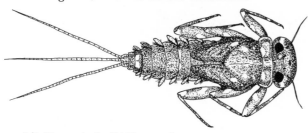

FIG. 6-7 *Heptagenia simplicioides* nymph

Eastern and midwestern anglers will find disappointing populations of this genus in their trout streams, though some species such as *H. hebe, H. diabasia,* and *H. lucipennis* are found commonly enough in the upper regions of the states of Michigan and Wisconsin to constitute fair hatches. Sporadic hatches of *H. hebe* can be found in eastern waters, but it appears that the time and the manner in which they emerge serve to cancel out their influence. Westerners get to enjoy the hatches and spinner falls of abundant *Heptagenia* species like *H. elegantula, H. solitaria,* and *H. simplicoides.* The dun and spinner stages of these species are impressively elegant and a common sight over the surface of trout streams during the summer months.

During a hatch, the nymphs reach the surface film very fast, and the duns waste no time in getting airborne. Both of these emergence traits tend to diminish the importance of *Heptagenia* hatches; however, the spinner falls are impressive by comparison. Nuptial flights are just over the riffled sections of streams with the actual downfall of the imagoes occurring at dusk.

Emergence Rationale and Artificial Patterns

Perhaps the once extensively used wet flies owe much of their past notability to the hatches produced by this family. In fact, *Epeorus pleuralis,* a member of Family *Heptageniidae,* was the first American hatch to be described. It is known to most anglers as the Gordon Quill and bears the name of the father of fly fishing on this side of the Atlantic. Preoccupation with the development of wet fly patterns continued and captured much of the attention of innovative fly tyers for the next few decades before slipping into a secondary position as more recent developments took their place. However, to date these types of artificials merit our attention, especially with the imitation of many of the hatches included in this chapter.

The method of subsurface emergence of *Heptageniidae* members appears to depend on their immediate surroundings during their hatches. Nymphs in the tranquil sections of rivers swim clear to the surface of the water before the subimagoes split the nymphal exoskeleton (*Stenonemas, Heptagenias*). Those in faster waters will escape the nymphal shuck while the nymphs are still attached to the bottom of the stream

FIG. 6-8 Good *Stenonema* water—Esopus Creek in New York. *Photograph by Austin M. Francis*

FIG. 6-9 The Flat-Body nymph

or when approaching the surface, and will make the rest of the journey as a folded-wing dun (*Epeorus, Rhithrogenas*). Consequently, two types of artificial patterns are required to imitate the subsurface stage of the genera of Family *Heptageniidae*: the Flat-Body Nymph for species of *Stenonemas* and *Heptagenias*, and the Emerging Wet-Fly artificial for the emergences of *Epeorus* and *Rhithrogenas*. Fortunately for anglers, not all types were found abundantly in the same waters or in all regions of the country, which greatly reduces the amount of artificial patterns the reader will need in order to match their numbers.

Practical patterns for the dry forms of these relatively large mayflies are: the Conventional Hackle and Duck-Wing dries.

FIG. 6-10 The ever-popular conventional-hackle and duck-wing dry fly imitations.

EASTERN AND MIDWESTERN HATCHES OF HEPTAGENIIDAE

This group of common mayflies begins to appear for the season during the month of April in most eastern waters and will continue to do so through the month of August. All are comparatively large in actual size and will emerge profusely enough to be significant to all anglers. Some of the better-known hatches produced by this family include the Gordon Quills, American March Browns, Gray Fox and Light Cahills, and the less popular Gray-Winged Yellow Quills.

Heptageniidae spinner falls will customarily take place in the evenings. Anglers should make it a point to be astream prepared with some of the large spinner imitations offered in this chapter, which are often prerequisites for success during these mayflies' spinner activity.

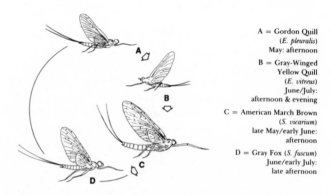

A = Gordon Quill
(*E. pleuralis*)
May: afternoon

B = Gray-Winged
Yellow Quill
(*E. vitreus*)
June/July:
afternoon & evening

C = American March Brown
(*S. vicarium*)
late May/early June:
afternoon

D = Gray Fox (*S. fuscum*)
June/early July:
late afternoon

FIG. 6-11 Seasonal cycle of eastern and midwestern *Heptageniidae* (actual sizes).

Perhaps no other family of mayflies is harder to simplify than the present one. The difficulty stems primarily from the fact that there are five genera to reckon with: *Epeorus, Rhithrogena, Cinygmula, Stenonema,* and *Heptagenia*. Fortunately, only certain types are important in each section. Every effort will be made here to clarify this complex group for the reader. No better method can be employed than to immediately divide those that are significant to either the eastern or midwestern angler.

Important Eastern Hatches

COMMON NAME	SPECIES	SEASONAL OCCURRENCE
Gordon Quill	*Epeorus pleuralis*	April 28–May 25
Gray-Winged Yellow Quill	*Epeorus vitreus*	June 1–August 10
American March Brown	*Stenonema vicarium*	May 25–June 15
Gray Fox (or Light Cahill)	*Stenonema fuscum* *Stenacron interpunctatum*	June 5–July 30

Table 6-1: Eastern members of Family *Heptageniidae*.

Important Midwestern Hatches

Gray-Winged Yellow Quill	*Epeorus vitreus* *Heptagenia hebe*	May 20–July 30
Gray Fox (or Light Cahill)	*Stenonema fuscum* *Stenacron interpunctatum*	June 1–August 30

TABLE 6-2: Midwestern members of Family *Heptageniidae*.

Gordon Quill (*Epeorus pleuralis*)

This hatch ranks as one of the favorites among eastern anglers, principally because it is the first appearance of a large-sized aquatic insect for the season. It also coincides with the time of the year when water temperatures permanently reach the high 40 mark, causing trout to become active and feed on insects riding the surface of the water. It's often a bitter-cold-weather hatch, but one gladly welcomed after eagerly awaiting the fishing season during the long winter.

Epeorus pleuralis (See Fig. 2-1d, page 15), like all members of its genus, thrives abundantly in the fastest sections of freestone rivers. Its nymphs, as those of *Rhithrogena*, are suited to survive in the treacherous white-water microhabitats. The bottom substrate is usually composed of large boulders, smoothly faced by the molding effect of the fast currents.

Expect its hatches during the first three weeks of the month of May or when the water temperature permanently reaches 50 degrees. Its midday appearance, as that of all other early-season emergers, is customarily between two and four o'clock, the warmest part of the day. During actual emergence, *E. pleuralis* duns often exhibit difficulty drying their wings and, consequently, leaving the surface of the water. As a result, they are compelled to float helplessly to the more placid portions of large pools and become easy victims to winter-starved trout.

Spinner swarms and falls often occur just after a hatch in the late afternoon. The thick gathering of the imagoes over the riffles is the only indication that anglers will have of the coming spinner activity. In typical *Heptageniidae* fashion, their nuptial flight consists of graceful three- to four-foot vertical rises and falls, which cannot be mistaken for that of any other mayfly that emerges during the same time of year.

Epeorus nymphs are perhaps the easiest ones to separate from other mayfly nymphs; they have *two tails* and *E. pleuralis* nymphs are the only mature *Epeorus* found in the streams so early in the season. Duns are

of a grayish brown color with slate-colored wings and exhibit only *two tails* as do all members of the *Heptageniidae* family.

Epeorus pleuralis Imitations

NATURAL	ARTIFICIAL

Flat-Body Nymph: An optional and very useful pattern to fish the fast-water stretches during nonhatch periods.

NATURAL	ARTIFICIAL
SIZE: 9–10mm	HOOK: Mustad 3906 #12, weighted with 1 amp lead wire
TAILS: dark olive brown, barred	THREAD: olive prewaxed 6/0
ABDOMEN: olive brown	TAILS: dark barred wood duck
GILLS: light dun	ABDOMEN: brown dubbing
THORAX: olive brown; mottled dark brown wing pads	GILLS: light dun ostrich herl ribbed into place with yellow 6/0 thread
LEGS: mottled olive brown	THORAX: olive brown dubbing; brown mottled turkey or hen pheasant for wing cases
	LEGS: brown olive partridge hackle fibers

Emerging Wet Fly*: This pattern is designed to be fished *wet*, thus tied in a heavy hook, and it is to imitate the rising folded-winged adult as it is traveling toward the surface.

NATURAL	ARTIFICIAL
SIZE: 9mm	HOOK: Mustad 3906 #12
TAILS: brown olive	THREAD: gray prewaxed 6/0
ABDOMEN: yellowish gray	TAILS: brown olive hackle fibers
THORAX: dark yellowish gray	ABDOMEN: yellowish gray dubbing ribbed with brown monocord 3/0
WINGS: medium gray, unmottled	THORAX: same as abdomen
	WINGS: four turns of medium dun hackle; two turns of brown grizzly for legs

Hen-Winged Spinner*:

NATURAL	ARTIFICIAL
SIZE: 9–10mm	HOOK: 94833 #12
TAILS: brownish olive	THREAD: brown prewaxed 6/0
ABDOMEN: tannish brown	TAILS: medium brown hackle fibers
THORAX: light reddish brown	ABDOMEN: rusty brown dubbing
WINGS: clear (hyaline)	THORAX: rusty brown dubbing
	WINGS: light dun hen-hackle tips tied spent; three turns of dun hackle, clipped top and bottom, for better floatability

*Most recommended

Small Gordon Quill (Cinygmula subequalis)
Cinygmulas, as a group, are of primary importance to western anglers; however, for a number of years I have fished to a fairly good hatch caused by *Cinygmula subequalis* in many eastern streams. To date, no angling book includes this hatch in its coverage. Yet it deserves some degree of importance, for its hatches

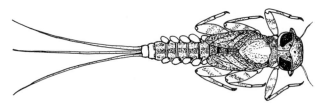

FIG. 6-12 *Cinygmula subequalis*

are not only predictable, but they usually manage to cause trout to feed semi-selectively.

C. subequalis nymphs are markedly more diversified than those of *Epeorus* in their selection of microhabitats, being found most commonly in the main currents as well as along the margins of freestone streams.

Their seasonal emergence begins in the wake of that of the Gordon Quills, which they happen to resemble closely in general appearance, though they are smaller by exactly two hook sizes. They will continue to emerge until June, when their evening hatches will follow the late-afternoon hatches of the Gray Fox.

Separation of *Cinygmula* nymphs from those taxonomically belonging to other mayfly groups is best accomplished by noting the lateral extensions that protrude from the sides of their heads. Only one species, *C. subequalis*, is reported by entomologists to exist in the eastern half of the country. The nymph phase is extremely variable. Two distinct color forms become apparent: a unicolorous olive type and a type that shows obvious pale dots and markings on the head, legs, and abdomen (segments 5, 9–10). The duns also exhibit great nonuniformity, ranging from pale cream to grayish brown in body color. The latter color form is by far the most common, thus the common name given this hatch in this book.

Gray-Winged Yellow Quill (*Epeorus vitreus*)

In comparison, *Epeorus vitreus* is not as important to the eastern angler as are the hatches of *Epeorus pleuralis* or Gordon Quill; nonetheless, the species produces good, dependable emergences in the evenings during the summer months. Moreover, *E. vitreus* is also more widespread than its sister species and produces fishable hatches for midwesterners.

E. vitreus nymphs are distinctly more tolerant of the slower and warmer sections of trout rivers than those of *E. pleuralis*. Consequently, its hatches are not restricted to only bouldered, freestone waters, but they will also take place in meandering, gravel-bottomed streams of varied sizes.

Hatches of Gray-Winged Yellow Quills are mainly summer events, during the months of June and July, and often lasting until the early part of August. In the beginning of their seasonal cycle, they will appear in the middle of the afternoon, but as the season progresses they will gradually adjust toward an evening timetable. Their spinner falls, which also take place late in the evening, can be as important to anglers as the hatches themselves since the duns that emerged over a period of hours the day before return to the stream, mate, and suddenly fall spent on the surface of the water. Trout will respond to them just as quickly.

Streamside identification of *E. vitreus* nymphs is simplified by the fact that like all *Epeorus*, they only exhibit two tails, and also that they are the only mature *Epeorus* nymphs found in the stream during early summer. Furthermore, each abdominal segment exhibits a pair of dark spots. Duns are also two-tailed and have a unique yellowish orange coloration. A very similar *Epeorus* species, though comparatively uncommon, is *E. fragilis*, which also appears in streams later in the year. Artificial patterns are not suggested for the Gray-Winged Yellow Quill, because in its nymph stage it is well represented by patterns given for *E. pleuralis*. Its dry form is very similar to summer *Stenonemas*, specifically *S. fuscum*.

Small Gray-Winged Yellow Quill (*Heptagenia hebe*)

This small mayfly looks, at first glance, like a miniature *Epeorus vitreus* which it happens to duplicate closely in general biology and geographical distribution. It is commonly found in eastern streams, though its best populations are in the trout waters of Michigan and Wisconsin.

In typical *Heptagenia* fashion, the duns of *H. hebe* leave the water instantaneously during actual emergence. This gives the trout little opportunity to capture them, and anglers little reason to imitate them in the first place. On the other hand, during ovipositing, the spinners are compelled to touch the surface

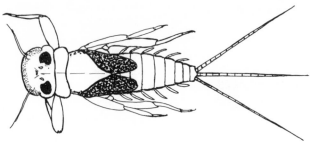

FIG. 6-13 *Heptagenia hebe*

of the water in order to extrude their eggs, thus presenting more of an opportunity for the trout and fly fishers. A similar pattern recommended for *E. vitreus*, except in two hook sizes smaller, will suffice during the spinner falls of *H. hebe*.

The nymphs are easily recognizable by their *three tails*, their small size (7mm), and their well-mottled bodies with pale areas. Duns and spinners resemble those of *E. vitreus*, though besides being smaller, they lack the orangish color flush of the latter species.

American March Brown (*Stenonema vicarium*)

This hatch, and that of its sister species, *Stenonema fuscum* or Gray Fox, are undoubtedly two of the most important ones of the entire season. Both are large mayflies, occur quite commonly in eastern streams, and emerge during the most pleasant period of the year—late afternoon during early June. The American March Browns are of principal importance to eastern anglers, while those of the Gray Fox are prolific in both eastern and midwestern streams.

S. vicarium and *S. fuscum* are extremely adaptable species of mayflies, and occupy most available microhabitat niches in trout-stream environments. Freestone rivers, weedy streams, and even silted waters contain them in good numbers. Prior to their seasonal occurrence, their nymphs will undergo great migrations along the bottom of streams, moving to the more placid margins. Trout appear to be aware of this phenomenon, for their stomachs will often be cramped with as many as 100 to 200 immature nymphs a week before the hatches will begin for the season. A flat-body artificial of either species will often prove deadly when fished dead drift during the cooler periods of the day and for the week before their hatching.

American March Browns appear in the season from the latter part of May (or when the water temperature reaches the mid-50's) and last until the middle of June, at which time they are fully replaced by the hatches of their sister species, *Stenonema fuscum*. They are customarily early- to late-afternoon emergers,

their hatches taking place for four to five hours in daily duration. As with all other mayflies, cloudy days will experience the best hatches.

Spinners and their consequential falls are profitable for anglers. The concentrated numbers of such large flies cannot help but entice the frenzied feeding activity of trout. Customarily, they fall at dusk or after dark, just after the angler will notice the low-flying squadrons of their spinners heading straight upstream, appearing as if they were preoccupied with reaching a preconceived destination.

Identification of *Stenonema vicarium* nymphs, and separating them at streamside from those of *S. fuscum*, is best accomplished by remembering the sizes in which they attain full maturity. Those over 13mm in length can safely be considered as belonging to *S. vicarium*, while *S. fuscum* nymphs are noticeably smaller, averaging only 10 to 11mm. The immature stages of both species are very hard to distinguish from each other; however, *S. vicarium* is reddish in general color, while those of *S. fuscum* are yellowish. Both are strongly banded with dark, horizontal markings.

Stenonema vicarium Imitations

NATURAL	ARTIFICIAL

Flat-Body Nymph*: A good nymph pattern to be employed during nonhatch periods for the week prior to the seasonal commencement of the *S. vicarium* emergence cycle.

NATURAL	ARTIFICIAL
SIZE: 15mm	HOOK: Mustad 3906 #8
TAILS: dark brownish olive, 1½ length of nymph	THREAD: amber prewaxed 6/0 or 3/0 monocord
ABDOMEN: dark amber distinctly ringed with black	TAILS: wood duck fibers dyed dark olive brown
THORAX: light amber; black wing pads	ABDOMEN: gills dun color ostrich herl; body dark amber dubbing ribbed with dark brown monocord
LEGS: mottled brown with amber	THORAX: light amber dubbing; dark turkey tail feather segment for wing cases
	LEGS: brown partridge hackle fibers

Hen-Winged Dun*: Pattern can also be tied with a second hackle in place of hen body feathers.

NATURAL	ARTIFICIAL
SIZE: 15mm	HOOK: Mustad 94842 or 94833 #8
TAILS: blackish brown	THREAD: amber prewaxed 6/0 or 3/0 monocord
ABDOMEN: reddish amber on top, yellowish tan on bottom	TAILS: dark reddish hackle fibers, twice the length of the entire body
THORAX: reddish amber on top, yellowish tan on bottom	ABDOMEN: yellowish tan dubbing blend, no ribbing
WINGS: mottled grayish brown	THORAX: same as abdomen
LEGS: dark amber	WINGS: mottled brownish hen body feathers
	LEGS: dark brown hackle

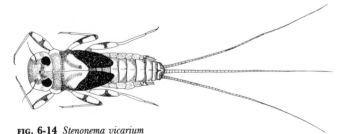

FIG. **6-14** *Stenonema vicarium*

Spinner*: An excellent pattern often needed for the excellent spinner falls of the *S. vicarium* in waters where they constitute a good hatch.

SIZE: 14–15mm
TAILS: dark amber, barred
ABDOMEN: brownish tan
THORAX: same as abdomen
WINGS: hyaline with pigmented crossveins
LEGS: mottled amber

HOOK: Mustad 94833 #8
THREAD: brown prewaxed 6/0
TAILS: dark amber hackle fibers, 1½ length of hook shank
ABDOMEN: brownish tan dubbing, ribbed with yellow monocord
THORAX: same as abdomen
WINGS: light dun hen-hackle tips or sparse amount of dun-colored poly fibers
LEGS: three turns of mottled amber hackle fibers, clipped top and bottom for added floatability

*Most recommended

Gray Fox *(Stenonema fuscum)*

The hatches of *S. fuscum* are complementary to those of its sister species, *S. vicarium*. They will commence to hatch for the season while the emergences of *S. vicarium* are still taking place. *S. fuscum* is identical in biology to *S. vicarium*, so that the preceding discussion is applicable to both species. However, it does appear that *S. fuscum* is a much more abundant species and of greater importance to anglers in the East *and* Midwest. (See Fig. 2-1e.)

S. fuscum hatches take place from the beginning of June until they are replaced by other related species, *S. interpunctatum* and *S. rubrum*. This will take the *Stenonema* seasonal cycle well into the month of August. By such time their daily occurrence is at dusk, and the late-season hatches are customarily referred to as those of Light Cahills, the species then being nearly white in color.

Stenonema fuscum (and related species) Imitations

NATURAL	ARTIFICIAL

Flat-Body Nymph*: A very effective nymph to be used during non-hatch periods for the week preceding the seasonal commencement of *S. fuscum*. This nymphal pattern and those that follow are also applicable to the summer hatches of other *Stenonema* species. Size and colorations are a compromise to imitate their *general* lengths and colors.

SIZE: 10–12mm
TAILS: dark amber, minutely barred
ABDOMEN: light amber distinctly ringed with dark blackish bands

HOOK: Mustad 3906 #10
THREAD: yellow prewaxed 6/0
TAILS: three fibers of yellow-dyed wood duck, 1½ length of hook shank
ABDOMEN: light amber

THORAX: light amber; dark brown wing pads
LEGS: mottled pale amber

dubbing and trimmed dun-colored ostrich herl for gills, ribbed with dark brown monocord 3/0 thread
THORAX: light amber dubbing; dark turkey tail feather segment for wing cases
LEGS: yellow-dyed wood duck

Hen-Winged Dun*: Pattern can be tied with a second hackle to replace hen body feathers.

SIZE: 10–11mm
TAILS: barred amber to tan
ABDOMEN: yellowish tan
THORAX: same as abdomen
WINGS: tan with pigmented crossveins
LEGS: light ginger

HOOK: Mustad 94833 #12
THREAD: tan prewaxed 6/0
TAILS: light ginger hackle fibers, 1½ length of hook shank
ABDOMEN: yellowish tan dubbing
THORAX: same as abdomen
WINGS: pale cream hen body feather; four turns with light ginger hackle for legs

Spinner: A useful spinner pattern practical to imitate the *Stenonema* spinners of summer.

SIZE: 10–11mm
TAILS: pale cream
ABDOMEN: yellowish brown
THORAX: same as abdomen
WINGS: clear (hyaline)

HOOK: Mustad 94833 #12
THREAD: tan prewaxed 6/0
TAILS: light ginger hackle fibers
ABDOMEN: yellowish brown dubbing, no ribbing
THORAX: same as abdomen
WINGS: pale dun hen body feather tips or light dun poly, tied very sparsely

*Most recommended

Gray Fox (Stenacron interpunctatum)

This species, comprised of four subspecies, will continue the *Stenonema* seasonal cycle until the middle of August and will provide sport to anglers during the late-summer evenings when most evening hatches have expired for the season. It occupies an important niche among the mayfly biota found in many trout streams, being most common in those with a hard substrate in their bottom. (See Fig. 6-6.)

S. interpunctatum is actually a complex of four other *Stenonemas* that have been included in many angling texts by their individual subclassifications. They are: *S. i. canadense, S. i. frontale, S. i. heterotarsale,* and *S. i. interpunctatum.* All these nymphs are separable from other *Stenonemas* by the presence of conspicuous pale stripes along their length. *S. rubrum,* another late-summer *Stenonema,* also complements the hatches of the preceding species, as does *S. pulchellum* the nearly white *Stenonema* that probably caused the common name Light Cahill to become synonymous with its hatches. The majority of these species are very similar in size and general appearance and can all be practically imitated with the dun artificial pattern given for *S. fuscum.*

WESTERN HATCHES OF HEPTAGENIIDAE

Members of this family are, generally speaking, the only mayflies of importance in the moderate-to-fast freestone rivers of the West. As in the East, some of them are the first to appear for the season. Of the five groups comprising this large family, *Rhithrogenas*, *Epeorus*, and *Heptagenias* are of greatest significance. As yet, most of their member species have not been assigned common names, making it necessary to propose a few new ones here.

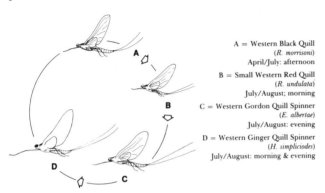

A = Western Black Quill
(*R. morrisoni*)
April/July: afternoon

B = Small Western Red Quill
(*R. undulata*)
July/August; morning

C = Western Gordon Quill Spinner
(*E. albertae*)
July/August: evening

D = Western Ginger Quill Spinner
(*H. simpliciodes*)
July/August: morning & evening

FIG. 6-15 Seasonal emergence cycle of western Heptageniidae (actual sizes).

Spinner gatherings and subsequent falls of most species within *Heptageniidae* take place in the evenings between the hours of six and nine o'clock. They customarily gather approximately eight feet over the banks of streams, and their falls are often remarkably potent in eliciting the action of feeding trout.

The identification of western members of *Heptageniidae* as to species is quite difficult at streamside. But, with a bit of practice, the reader will find that deter-

mining specimens to the generic level becomes a routine matter, and in most cases that is all that is needed. Table 6-3 is a breakdown of the most important hatches of Western *Heptageniidae* that are described in this section.

Western Black Quill (*Rhithrogena morrisoni*)

This is the first of three very important *Rhithrogenas* that will emerge throughout the season in western waters. It is also the first medium-sized mayfly to appear for the year. The Black Quills are an excellent hatch during the months of April and May, a full month before spring runoff has begun in western mountains. It's a favorite of those hardy souls willing to get out to the streams so early in the year. (See Fig. 6-2.)

Slow to moderate flowing streams and rivers, where trout can afford to be selective, produce good *R. morrisoni* hatches. The Henry's Fork in Idaho is a classic example. Seasonal occurrence takes place from early April to the middle of May, when it is replaced in the cycle of chronological emergence by other *Rhithrogena* species. Daily appearances are normally in the middle of the afternoon.

R. morrisoni nymphs are the only ones of its genus to be found fully matured in trout streams so early in the season. However, in mid-May they can be found with ready-to-emerge nymphs of *R. futilis* and *R. robusta*. The small, dark reddish *R. morrisoni* nymphs are easy to distinguish from the tannish nymphs of these two related species. *R. futilis* is a large and uncommon mayfly, and though found in the trout streams of the Rockies, its best populations occur in northwestern waters. *R. robusta*, on the other hand, is fairly common throughout the West, ranging from Colorado to Canada and in the rapidly flowing streams of California. The artificial recommended for *R. morrisoni* also works well for the late-May hatches of *R. robusta*, though if tied specifically for its hatches it should be one hook size larger and slightly lighter in color.

Rhithrogena morrisoni (and related species) Imitations

NATURAL	ARTIFICIAL

Flat-Body Nymph*: Tied with a heavy hook to sink down to the bottom and to be fished during nonhatch periods in the fast-water environments that support good populations of *Rhithrogenas* and other members of Family *Heptageniidae*.

SIZE: 9mm   HOOK: Mustad 3906 #12

Important Western Hatches

COMMON NAME	SPECIES	SEASONAL OCCURRENCE
Western Black Quill	*Rhithrogena morrisoni* *Rhithrogena hageni*	April-May June-July
Small Western Red Quill	*Rhithrogena undulata*	July-August
Western Gordon Quill Spinner	*Epeorus longimanus* *Epeorus albertae*	July-August
Western Pink Quill Spinner	*Heptagenia elegantula*	June-July
Western Ginger Quill Spinner	*Heptagenia simpliciodes*	July-September

Table 6-3 Western members of Family *Heptageniidae*.

TAILS: light brown, speckled
ABDOMEN: dark reddish brown
THORAX: dark reddish brown;
  black wing pads
LEGS: dark brown, mottled

THREAD: brown prewaxed 6/0
TAILS: three pale partridge
  fibers
ABDOMEN: dark reddish brown
  dubbing
THORAX: dark reddish brown
  dubbing; dark black goose
  quill for wing cases
LEGS: dark partridge fibers,
  soft texture

Emerging Wet Fly*: Designed to be fished *wet* and thus tied with a heavy hook. *Rhithrogenas* escape the nymphal exoskeleton approximately 6–8 inches below the surface film during their actual emergence.

SIZE: 9mm
TAILS: dark grayish brown
ABDOMEN: purplish black
THORAX: purplish black
WINGS: mottled brown (in a
  folded-back position)

HOOK: Mustad 3906 #12
THREAD: brown prewaxed 6/0
TAILS: dark dun hackle fibers
ABDOMEN: purplish black
  dubbing, ribbed with dark
  brown monocord
THORAX: purplish black
  dubbing, ribbed with dark
  brown monocord
WINGS: three turns of a grizzly
  hackle dyed brown, and
  three turns of a soft dun-
  colored hackle—to represent
  legs and wings

Hen-Winged Dun: In the type of waters where *R. morrisoni* is often found, smooth-flowing western spring creeks, the No-Hackle dry fly is recommended over the Hen-Winged style; however, this type of pattern is better suited for the faster stretches where the best *R. hageni* hatches occur.

SIZE: 9mm
TAILS: dark grayish brown
ABDOMEN: purplish black
THORAX: purplish black
WINGS: mottled grayish brown
LEGS: dark gray

HOOK: Mustad 94840 #12
THREAD: brown prewaxed 6/0
TAILS: dark dun hackle fibers
ABDOMEN: purplish black
  dubbing, ribbing optional
THORAX: purplish black,
  dubbing, ribbing optional
WINGS: dark dun hen body
  feathers
LEGS: dark dun hackles, three
  to four turns

Spinner*: Customarily, the spinner falls of *Rhithrogenas* are probably the most important ones produced by any of the members of Family *Heptageniidae* for the angler.

SIZE: 9mm
TAILS: dark grayish brown
ABDOMEN: dark grayish brown
THORAX: dark grayish brown
WINGS: clear (hyaline)

HOOK: Mustad 94840 #12
THREAD: dark gray prewaxed
  6/0
TAILS: dark dun hackle fibers,
  one inch in length
ABDOMEN: dark grayish brown
  dubbing
THORAX: dark grayish brown
  dubbing
WINGS: light dun hen-hackle
  tips tied spent; three turns
  of light dun hackle tied in
  front of hackle tips adds
  floatability; clipped

*Most recommended

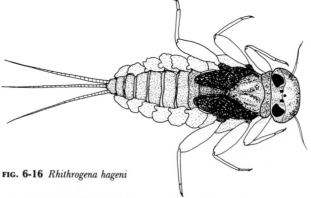

FIG. 6-16 *Rhithrogena hageni*

Western Black Quill (R. hageni)

This is a second extremely common *Rhithrogena* found in western streams; however, its seasonal occurrence does not commence until the early part of June. Many of its earliest hatches are nullified by the fact that spring runoff will be taking place in the West. Nonetheless, it is an excellent hatch throughout the Rockies and many of the streams in northern Utah. This species and *Rhithrogena undulata*, which follows, are the two most common mayflies in faster waters. Both provide sport to the western fly fisher unparalleled by any other species covered in this chapter.

R. hageni is a common species in the fast-water sections of large rivers and streams above 5,000 feet in altitude. Rivers like the Madison and Rock Creek in Montana produce impressive hatches, as does the smaller Frying Pan in Colorado.

The months of June and July are the best for summer emergences of *R. hageni*, and their midday hatches will last about two hours. The duns escape the nymphal exoskeletons approximately four inches below the surface of the water and leave the stream very quickly. The hatches of *R. hageni* then are best imitated by the wet fly given for *R. morrisoni*. Its spinners are also identical to those of its closely related sister species.

Spinner flights occur when the air temperature is in the low 60's, and their concentrated swarms will hover five to ten feet above the margins of streams late in the afternoon. Mating takes place high above the water, and spinner falls just before dusk. The impact they have on trout often surpasses that of the hatch itself. Trout and whitefish will respond savagely to these imagoes, and it is hard to understand why they become so selective during such times.

Identification of *R. hageni* nymphs is best accomplished in the stream by remembering their dark, reddish brown color and their size; those *Rhithrogenas*

9mm or longer can be attributed to this species, those under 8.5mm are, in all likelihood, nymphs of their seasonal successor, *Rhithrogena undulata*.

Small Western Red Quill (*Rhithrogena undulata*)

The hatches of the Small Western Red Quills are frequent, predictable, and dense. In my personal experience, they rank above those of any other mayfly that thrives in the faster water sections of western trout streams and rivers. Their emergences will take place during the latter part of summer, when the waters are wadable and the weather is at its best. These hatches will consistently produce trout in the 16- to 20-inch class, which is more than can be said of most insect hatches that take place in trout waters that run at a moderate to fast tempo. In addition to its importance in such waters, the species is also common in slow to moderate environments, and even in silted and warm rivers unable to support trout.

Of all western *Rhithrogenas*, *R. undulata* is the most abundant and significant to anglers. Their nymphs are found in numbers in rivers like the Beaverhead, Big Hole, and Madison in Montana, Henry's Fork of the Snake River in Idaho, the Shoshone River in Wyoming, and Roaring Fork and Colorado rivers in Colorado. Seasonal emergence takes place during the months of July and August, customarily appearing at 10 or 11 o'clock every morning, though best occurrences will be on cloudy mornings. The optimal pattern for this hatch I find to be the subsurface little wet fly. I have found that its duns leave the water much too fast to give trout the opportunity to capture them on the surface.

Late afternoons will induce the gathering of its spinners, and they will collect five to ten feet over the banks. Their nuptial flight, in typical *Heptageniidae* fashion, consists of graceful three-foot vertical rises and falls. Spinner falls occur at dusk and all at once, consistently causing trout to rise oftentimes ultra-selectively. During these troublesome but exciting spinner falls, the exact size and basic color are needed to succeed.

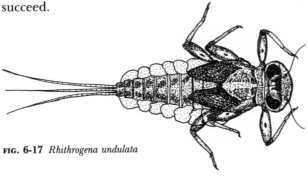

FIG. 6-17 *Rhithrogena undulata*

Rhithrogena undulata Imitations

NATURAL	ARTIFICIAL

Flat-Body Nymph: The species in the nymphal stage is identical in color to *R. morrisoni* or *R. hageni* nymph, though conspicuously smaller and thus should be tied in a size #16. It is an effective "hunting" pattern during nonhatch periods during late-summer months in medium- to slow-flowing waters.

Emerging Wet Fly*: To be fished as a *wet* fly just below the surface during *R. undulata* hatches.

SIZE: 7mm	HOOK: Mustad 3906 #16
TAILS: speckled light brown	THREAD: rusty brown prewaxed 6/0
ABDOMEN: reddish brown	TAILS: pale partridge hackle fibers
THORAX: reddish brown	ABDOMEN: reddish brown dubbing, ribbed with fine gold wire
WINGS: mottled grayish brown	THORAX: reddish brown dubbing, ribbed with fine gold wire
	WINGS: three to four turns of dyed dark brown grizzly

Spinner*:

SIZE: 7mm	HOOK: Mustad 94833 #16
TAILS: mottled brown	THREAD: rusty brown prewaxed 6/0
ABDOMEN: rusty brown	TAILS: brown hackle fibers
THORAX: rusty brown	ABDOMEN: rusty brown dubbing
WINGS: clear (hyaline)	THORAX: rusty brown dubbing
	WINGS: light dun hen feather tips

*Most recommended

Western Gordon Quill Nymph (*Epeorus longimanus*)

This is a fairly common species in western waters, but, ironically, it produces disappointing hatches for anglers. Only occasionally is it of any significance to anglers when it emerges. This is largely due to the fact that the nymphs will migrate to the shallows of a stream before emerging, and the duns escape so swiftly from the surface of the stream that they awaken little interest on the part of trout. It also exhibits the disadvantageous habit, from the fly fisherman's point of view, of emerging sporadically throughout the day with little consistency or density.

In general, *E. longimanus* nymphs are found commonly in the faster, cold waters of small- to moderate-sized streams above 5,000 feet in altitude. They are June emergers appearing at the same time of year as *Rhithrogena hageni*, which greatly overshadows them in importance. Daily emergences are customarily between the morning and late afternoon. The hatches of this species are often joined in smaller-creek environments by *E. grandis*, a robust, dark *Epeorus* instantly recognized by the row of thick hairs that run along the middle of the abdomen (see Appendix II). I have found this second *Epeorus* and encountered its mediocre hatches in some of the smaller creeks in the states of Montana, Wyoming, and California, and even in the lovely Oak Creek below Flagstaff, Arizona. In California waters, *Epeorus nitidus* will also be found in similar habitats. It produces fair hatches in rivers like the Kern and Mono Creek area as well as in numerous creeks that drain the eastern slopes of the Sierra Mountains.

For the nymphs of all these species no better pattern probably can be employed than the popular Hare's Ear, extensively used in the East to imitate the eastern counterparts of the previously mentioned *Epeorus* species.

Epeorus longimanus Nymph Imitation

NATURAL	ARTIFICIAL

Flat-Body Nymph: This pattern as well as those two required for *Rhithrogena* species is very useful in faster stretches of waters during nonhatch periods. The pattern for *E. longimanus* imitates most *Epeorus* species found in western waters very closely, like *E. albertae, E. deceptivus,* and species indigenous to the streams that drain both sides of the Sierras and Cascade mountains, like *E. nitidus* and *E. grandis*.

NATURAL	ARTIFICIAL
SIZE: 9–10mm	HOOK: Mustad 3906 #12; weighted with 1 amp lead wire
TAILS: light olive brown	THREAD: gray prewaxed 6/0
ABDOMEN: medium olive brown; gray gills	TAILS: hackle fibers light olive brown in color
THORAX: medium olive brown; black wing pads	ABDOMEN: olive brown dubbing, ribbed with a fine gold wire; dubbing should be fuzzy and clipped on top and bottom; gray ostrich herl for gills
LEGS: mottled olive brown	THORAX: same color and procedure as in abdomen; black mallard quill segments for wing cases
	LEGS: olive brown partridge hackle fibers

Western Gordon Quill Spinner (*E. albertae*)

In comparison, this species is more common than *E. longimanus*, which it replaces in the warmer sections of large rivers. Its seasonal occurrence also complements that of its sister species and will take the *Epeorus* emergence cycle through the month of August. Like its predecessor, it is a poor hatch and one deserving little attention from anglers; however, its late-afternoon or evening spinner falls can be very productive.

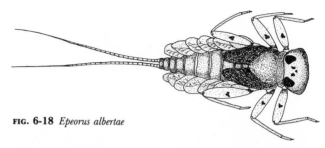

FIG. **6-18** *Epeorus albertae*

E. albertae appears in the season from the middle of July until the end of August. Many western rivers, such as the following, have good populations: Big Hole and Madison in Montana, the Box Canyon of the Henry's Fork, and Frying Pan and Roaring Fork in Colorado. Smaller waters like the Gibbon and Slough Creek in Yellowstone National Park have fair hatches.

Another *Epeorus* often found with the nymphs of *E. albertae* is *E. deceptivus*, which is fairly uncommon and indigenous to medium-sized rivers and emerges during August and September. The nymphs of *E. deceptivus* lack the dark spots on their legs, exhibited by those of *E. albertae*. The duns of both species are identical.

Epeorus albertae Spinner Imitation

NATURAL	ARTIFICIAL

NATURAL	ARTIFICIAL
Hen-Winged Spinner:	
SIZE: 10mm	HOOK: Mustad 94833 #12
TAILS: grayish brown	THREAD: gray prewaxed 6/0
ABDOMEN: light grayish brown	TAILS: dark dun hackle fibers
THORAX: grayish brown	ABDOMEN: light grayish brown dubbing
WINGS: clear (hyaline)	THORAX: grayish brown dubbing
	WINGS: light dun hen-hackle tips; three turns of dun hackle in front of wings for added floatability; clipped

Small Western Gordon Quill (Cinygmula ramaleyi)

This is a small, slightly darker olive mayfly than the *Epeorus* species. It is indigenous to the same type of waters as the *Epeorus* species, though it is comparatively less common. Its late-summer hatches are often observed taking place with those of *E. deceptivus*. It possibly has some significance as a nymph, for the species is apparently a poor swimmer and constantly shows up in the stomach contents of trout even during nonhatch periods.

I have encountered *C. ramaleyi* emerging only once, in the Gallatin River of Montana; however, Dr. George Edmunds of the University of Utah reports

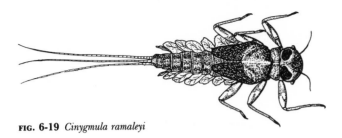

FIG. **6-19** *Cinygmula ramaleyi*

excellent populations from the Provo, Weber, and Duchesne rivers in northern Utah and in the Metolius of Oregon. In case the reader discovers that this species is of importance in the waters he normally fishes, a size 16 version of the nymph pattern given for *E. longimanus* and the dry form for *R. morrisoni* should suffice for this hatch.

Western Pink-Quill Spinner *(Heptagenia elegantula)*

This is one of the most beautiful mayflies inhabiting western waters. Its hatches are characterized, unfortunately, by the duns leaving the surface of the water too fast to allow its actual emergences to be of value to anglers. However, its spinner falls, as those of its sister species, *H. simplicoides*, are very impressive by way of comparison.

H. elegantula is very much at home in large, slow-moving rivers, such as the Big Hole in Montana (Twin Bridges) and the Colorado River in northern Colorado. The bottom substrate in these waters is usually marginal, consisting of gravel and silt, which is the same type of microhabitat able to support populations of the burrowing mayfly *Ephemera simulans* or Brown Drake.

Seasonal emergence occurs any time after the water temperature permanently reaches the 50-degree mark for the season, usually after the middle of June. Hatches are in the mornings. Spinner swarms, however, will become apparent over the riffles in the evenings. In typical *Heptageniidae* fashion, fertilized females will repeatedly drop to the water to extrude a few eggs at a time.

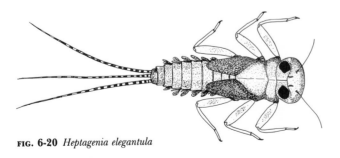

FIG. **6-20** *Heptagenia elegantula*

In order to separate these nymphs from those of their sister species that follow, study the color pattern of the specimen in question; those of *H. elegantula* are basically unicolorous, while those of *H. simplicoides* exhibit conspicuous pale markings on their head, thorax, and abdomen.

Heptagenia elegantula Spinner Imitation

NATURAL	ARTIFICIAL

Hen-Winged Spinner: The pattern serves nicely to also imitate *H. solitaria*, a similar-sized though a bit more yellowish *Heptagenia*.

NATURAL	ARTIFICIAL
SIZE: 11mm	HOOK: Mustad 94840 #10
TAILS: pale cream	THREAD: rusty reddish prewaxed 6/0
ABDOMEN: light gray, almost translucent	TAILS: light tan hackle fibers
THORAX: rusty red	ABDOMEN: pale dun dubbing
WINGS: clear (hyaline)	THORAX: rusty reddish dubbing
	WINGS: light dun hen feather tips; three turns of a light tan hackle for floatability

Western Ginger-Quill Spinner *(Heptagenia simplicoides)*

In population, *H. simplicoides* is up to par with that of its sister species, and it also is an important mayfly to anglers in its spinner stage. It differs from the spinner of *H. elegantula* only in color. (See Fig. 6-7.)

Its seasonal duration lasts two full months—from the middle of July until September—and takes place after that of *H. elegantula*. Western rivers representative of the type of running-water environment it prefers are: the Ruby River in Montana, the South Fork of the Snake River in Idaho, and the Upper Colorado and Eagle rivers in Colorado.

Spinners are easy to detect at streamside by their curious snakelike hoverings just above the water. Eventually they will form into groups six to eight feet about the surface in the evenings and, after ovipositing, will fall spent on the water. Occasionally they will become active in the mornings.

Another related and similar *Heptagenia* is *H. solitaria*; however, it is less numerous and of limited significance to fly fishermen. *H. criddlei* is markedly smaller and is easily identifiable by the dark, chevron markings on its abdomen. *H. rosea* is only common in the coastal steelhead rivers of the Pacific Northwest. An unrelated mayfly that is similar in appearance is *Cinygma dimicki*, which I have encountered but once in the Lewis River in Yellowstone National Park. For all intents and purposes it can be imitated by the spinner pattern recommended for *H. simplicoides*, though it should be somewhat smaller. *Stenonema reesi* is the only species in that genus reported from the western half of the country, and it is indigenous to slow-moving, silted rivers like the Yellowstone in Montana below its junction with the Musselshell River.

Heptagenia simplicoides Spinner Imitation

NATURAL   ARTIFICIAL

Hen-Winged Spinner: This pattern differs from that given for *H. elegantula* not only in color but in size, and in all likelihood the western angler will find many more occasions to use it than that of its sister species. The color and size recommended are in consideration of the size and general appearance of *H. simplicoides* late in the season, when it is of most importance to the fly fisher.

SIZE: 9mm

TAILS: tannish, barred

ABDOMEN: pale cream to whitish

THORAX: yellowish cream

HOOK: Mustad 94833 #14

THREAD: beige prewaxed 6/0

TAILS: tan hackle fibers

ABDOMEN: pale cream dubbing

THORAX: light yellow dubbing

WINGS: clear (hyaline)

WINGS: light dun hen-hackle tips; three turns of light tan hackle for added floatability, clipped top and bottom

Small Western Ginger Quill (Cinygmula reticulata)

This mayfly will occasionally be encountered emerging from cold, gravel-bottom streams at midday during the months of July and August. It's an elegant little fly, with a reddish ginger body and yellow wings. Its numbers and frequency do not warrant a specific artificial imitation for its hatches; nonetheless it is common enough to merit some mention in this work. I have witnessed its emergence in Rock Creek and the South Fork of the Madison in Montana, Slough Creek and Little Firehole in Yellowstone National Park, and Henry's Fork of the Snake River in Idaho. Its nymphs often exhibit red-colored gills, making them quite conspicuous when picked up from the stream. (See Fig. 6-4.)

CHAPTER 7: The Early and Late-Season Hatches of Black Quills and Slate-Winged Mahogany Duns (Family *Leptophlebiidae*)

AT the same time that members of Family *Heptageniidae* are making their seasonal debut, anglers will most likely encounter the hatches of the Early Black Quill or Slate-Winged Mahogany Dun, appropriate common names for the duns of the two genera belonging to Family *Leptophlebiidae*. *Leptophlebias* and *Paraleptophlebias* produce fair-to-good hatches for anglers at the very beginning and end of the fishing season. At these times of the year their emergences are concentrated and predictable, and they receive little competition for the trout's attention from other insect hatches.

In eastern and midwestern states, their emergences do not commence until the water temperature of streams permanently reaches the 50's. This customarily takes place during the interim between the seasonal occurrences of the Gordon Quills and the prolific Hendricksons. Western species begin their seasonal cycle in May in the wake of the early-season hatches of the important Western Black Quills (*Rhithrogena morrisoni*). *Paraleptophlebias* once again surge during the months of September and October, when the prolific species *P. debilis* emerges in most northern states throughout the entire country.

The nymphal stage of both genera is easily recognizable even by a neophyte on aquatic entomology. They have conspicuous filamentous gills discernible even with the naked eye. The dry forms are either uniformly black, in the case of *Leptophlebias*, or mahogany brown as are the majority of *Paraleptophlebia* species.

A morphological characteristic that distinguishes duns or spinners belonging to this family from the three-tailed and similar sized *Ephemerellas* is the absence of an angular process or point on the fore margin of their hind wings. In addition, all growth stages of *Leptophlebiidae* have obvious pale cream legs without visible markings, a distinctive characteristic that helps to separate them from those of other mayflies.

Though the two genera have common morphological properties that suggest their similarity of nature, *Leptophlebias* and *Paraleptophlebias* do differ in biology and, most importantly, in their relative importance to the fly fisherman.

FAMILY LEPTOPHLEBIIDAE

Genus Leptophlebia *(West: uncommon; Midwest: uncommon; East: uncommon)*

Leptophlebia nymphs are the larger of the two and customarily prefer backwaters, side eddies, and cut-off pools of trout streams. They have large lamellated gills with conspicuous threadlike extensions, and their efficiency in processing great amounts of oxygen permits these nymphs to thrive in slow, nearly stagnant waters. *Leptophlebias* are found in lakes and ponds as well as in large warm rivers that can support other species of fish besides trout.

Hatches of the most common species (*L. cupida*) take place early in the season in eastern and midwestern waters, usually during the months of April or May. In the West, *L. gravastella* appears a month later. The duns of both species are fairly large and nearly

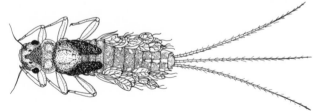

FIG. 7-1 *Leptophlebia* nymph

black in color, with their middle tail always distinctly shorter than the two outer ones.

A few days prior to emergence the nymphs gather in minnow-like schools and migrate upstream along the margins. Daily emergence is in placid sections of waters with the nymphs swimming to and from the surface film for an hour before emergence begins in earnest.

One issue that should be taken up at this point is whether *Leptophlebias* are important enough to fly fishermen for their hatches to be promoted by angling authors. It does appear that its common name, the Early Black Quill, is certainly more famous in print than the hatch that is actually encountered in the stream.

Ernest Schwiebert, Carl Richards, Doug Swisher, and other angling authors report that *Leptophlebias* are indeed important to fly fishermen who fish well-known eastern and midwestern waters. Supposedly the Schoharie, West Branch of the Delaware and Beaverkill rivers of New York have good populations. Penn's Creek and Big Fishing Creek of Pennsylvania, and the Pere Marquette and AuSable rivers in Michigan are also producers of its hatches. One of my closest fishing partners, Pete Laszlo, wrote an excellent article with Wally Blanchard in *Fly Fisherman* magazine (April '74) concerning its emergence in the Parker River of New Hampshire. On the other hand, Al Caucci and Bob Nastasi proposed the theorem, in their book *Hatches*, that *Leptophlebias* are of questionable importance to most anglers; undoubtedly, a similar conclusion reached by many other angling authors.

My own research and conclusions do not contradict those of past authors, but they do place some qualifications on the importance of these mayflies and perhaps offer a plausible explanation for the apparent contradiction in their information. Throughout the years, I discovered a number of local populations of *Leptophlebias* in the previously mentioned trout streams in addition to many others, but, with few exceptions, they were always in specific stretches. The dead-flow, meandering beginnings of many eastern streams contain fair to good populations as do the lower, warmer sections where, once again, the speed of the current slows down to a crawl. These two areas may be as much as 50 miles from each other and differ 20 degrees in average water temperature throughout the year. Specific examples are the Schoharie and Willowemoc rivers of New York. This suggests that the peculiar distribution of these nymphs is a result of their strict microhabitat requirements; only sections

that permit accumulations of leaves, sticks, and other detritus to form along the bottom will contain *Leptophlebia* populations. On the other hand, sections of freestone or semi-fast rivers that flow like water troughs for most of their length cannot support their numbers.

The West has sparse populations of *Leptophlebias*, and when found, they are usually in big, unwadable rivers. The mighty Yellowstone River near Livingston, Montana, and Clark's Fork of the Columbia (below the town of Missoula) sport fair populations. However, because of the difficulty of fishing these waters, especially during spring runoff, hatches of *Leptophlebia* turn out to be of little consequence to most western anglers.

The main concern of this book is to introduce the reader to the mayfly hatches he can *expect* to encounter whenever and wherever he fishes. In all likelihood, emergences of *Leptophlebia* (Early Black Quill) will not be one of them. The reader should first encounter a *Leptophlebia* hatch before going through the trouble of tying and carrying a specific artificial to imitate it; otherwise, he should put this mayfly mentally aside until further notice.

Genus Paraleptophlebia *(West: common; Midwest: common; East: common)*

Unlike species of *Leptophlebia*, members of this genus are found commonly in the shallower, wadable portions of trout streams. Resulting from their aquatic preference, *Paraleptophlebias* are important to the fly fisherman, especially during the margins of the fishing season.

Paraleptophlebia nymphs are instantly recognizable by their tuning-fork gills. The West contains a few larger species that, in addition, have very visible sickle-shaped mandibular projections unlike those of other mayfly nymphs. (See also Fig. 2-1g.)

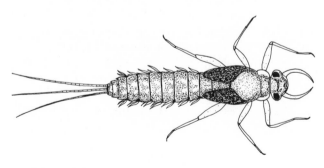

FIG. 7-2 *Paraleptophlebia bicornuta*

FIG. 7-3 Good artificial patterns for hatches of *Paraleptophlebias*.

The dun stage of *Paraleptophlebias* is a unicolorous mahogany color with slate wings and pale yellow legs. Imitations of almost all the species found throughout the country are accomplished by one artificial pattern in a single size or, at most, two sizes.

Paraleptophlebia nymphs are prone to similar migratory habits as those of their sister genus but only to the extent that, as they attain maturity, they gradually travel to the more placid margins of fast streams.

General Emergence

The migratory habits of both genera cause their best hatching to occur in the protected eddies near the banks of streams or behind boulders, log-jams, or other natural shelters. *Leptophlebias* and *Paraleptophlebias* are both late-morning or early-afternoon emergers.

An hour before actual emergence begins, the nymphs become very active along the bottom of the stream and make repeated trips to the surface and back again to the bottom. During such times, the trout may become aroused to chase the tantalizing nymphs that move in snakelike fashion through the water. They are markedly different in their motion from *Ephemerellas* that hold their thorax in a stiff position when swimming or the little *Baetidae* and larger *Siphlonuridae* species that streak through the water by flicking their setaceous tails. *Leptophlebiidae* nymphs closely resemble the exaggerated undulations of the much larger burrowing nymphs.

Eventually the nymphs stop their practicing and swim clear to the film, allowing the duns to escape from their exoskeleton. The reader will notice that after the duns leave the nymphal shuck they then float for as much as 50 to 60 feet before finally attempting to make use of their wings. This peculiarity causes *Paraleptophlebias* in particular to produce unusual dry fly action for anglers.

Approximately 24 hours after the hatch, the spinners of the same flies return to the stream in the evening. Males and females assemble in small groups at eye level over the margins of the water, their nuptial flight consisting of vertical one- to two-foot rises and falls. The females oviposit by jettisoning their egg cargoes either while still a few feet from the water or by physically dipping their lower abdomen momentarily into the surface film.

In general, the numerous but very similar species in this family can be exactly imitated by one or two patterns representing each stage of development. A gilled nymphal imitation and hackled dun are the most practical artificials to fish these hatches.

EASTERN, MIDWESTERN, AND WESTERN HATCHES OF PARALEPTOPHLEBIAS

Throughout the country *Paraleptophlebias* demonstrate a remarkable similarity of size, overall appearance, and general biology. The common eastern species, *P. adoptiva*, can serve as a neotypical form for all their hatches. They are of principal importance during the spring and fall months when their sporadic hatches

FIG. 7-4 *Paraleptophlebia* (actual size)

will take place in the afternoons. They will receive little competition for the trout's attention from other aquatic insects, for most have completed their seasonal cycle. Fall hatches are curiously brought about by the same species, which begins to emerge in September in all waters throughout the country.

Slate-Winged Mahogany Dun (*Paraleptophlebia adoptiva E,M*)

P. adoptiva, a fairly common and important mayfly to eastern and midwestern anglers at the beginning of the fishing season, will partly satisfy their winter-long appetite for dry fly action. Emergence of *P. adoptiva*, however, is only a preliminary event in a series of more impressive mayfly and caddis hatches that anglers will begin to encounter within a week after the first appearance of this mayfly. Nonetheless, it is an important, though short-lived, hatch and remains the best known of the *Paraleptophlebias*.

Moderate to fast streams usually of a microhabitat consisting of smoothly washed, fine gravel or pebble will support better nymph populations. Sandy-bottomed, cold, meandering streams are also an ideal environment for *P. adoptiva*.

In the chronological order of seasonal emergence, *P. adoptiva* lies between the hatches of the Gordon Quill (*Epeorus pleuralis*) and those of the Dark Hendricksons (*Ephemerella subvaria*), establishing its seasonal cycle during the first two weeks of May. Cloudy, bitter-cold days will produce the best hatches, and typical of its genus, the protected side eddies and pockets of fast waters have exceptional concentrations. Daily emergence is at midday, from 11 in the morning to 5 in the afternoon. During the hatch, the duns ride the swirling eddies of the surface current for long distances before getting on the wing, which offers trout an unusual opportunity to consume them in numbers. Those that escape will come back the following day as spinners to mate, oviposit, and complete the life cycle of the species.

At the time of the season when *P. adoptiva* emerges,

FIG. 7-5 A close look at the streamside vegetation can often reveal clues to the observant angler as to the prevailing hatches of a trout stream. These are duns of *P. debilis* on the banks of a western stream during September.

the bottom of the trout stream is covered with drifting and foraging nymphs of a much larger and more common species of insects. It would therefore be impractical for anglers to hunt the waters with a small *P. adoptiva* imitation before their actual hatch. During nonhatch times, drifting a weighted-nymph imitation of *Epeorus pleuralis*, better known in the nymph stage as the Hare's Ear, is really the angler's best bet. However, when the *P. adoptiva* hatch begins and trout focus their attention on the surface of the water, a light-wire nymph imitation of this species, fished dead drift, becomes the most effective imitation and approach for the angler. The pattern suggested, when tied in the recommended hook sizes, will closely imitate the nymph of *P. adoptiva* as well as that of *P. mollis* and *P. debilis*, closely related and equally abundant sister species.

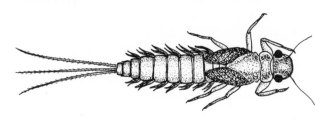

FIG. 7-6 *Paraleptophlebia adoptiva*

Paraleptophlebia adoptiva (and related species) Imitations

NATURAL | ARTIFICIAL

Conventional Nymph*: This nymph is tied with a dry fly hook and is intended to *float.* It is fished on the surface *during* the actual hatch. Dry fly materials are needed for its construction. It is a "catch-all" pattern for all North American *Paraleptophlebia* species, eastern and western. Colors are those of the bottom side of the nymph.

SIZE: 8mm
TAILS: amber
ABDOMEN: tannish brown
THORAX: same as abdomen
LEGS: amber, no markings

HOOK: Mustad 94833 #16
THREAD: brown prewaxed 6/0
TAILS: light ginger hackle fibers
ABDOMEN: tannish brown dubbing; gills of dark ostrich herl and ribbed with fine gold wire (optional)
THORAX: same as abdomen
LEGS: light ginger hackle fibers

No-Hackle*: In freestone rivers, *Paraleptophlebias* appear from the most placid areas or margins; also they are often found in lakes. Thus a credible and more exacting imitation like the No-Hackle is best suited for the imitation of *Paraleptophlebia* duns.

SIZE: 8mm
TAILS: dark brown
ABDOMEN: dark reddish brown
THORAX: same as abdomen
WINGS: medium gray or slate
LEGS: dark brown

HOOK: Mustad 94833 #16
THREAD: dark brown prewaxed 6/0
TAILS: dark brown hackle fibers
ABDOMEN: dark reddish brown, no ribbing
THORAX: same as abdomen
WINGS: gray or natural mallard quill segments
LEGS: none

Spinner: Spinner falls of *Paraleptophlebias* are usually never terribly thick and thus important, though they are quite common in trout waters. Moreover, *Paraleptophlebia* spinners land continually on the water surface with their wings in an upright position. Their body color is very close to that of their dun; consequently, the No-Hackle pattern recommended serves very nicely during their spinner falls, with the natural mallard quill segment blending well with the grayish natural tone of the sky. Besides, their spinners are well imitated with some of the *Ephemerella* spinner patterns given in the following chapter, which are of greater significance than those of *Paraleptophlebias.*

*Most recommended

Slate-Winged Mahogany Dun (P. mollis E,M)

This is a slightly smaller *Paraleptophlebia* that follows *P. adoptiva* in seasonal emergence and is also as commonly found. It is tolerant of slower and warmer waters and, consequently, inhabits areas like the dead-flow beginnings of freestone streams in the East and many of the silted rivers of the Midwest, waters that cannot support populations of its sister species.

P. mollis hatches complement those of *P. adoptiva,* taking place during the months of June and July and

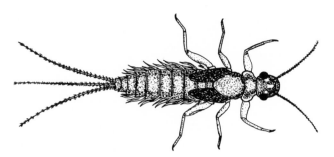

FIG. 7-7 *Paraleptophlebia mollis*

only differing in biology by emerging earlier in the day, from ten to noon in the morning. Their hatches can produce excellent dry fly action for anglers, since the duns also demonstrate the peculiar trait of floating unnecessarily long distances during emergence. The reader should keep in mind that, unlike its seasonal predecessor, *P. mollis* now faces some stiff competition for the trout's attention from the superior hatches of the Blue-Winged Olives (*Ephemerella cornuta* and *cornutella*) that also emerge every morning during the summer months.

Their spinner flights occur in the late afternoon over the banks, and the ovipositing of the females can cause trout to feed on them quite selectively. Male spinners differ from those of *P. adoptiva* by having whitish abdominal segments. Somewhat paler but similar species to *P. mollis* are *P. strigula* and *P. guttata,* which also emerge during the same time of year and, in essence, enhance the hatches of *P. mollis.*

Slate-Winged Mahogany Dun (P. debilis E,M,W)

Though this mayfly is found emerging throughout the summer, it does not constitute a good hatch until the fall when its hatches finally attain a marked level of concentration. The species is the late-season counterpart to *P. adoptiva,* and the artificial pattern needed to match the latter, once again, can be put to service. Another *Paraleptophlebia* often appearing with *P. debilis* is *P. praedipita,* which is of importance in warmer and larger rivers in the East and Midwest. (See Fig. 2-1g.)

During the months of September and October, the trout streams are more peaceful than at any other time of the year. As a result, *P. debilis* nymphs have no need to migrate to the shallower margins of the water during their emergence as the nymphs of *P. adoptiva* and *P. mollis* were compelled to do. Anglers can expect this hatch to take place in all sections. The water temperature is once again in the 50's as it was during the emergences of *P. adoptiva* five months earlier; in a sense, this hatch marks the end of the seasonal cycle of *Ephemeroptera* for the year.

Slate-Winged Mahogany Dun (P. heteronea W)

This species is a fairly common mayfly found emerging during the summer in western waters; however, its hatches are never too consistent or dense enough to entice the feeding activity of trout. It inhabits a diversity of water types ranging in general character from fast, freestone streams, like Rock Creek in Montana and the Frying Pan of Colorado, to slower, larger rivers like the Big Hole and the Henry's Fork. Its hatches customarily take place from the early part of June until the end of July; its daily emergences are during the afternoon. *P. temporalis* will seasonally complement its occurrence by appearing in late-June through August.

Large Slate-Winged Mahogany Dun (P. bicornuta W)

This is the largest *Paraleptophlebia* found in North American trout streams. Because of its conspicuous sickle-shaped frontal horns, it is the easiest to identify. Large western waters will produce its fall hatches, such as the Colorado and South Platte rivers in

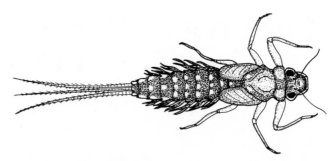

FIG. **7-8** *Paraleptophlebia heteronea*

Colorado, the Yellowstone and Missouri in Montana, and many of the steelhead rivers of the Northwest, like the beautiful Lochsa in Idaho and Chetco in Oregon. (See Fig. 7-2.)

The nymphs will migrate to the margins of the water prior to actual emergence, and the trout will also move close to the banks to snatch up the large, fluttering duns. Many California streams also support fair populations of *P. helena*, a similar *Paraleptophlebia* in size, structure, and streamside biology.

CHAPTER 8: Hendricksons, Pale Duns, and Blue-Winged Olives (Family *Ephemerellidae*)

THIS family of mayflies produces the majority of the most important hatches throughout the country, and regardless of the type of waters an angler fishes, he will encounter their hatches. Many *Ephemerellas* are well-known to the angler, if not by scientific names, at least by their common ones. Some eastern examples are the Hendricksons, Pale Evening Duns, and Blue-Winged Olives. Western *Ephemerellas* include the extremely prolific and reliable hatches of Pale Morning Duns, Western Green Drake, and Small Western Green Drake of midsummer.

Ephemerella species are often found in awesome numbers in many trout streams. In the Beaverkill River, just below the town of Roscoe, I once observed 57 ready-to-emerge Hendrickson nymphs (*E. subvaria*) clinging to one medium-sized boulder just before the hatch had begun. *E. inermis* and *E. infrequens*, which produce the unexcelled Pale Morning Dun hatches of the West, in one sampling numbered 237 nymphs in approximately one square-foot section of a Montana spring creek. Entomologists report that well over 1,000 nymphs of just one *Ephemerella* species have been found in similarly small areas of many trout streams. It is not at all surprising why *Ephemerellas* tend to produce such heavy hatches and consequently cause trout to become ultra-selective.

One interesting fact about *Ephemerella* species is that the males and females of the same species appear from different pools or areas of a stream during a hatch. Furthermore, unlike the species of other mayfly families (with the exception of *Tricorythidae*), the two sexes differ in color and size. This phenomenon is well understood by anglers who are familiar with the Hendrickson hatches of the East and Midwest. Due to the sexual differences, two artificial patterns are required to fish this hatch: the Red Quill for the male or the larger and lighter Hendrickson imitation for the female. Actually, all *Ephemerella* species are prone to sexual separations in a stream, and the females are always slightly larger and paler than their respective mates. It is doubtful that the angler needs to go to such lengths to imitate the dry fly forms exactly, but he should bear this fact in mind if the trout appear to be concentrating on one sex over the other during an *Ephemerella* hatch. Careful streamside observation will always provide him with the answer.

FIG. 8-1 Trout concentrating on emerging duns during an *Ephemerella* hatch.

General Emergence

All *Ephemerellas* have a similar emergence pattern. Approximately one hour prior to actual emergence, the nymphs will become quite active along the bottom of the stream, and during hatching they will slowly wriggle to the surface film where the duns will break out of the nymphal cases. Because *Ephemerella* duns take a noticeably long time to raise their wings to the upright position, the folded-winged duns are very vulnerable on the surface. Even when a hatch is at its height, an "emerging-dun" imitation, fished just like a dry fly, remains the most effective method for catching trout.

Spinners

As a general rule, *Ephemerella* duns require approximately 24 hours to molt into spinners. They then return to the stream to mate, and the females oviposit their fertilized eggs. The spinner falls of both sexes quickly follow the mating-ovipositing process, often causing the trout to feed on the spinners as earnestly and selectively as they do on the nymphs and duns of the same species during the hatch.

The female spinners of *Ephemerella* species are easily recognizable when in flight by the peculiar manner in which they carry their visible egg sacks and their steady, upstream flights. Their presence should serve as a warning to the angler, since the actual falls on the water are very hard to detect and the trout start rising to what appears to be "invisible" flies.

Identification and the Groups

As already pointed out in Chapter 2, *Ephemerellas* are distinguishable from all other mayflies in the nymphal stage by the presence of small, platelike gills on the top or dorsal side of the abdomen. The dry forms of both duns and spinners have *three* tails and exhibit hind wings with pronounced points (or angulation)

FIG. 8-2 Female with eggs ready to oviposit.

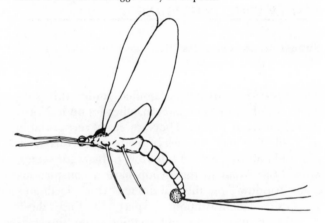

FIG. 8-3 The type of waters in which spinners of *Ephemerella* prefer to oviposit their eggs.

along the frontal margin. This characteristic helps to separate them from duns belonging to Family *Leptophlebiidae* whose species were covered in the preceding chapter. To facilitate identification further, entomologists divide the family into eight subgenera or groups.

These taxonomic distinctions are important to anglers, for the species belonging to each group emerge in close chronological sequence during the fishing season, and they also resemble each other quite closely in general appearance.

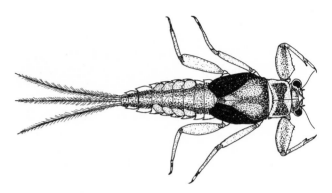

FIG. 8-4 *Ephemerella cornuta*

FAMILY EPHEMERELLIDAE

Subgenus Ephemerella *(West: abundant; Midwest: abundant; East: abundant)*

The *Ephemerella* nymphs classified under this subgenus are the most common mayflies found in North American trout waters. They are easily recognizable by feeble-like legs, the lack of teeth on the fore margin, and tails that exhibit fine rows of hairs (or setae). Most *Ephemerellas* in this group have a conspicuous pale "window" on their abdomen which facilitates streamside identification. Expect to find these nymphs in just about any running-water environments. (See Fig. 2-1i.)

Duns of this subgenus are responsible for the prolific Dark Hendrickson, Light Hendrickson, and Pale Evening Dun hatches in the East and Midwest, which customarily take place from late spring to early summer. Western members produce the unsurpassed Pale Morning Dun hatches appearing in June and July, and up until August, and in some localities, as late as September.

Subgenus Drunella *(West: abundant; Midwest: abundant; East: abundant)*

These are robust-looking nymphs, which are best differentiated from other *Ephemerellas* by their crab-like fore legs. In most species, they also exhibit a set of teeth along the frontal margins. In addition, the great majority of eastern and midwestern members have horns on their heads and thus are known to entomologists by scientific names such as *E. cornuta*, *E. longicornis*, and *E. cornutella*. Others are described by their size, as is the case of the impressive western species, *E. grandis*.

All hatches produced by subgenus *Drunella* are known to anglers as Blue-Winged Olives. In this work, eastern and midwestern species are given the common names of Large and Small Blue-Winged Olives; those of the West are called Large and Small Green Drakes. The author hopes that the liberty he has taken will prove beneficial to the reader and will help him remember these extremely important mayflies, which emerge during the summer months.

Subgenus Serratella *(West: fairly common; Midwest: fairly common; East: fairly common)*

Comparatively speaking, the members of this group are not nearly as important to anglers as those of the two types we just described; nonetheless, the eastern, midwestern, and western regions do contain a single species that will produce a dependable and concentrated hatch of significance to fly fishers. Scientifically, they are separable from those of subgenus *Ephemerella* because of the coarse, spine-like hairs on their tails. Their unique coloration is a more practical characteristic which facilitates streamside identification. Both western and eastern species are dark, nearly blue-black nymphs usually exhibiting a distinctive pale area or stripe along their entire length.

The small duns of subgenus *Serratella* are a dark mahogany color and will be given the common name of Little Dark Hendricksons. Eastern and midwestern states support populations of *E. deficiens* and *E. needhami* and will emerge at midday during the months of June and July. The western *E. tibialis* is a prolific *Ephemerella* which appears from August to September.

Family *Ephemerellidae* contains other groups whose members do not produce as important hatches as those members previously discussed. Consequently, in this work, their emergences are placed under one of the above *Ephemerella* "super species." The reader,

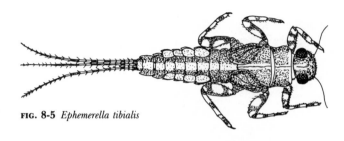

FIG. 8-5 *Ephemerella tibialis*

however, is advised to consult the nymph chart in Appendix II to make a mental note of the morphological characteristics utilized by entomologists to make the further distinction of groups composing this large mayfly family.

The Hatch and Artificial Imitations

Many angling texts advise the fly fisherman to fish a nymph prior to and during a hatch, up to the time that the trout begin to take the dry fly form. Since most anglers would rather use an artificial imitation that they can see, the time to use the dry fly is a welcomed point during a hatch. The reader should bear in mind, however, that this how-to-fish method has an inherent limitation when applied to a good *Ephemerella* hatch or any hatch in which trout tend to get selective at the most vulnerable emerging stages. Prior to actual emergence, the trout are indeed foraging for active nymphs along the bottom of a stream. They will also proceed to take the emerging nymphs and duns on the surface when the hatch begins. But, as a hatch heightens in density, the water surface will become covered with the helpless nymphs and emerging duns. The trout will inevitably begin to concentrate on these two vulnerable stages, consuming the naturals in great numbers with little expenditure of energy on their part. These are also the same stages that anglers should be preoccupied in matching during the difficult enough dense hatches of *Ephemerellas*. The nymph fished just under the surface is a very potent method, as is the Emerging Dun pattern recommended in the fly tying section to be employed during these hatches. Besides its effectiveness, the Emerging Dun imitation is highly visible when on the water, especially when it is tied with very buoyant, first-quality hackle. In effect, it's as visible as a dry fly artificial.

Under each major *Ephemerella* species, tying instructions are included for both the nymphal and emerging-dun stages. The dry fly imitations can be tied in either the No-Hackle or Conventional Hackle styles. The No-Hackle is an authentic and extremely effec-

tive artificial that works very well when fishing the smooth flats of freestone and limestone streams, waters in which trout can afford to become ultra-selective. However, the pattern is not designed to be used in fast, choppy waters or during windy weather, when the Conventional Hackle dry fly would be more practical.

The angler who is equipped with the patterns recommended in this chapter is prepared to match some of the most important hatches in the country. This, however, should not necessarily preclude exercising the best possible presentation when using those imitations. During *Ephemerella* hatches, the likelihood of extreme selectivity on the part of the trout is high. Consequently, careful approach, exact delivery, and drag-free floats also remain imperative for the angler's success. An artificial imitation (regardless of its authenticity), when allowed to skitter across the water like a minuscule sailboat, is as pointless an approach as stubbornly flogging the water with an oversized or grossly off-colored imitation.

Identification

The average size of *Ephemerella* nymphs is small, about 9mm. The species are often differentiated by minute morphological characteristics, making naked-eye identification usually difficult. However, with a ten-power hand lens the novice will have little problem keying any nymph specimen down to its species level.

During the majority of *Ephemerella* hatches, live nymphs can be obtained simply by holding a small

FIG. 8-6 The No-Hackle fly

FIG. 8-7 A 22-inch rainbow trout that fell to a size No. 20 No-Hackle during a Pale Morning Dun hatch. It was promptly released.

aquarium net in the first few inches of the surface film. As is often the case, the dun will escape out of the nymphal shuck when the live nymph is lifted out of the water. Empty nymphal shucks, always available during a hatch, are just as suitable for determining the species that happens to be emerging.

EASTERN AND MIDWESTERN HATCHES OF EPHEMERELLAS

The eastern angler can expect *Ephemerella* hatches from the latter part of April through the month of August. Dark Hendricksons (*E. subvaria*) are always the first to emerge for the season, followed by the Light Hendricksons and Pale Evening Duns. By the time the Pale Evening Duns start to emerge, usually in June, a series of Blue-Winged Olive species start to hatch, their morning emergence lasting until the month of August.

Spinner swarms of eastern *Ephemerella* usually gather in the late afternoon. Mating and ovipositing take place over the riffles at dusk, with the spinner falls occurring between 7 p.m. and 9 p.m. in the evening. During unseasonably cold days, the entire process may be postponed until the following morning. All three spinners included in this section belong in the well-equipped fly fisherman's fly box.

Entomologists divide eastern *Ephemerella* species into six genera, based on the taxonomic characteristics given in Appendix II. The entomological-oriented reader should note a few of the more important deviations in the information given here from that included in past angling texts. In the Blue-Winged Olive Group, *E. cornutella* is introduced for the first time to the angler. The species is found in excellent numbers in most eastern streams and is responsible for the hatches of little Blue-Winged Olives during the summer. *E. lata*, often said to exist only in the midwestern states, is also found in eastern streams. *E. attenuata* is of little importance to anglers, despite the fact that it has been credited in angling texts with all the Blue-Winged Olive hatches that are in fact produced by the two species already mentioned.

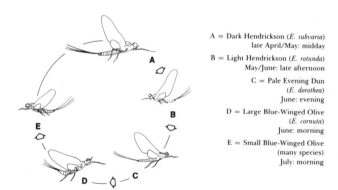

A = Dark Hendrickson (*E. subvaria*)
late April/May: midday

B = Light Hendrickson (*E. rotunda*)
May/June: late afternoon

C = Pale Evening Dun
(*E. dorothea*)
June: evening

D = Large Blue-Winged Olive
(*E. cornuta*)
June: morning

E = Small Blue-Winged Olive
(many species)
July: morning

FIG. 8-8 Seasonal cycle of eastern *Ephemerellas* (actual sizes).

Emergence Dates of Eastern Ephemerellas

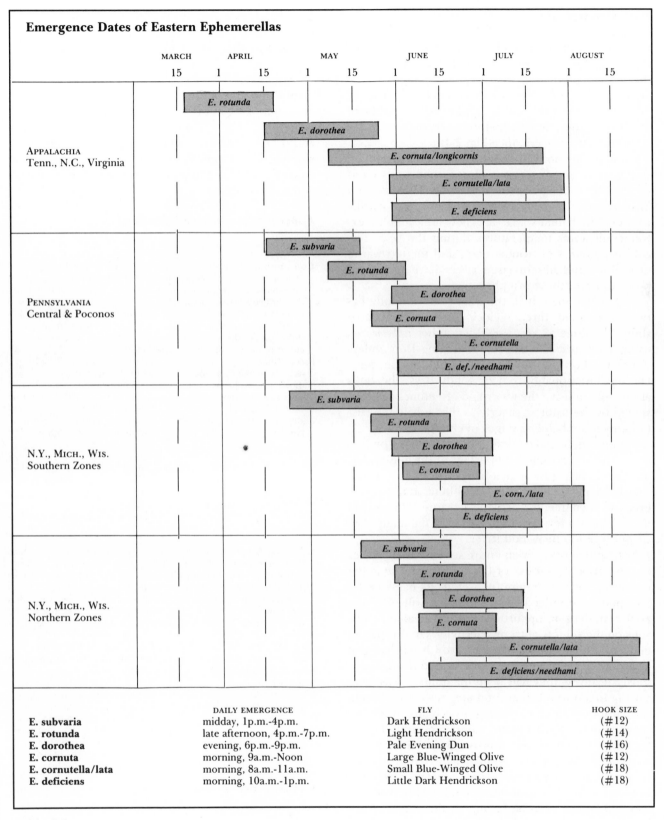

	DAILY EMERGENCE	FLY	HOOK SIZE
E. subvaria	midday, 1p.m.-4p.m.	Dark Hendrickson	(#12)
E. rotunda	late afternoon, 4p.m.-7p.m.	Light Hendrickson	(#14)
E. dorothea	evening, 6p.m.-9p.m.	Pale Evening Dun	(#16)
E. cornuta	morning, 9a.m.-Noon	Large Blue-Winged Olive	(#12)
E. cornutella/lata	morning, 8a.m.-11a.m.	Small Blue-Winged Olive	(#18)
E. deficiens	morning, 10a.m.-1p.m.	Little Dark Hendrickson	(#18)

Table 8-1

Dark Hendrickson (*Ephemerella subvaria*)

E. subvaria is the first and most important *Ephemerella* to emerge for the season, and its hatches are usually the first to produce dry fly action for anglers. The Hendricksons normally last three weeks and usually take place during the end of April until the middle of May, when the water temperatures in streams range from 55 to 65 degrees. (See Fig. 2-1i.)

Good populations of *E. subvaria* nymphs are found in the slow-current sections of deep pools, as well as in the slick runs of fast-water streams. Their general distribution in a given stream, however, is normally confined to habitats that are not subjected to extremes in water temperatures during the year. Icy-cold headwaters of trout streams and the too warm, dead-flow stretches of large rivers have very poor populations of these nymphs.

Daily emergence is in the afternoon normally between one and three o'clock. Fishing this hatch should be done as you would any other *Ephemerella*, using a subsurface nymph or Emerging Dun, unless the trout show an equivalent interest for the duns. During unseasonably cold or windy days, the duns are unable to leave the water and oftentimes are consumed by the trout as eagerly as they inhale the customarily more helpless stages of emergence.

Spinner flights take place in the afternoons or evenings and are extremely important to the angler. Often they appear just after a hatch and the trout may switch to the fallen spinners without a noticeable break in their feeding activity. I learned this lesson the hard way a few years ago in one of the many classic pools of the Beaverkill River.

Fishing this river for an entire season, or any other of the "insect factories" of the country, is like going to college for a degree in fly fishing. Its many excellent pools are indeed classrooms that will offer the angler/student an opportunity to learn valuable lessons on the subject of trout selectivity. On this particular day, an exceptional Hendrickson hatch had just ended when the trout once again started rising as enthusiastically as they had been for hours. I was soon casting to a dozen fish around me, but none of them was curious enough to even approach any of my dry fly imitations. When I finally stopped beating the water long enough to look downstream, I noticed that other anglers were also failing in their repeated attempts to fool a single fish. There was one exception, however. One individual near me was taking fish after fish and appeared to be having all the "luck." After his ninth fish I couldn't take it any longer. I swallowed my pride long enough to ask him what pattern he was using.

"Look at the water," he commanded with a knowing glance.

"Spinners," I blurted out in total disbelief when I scrutinized the surface film. Other anglers near us started looking at the water surface as if they had lost something in it. It was not long, however, before you could hear the loud snaps of plastic boxes and reels singing. It is a timeless lesson. Whenever in doubt, study the surface of the water, and it will tell you what you need to know.

Ephemerella subvaria Imitations

NATURAL	ARTIFICIAL

Conventional Nymph: This pattern as well as the Conventional Nymph imitation recommended for the other *Ephemerella* species included in this section are designed to be fished at or just under the surface *during* an actual *Ephemerella* hatch. Thus they are tied in a light dry fly hook, and take into consideration the *bottom* coloration of the nymph—the side trout will see when approaching them from underneath. The pattern is an alternative imitation to either of the two dry fly patterns below.

SIZE: 11mm	HOOK: Mustad 94840 #10
TAILS: dark amber, banded	THREAD: medium brown prewaxed 6/0
ABDOMEN: olive brown	
THORAX: olive brown; dark brown wing pads	TAILS: light amber pheasant or wood duck fibers
LEGS: light brown, alternately banded	ABDOMEN: light olive brown dubbing ribbed with gold wire
	THORAX: olive brown dubbing, dark brown partridge hackle fibers pulled tight over thorax to represent wing cases
	LEGS: brown partridge hackle fibers

Emerging Dun*: *Ephemerellas* produce perhaps the most profuse flush emergences of all aquatic insects, and their hatches are customarily characterized with very selective and cautious trout. The Emerging Dun given here and for all *Ephemerellas* in this chapter is an imitation that imitates a yet-unfolded wing dun struggling at the surface film and appeals to the opportunistic nature of trout. It will undoubtedly turn the odds in the angler's favor.

SIZE: 11mm	HOOK: Mustad 94833 #12
TAILS: brown	THREAD: olive brown prewaxed 6/0
ABDOMEN AND THORAX: reddish brown	
WING: medium gray, in a folded-back position	TAILS: brown hackle fibers
	ABDOMEN AND THORAX: light rusty tan dubbing ribbed with dark brown monocord
	WINGS: two hackles: four turns of dark dun hackle for wings; two turns of dark ginger hackle for legs

No-Hackle Dun: As with this species and all *Ephemerellas* that follow, this is an alternative pattern to the Emerging Dun. Whenever trout are taking the fully upright-winged duns, it is just as effective as the Emerging Dun; however, during the majority of circumstances the latter is comparatively much more effective. The No-Hackle differs only in employing mallard quill segments for the wings, which are positioned in a fully upright direction.

SIZE: 11mm
TAILS: brown
ABDOMEN AND THORAX: reddish brown
WINGS: medium gray

HOOK: Mustad 94833 #12
THREAD: olive brown prewaxed 6/0
TAILS: brown hackle fibers
ABDOMEN AND THORAX: light rusty tan dubbing ribbed with a dark brown monocord
WINGS: dark slate gray mallard quill segments

Spinners*: Spinner falls of *E. subvaria,* *E. rotunda,* and *E. dorothea* are as impressive as their actual emergences and cause trout to get just as difficult and particular to size and color as they do to their corresponding duns. All three spinner patterns given for them take in consideration the coloration of the *Ephemerella* female.

SIZE: 11mm
TAILS: dark brown
BODY: blackish brown
WINGS: translucent (hyaline)

HOOK: Mustad 94833 #12
THREAD: black prewaxed 6/0
TAILS: dark brown hackle fibers
BODY: blackish brown dubbing ribbed with fine gold wire
WINGS: light dun hen-hackle tips or *sparse* amount of light dun poly fibers

*Most recommended

Light Hendrickson *(Ephemerella rotunda)*

The nymphs of *E. rotunda* start to emerge three weeks after *E. subvaria;* in fact, both species may often hatch together. Its hatches, however, are customarily a week after the last emergences of *Brachycentrus numerosus,* or Shad Fly. After approximately ten days, the importance of *E. rotunda* is supplanted by its sister species, *E. invaria.* Both *Ephemerellas* may be treated as one by the angler since the two are practically identical.

E. rotunda and *E. invaria* are the most abundant and widely distributed mayflies in the East and Midwest. Their extremely versatile nymphs can thrive almost

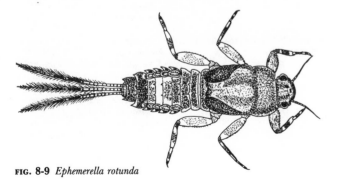

FIG. 8-9 *Ephemerella rotunda*

anywhere and can tolerate extremes in water temperature or currents.

Light Hendrickson hatches take place late in the afternoons or evenings, usually between four and six o'clock. The brown-bodied *E. rotunda* spinners gather at dusk over the riffles, and occasionally its spinner falls take place during an *E. rotunda* hatch. As with *E. subvaria,* the spinner falls of this species are very important to anglers.

Streamside identification of *E. rotunda* nymphs is accomplished by detecting the small, incurved spines on their abdominal segments, which are unlike the large, black spines exhibited by the *E. subvaria* nymphs. The second segment of their legs is doubly banded, and their abdomen shows two, instead of three, light cream segments.

Ephemerella rotunda and *E. invaria* Imitations

These two species have traditionally been erroneously grouped with *E. subvaria,* for the two differ markedly in size and color. They are closer to *E. dorothea* in size and coloration. When considering the fact that *E. rotunda* and *E. invaria* are *the* most abundant mayflies in trout environments, specific patterns should be employed to tackle the profuse and selective trout that they customarily cause.

NATURAL	ARTIFICIAL

Conventional Nymph: See comments under *E. subvaria.*

SIZE: 9mm
TAILS: light brown, faintly banded
ABDOMEN: mottled medium brown
THORAX: light tannish cream; medium brown wing pads
LEGS: mottled dark amber

HOOK: Mustad 94840 #12
THREAD: brown prewaxed 6/0
TAILS: light brown hackle or pheasant fibers
ABDOMEN: tannish cream dubbing ribbed with fine gold wire
THORAX: tannish cream dubbing; brown turkey or pheasant quill for wing cases
LEGS: light hen pheasant body feathers

Emerging Dun*: See comments under *E. subvaria.*

SIZE: 9mm
TAILS: light brown, barred
BODY: light olive brown
WINGS: light bluish gray, in a folded-back position
LEGS: light olive brown

HOOK: Mustad 94833 #14
THREAD: yellow prewaxed 6/0
TAILS: light brown hackle fibers
BODY: light olive brown dubbing
WINGS: two hackles: four turns of a light dun hackle for wings; two turns of a tan or ginger hackle for legs

No-Hackle: An alternative for the Emerging Dun pattern. See discussion under *E. subvaria.*

SIZE: 9mm
TAILS: light brown, barred
BODY: light olive brown
WING: light bluish gray

HOOK: Mustad 94833 #14
THREAD: yellow prewaxed 6/0
TAILS: light brown hackle fibers
BODY: light olive brown dubbing

WING: light dun mallard quill segments tied in an upright position

Spinner*: See discussion under *E. subvaria.*

SIZE: 9mm
TAILS: barred olive brown
BODY: olive brown
WINGS: translucent (hyaline)

HOOK: Mustad 94833 #14
THREAD: brown prewaxed 6/0
TAILS: olive brown or similar hackle fibers
BODY: olive brown
WINGS: very pale dun hen feather tips or light dun poly fibers tied very sparsely

*Most recommended

Pale Evening Dun *(Ephemerella dorothea)*

E. dorothea is the last *Ephemerella* to hatch in the afternoon or evening for the season. It begins its seasonal cycle about two weeks after *E. rotunda* and *E. invaria* first appeared. It's an excellent hatch, up to par with those of Dark and Light Hendricksons. Pale Evening Duns are primarily June emergers.

The nymphs of this species generally prefer the calmer sections of swift-flowing rivers, but they are indigenous to the myriad water types that support good populations of *E. rotunda* and *E. invaria.*

Its hatches take place at dusk, during the most pleasant time of the season—balmy, intoxicating evenings of early summer. Actual emergence may begin as early as six o'clock or as late as nightfall. Spinner falls are always in the evenings, and they usually occur just after a hatch. The spinners have a curious S-shaped flight pattern and hover just over the riffles; the angler will have little trouble recognizing them.

E. dorothea nymphs do not have spines on their abdominal segments, distinguishing them from those of either *E. subvaria* or *E. rotunda.* Moreover, their legs are practically devoid of bands and are markedly smaller in size than the *Ephemerella* species thus covered.

A midwestern *Ephemerella* quite similar to *E. dorothea*

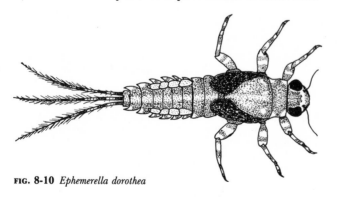

FIG. **8-10** *Ephemerella dorothea*

is *E. excrucians,* a fairly common species in the swift-flowing streams and rivers of Michigan and Wisconsin. The nymphs are almost identical to those of *E. dorothea* and can only be distinguished by the fact that they lack bands on their tails.

Ephemerella dorothea Imitation

NATURAL   ARTIFICIAL

Conventional Nymph: See discussion under *E. subvaria.*

SIZE: 8mm
TAILS: light amber
ABDOMEN: medium amber
THORAX: medium amber; light brown wing pads
LEGS: light amber lacking any noticeable markings

HOOK: Mustad 94840 #14
THREAD: light brown prewaxed 6/0
TAILS: pale amber wood duck or hen pheasant fibers
ABDOMEN: medium amber dubbing
THORAX: medium amber dubbing; light brown dubbing or poly for wing cases
LEGS: pale cream pheasant fibers or cock hackles

Emerging Dun*: See discussion under *E. subvaria.*

SIZE: 8mm
TAILS: pale cream
BODY: light cream, thorax orangish yellow
WINGS: pale dun, in a folded-back position
LEGS: pale cream without markings

HOOK: Mustad 94840 #16
THREAD: beige or light tan prewaxed 6/0
TAILS: light ginger hackle fibers
BODY: light cream dubbing, thorax with orangish yellow dubbing
WINGS: two hackles: four turns of light dun hackle for wings; two turns of cream or tan hackle for legs

No-Hackle Dun: See discussion under *E. subvaria.* Alternative pattern for Emerging Dun.

SIZE: 8mm
TAILS: pale cream
BODY: light cream, thorax orangish yellow
WINGS: pale dun in an upright position

HOOK: Mustad 94833 #16
THREAD: beige or light tan prewaxed 6/0
TAILS: light ginger hackle fibers
BODY: light cream dubbing for abdomen, orangish yellow dubbing for thorax portion
WINGS: pale dun or faded natural mallard quill segments

Spinner*: See discussion under *E. subvaria.*

SIZE: 8mm
TAILS: pale cream
BODY: whitish, lacking any coloration; however, thorax is orangish yellow
WINGS: translucent (hyaline)

HOOK: Mustad 94833 #16
THREAD: light tan prewaxed 6/0
TAILS: pale cream hackle fibers
BODY: pale dun or white for abdomen, orangish yellow dubbing for thorax
WINGS: light dun feather tips or light dun poly fibers tied very sparsely

*Most recommended

Large Blue-Winged Olives (*Ephemerella cornuta*)

The duns of *E. cornuta* represent the whole *Ephemerella* group of species known to anglers as the Blue-Winged Olives, which emerge during midsummer mornings in eastern and midwestern streams. The Blue-Winged Olive group comprises seven *Ephemerella* species that can be divided into two hook sizes: No. 12 (10mm) and No. 16 (7mm), of which *E. cornuta*, *E. cornutella*, and *E. lata* are the most common. Because of the similarity of the species, only one artificial pattern in two sizes is necessary to match their hatches. (See Fig. 8-4.)

The group of larger species emerges first, during the month of June. They are followed by the smaller *Ephemerellas* that are responsible for the many excellent morning Blue-Winged Olive hatches that take place in July and August.

The nymphs of *E. cornuta* and those of their closely related species inhabit medium- to fast-running portions of streams. They may also be found in the sluggish margins of deep pools, clinging to the debris and organic detritus that collect in them.

Daily emergence of *E. cornuta* and all species that follow is from nine in the morning until noon. As a general rule, spinner falls of these species appear to be of limited importance to anglers with the exception of *E. lata*, an extremely common midwestern species that emerges during July and August.

In the stream, identification of *E. cornuta* nymphs is accomplished by detecting their well-developed horns, visible with a ten-power hand glass. Their large size (10mm) and early seasonal occurrence in June serve to separate them from *E. cornutella*, which is almost morphologically identical though noticeably smaller, and which follows it in emergence.

Blue-Winged Olive Group Imitations

The following patterns are to be tied in two sizes. In the East, they will imitate the prolific *Ephemerella* species: *E. cornuta* and *E. cornutella*, which emerge back to back during the months of June and July. In the Midwest, *E. cornuta* is followed in turn by *E. lata*, which replaces the similar-sized *E. cornutella* in that area of the country. As a general rule, their spinner falls occur in the early hours of morning and thus are rarely encountered by anglers, with one exception; *E. lata* and the spinner pattern given here is specifically for that species which emerges best in midwestern waters. Again a light-wire Conventional Nymph, Emerging Dun, and No-Hackle are offered as three alternatives to meet the Blue-Winged Olive *Ephemerella* hatches. The choice between the three approaches is a matter of personal preference and custom, though the reader will undoubtedly find that the Emerging Dun imitation is the most effective during their actual emergences.

NATURAL	ARTIFICIAL
Conventional Nymph: See discussion under *E. subvaria*.	
SIZE: *E. cornuta*, 10mm; *E. cornutella* and *E. lata*, 7mm	HOOK: Mustad 94840 #12 and #16
TAILS: light olive brown	THREAD: olive prewaxed 6/0
ABDOMEN: grayish olive	TAILS: light brown hen pheasant fibers
THORAX: light olive brown; black wing pads	ABDOMEN: grayish olive dubbing
LEGS: amber, unbanded	THORAX: light olive brown dubbing; black goose, black dubbing, or poly for wing cases pulled very tightly and flat over thorax portion
	LEGS: unbanded tan or amber hen pheasant fibers
Emerging Dun*: See discussion under *E. subvaria*.	
SIZE: 10mm; 7mm	HOOK: Mustad 94833 #12 and #18
TAILS: dark olive brown	THREAD: olive prewaxed 6/0
BODY: medium olive	TAILS: dark brown hackle fibers
WINGS: dark slate or gray, folded-back position	BODY: medium olive dubbing ribbed with 6/0 yellow thread
LEGS: mottled olive and brown	WINGS: two hackles: four turns of dark dun hackle for wings; two turns of dyed olive grizzly for legs
No-Hackle Dun: An alternative pattern for the preceding pattern. See discussion under *E. subvaria*.	
SIZE: 10mm; 7mm	HOOK: Mustad 94833 #12 and #18
TAILS: dark olive brown	THREAD: olive prewaxed 6/0
BODY: medium olive	TAILS: dark brown hackle fibers
WINGS: dark slate or gray, upright position	BODY: medium olive dubbing ribbed with 6/0 yellow thread
	WINGS: dark slate mallard quill segments
Spinner*: Specific tie for *E. lata*, an important Blue-Winged Olive *Ephemerella* in midwestern waters. Same pattern in a hook size #12 will imitate the spinner of *E. cornuta* very closely, if needed.	
SIZE: 7mm	HOOK: Mustad 94833 #18
TAILS: dark brown	THREAD: rust prewaxed 6/0
BODY: dark reddish brown	TAILS: dark brown hackle fibers
WINGS: translucent (hyaline)	BODY: dark reddish brown dubbing
	WINGS: light dun hen-hackle feather tips

*Most recommended

Large Blue-Winged Olive (Ephemerella walkeri)

The robust, dark olive duns of *E. walkeri* cause fair hatches in certain localities. It's a mid-June to July emerger, and in typical Blue-Winged Olive hatches it occurs in the morning. Good populations of *E. walkeri*

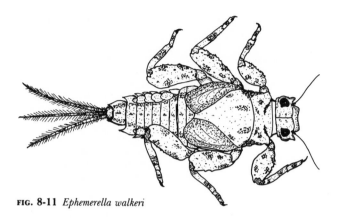

FIG. 8-11 *Ephemerella walkeri*

are found in the Platte River of Michigan, the Delaware River of New York (Hamilton), the Yellow Breeches of Pennsylvania, and the Broadheads River of New Jersey.

At streamside, its nymphs are unmistakable from those of any other mayflies because of the robust, strong-arm configuration of all three sets of legs.

Large Blue-Winged Olive (Ephemerella longicornis)

Good populations of *E. longicornis* are found in the trout streams of North Carolina and Tennessee, and the species is capable of causing fair Blue-Winged Olive hatches for the Smoky Mountain angler. Its seasonal emergence takes place from the early part of June until the end of July, with daily appearances between ten and one o'clock in the afternoon. Allens Creek, Flag Creek, and Big Creek (Macon County) of North Carolina have good hatches, as does LeConte Creek near Gatlinburg, Tennessee.

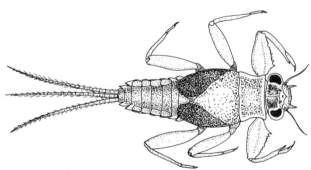

FIG. 8-12 *Ephemerella longicornis*

Small Blue-Winged Olive (*Ephemerella cornutella*)

This is the principal species that produces the hatches of Small Blue-Winged Olives in eastern trout waters. Its little duns appear about a week after the larger subimagoes of *E. cornuta* have completed their cycle for the season. Despite the difference in size,

the hatches of *E. cornutella* are just as important to the angler as the hatches of its predecessor.

Seasonal emergence takes place from late June through August, with daily occurrences during the morning from 9 until 11 o'clock. The best hatches are in moderate-flowing streams common throughout the Allegheny mountain ranges.

Differentiating *E. cornutella* nymphs from the near-identical ones of *E. cornuta* is best accomplished by size comparison. Those smaller than eight millimeters can be safely attributed to this species; specimens larger than nine millimeters belong to *E. cornuta*.

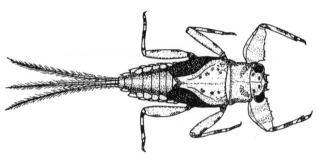

FIG. 8-13 *Ephemerella cornutella*

Small Blue-Winged Olive (Ephemerella lata)

E. lata is another small Blue-Winged Olive that produces excellent hatches, but, unlike *E. cornutella*, its primary importance is to the midwestern angler. Some rivers in the East, such as the Beaverkill and Saranac, support fair to good populations, where they will be found emerging with *E. cornutella*.

Morning hatches can be expected to occur from late June until the end of August. Immense spinner swarms gather at dusk. The spinner falls are very impressive, and usually entice the frenzied feeding activity of trout.

Identification of these little nymphs is often only a routine matter for it is one of the most conspicuous among mayfly biota of eastern and midwestern states. They usually exhibit bright, crimson dashes on their legs, thorax, and abdomen; however, the species is

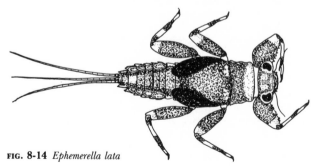

FIG. 8-14 *Ephemerella lata*

known to have distinctive and different color phases. It is a wonder that such an obvious nymph has been overlooked in eastern trout waters.

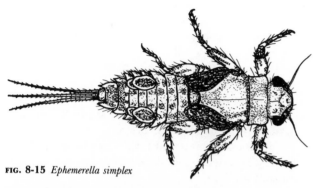

FIG. 8-15 *Ephemerella simplex*

Small Blue-Winged Olive (Ephemerella simplex)

Though *E. simplex* is not as common to anglers as the two species just discussed, it does produce good to excellent emergences during the months of June and July. It replaces *E. cornutella* and *E. lata* in the tail ends of large, silted pools, since it is well equipped to survive in the same waters that support populations of the little Tricos. *E. simplex* exhibits a large, protective third gill on segments four to seven which prevents it from choking on the silt that is perpetually settling to the bottom in its placid-water microhabitat. This species has produced excellent hatches for me in many Catskill, Pennsylvania, and midwestern streams. I suspect it is much more important than has been given credit in past angling texts.

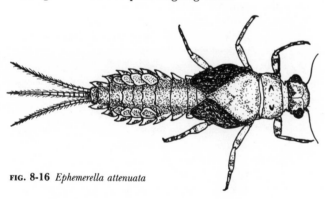

FIG. 8-16 *Ephemerella attenuata*

Small Blue-Winged Olive (Ephemerella attenuata)

E. attenuata is relatively unimportant to the trout fisherman, excepting in the Broadheads, as reported by Ernest Schweibert in his little classic *Matching the Hatch*. The species, however, has since received most of the credit in angling literature for what most likely are hatches of the more common *E. cornutella, E. lata,* and *E. simplex.* The little nymphs of *E. attenuata* are only occasionally found in silted sections of large riv-

ers. Entomologists report populations of *E. attenuata* from the states of Massachusetts, Pennsylvania, Virginia, South Carolina, and Florida (though they can also be occasionally found in the slow-moving waters of most states east of the Mississippi).

Little Dark Hendrickson (*Ephemerella deficiens*)

This is an excellent hatch in many eastern, midwestern, and Appalachian trout waters. Surprisingly, the species has been largely ignored by angling authors. It is widely distributed and abundant in swift sections of weedy streams and in the medium-flowing portions of freestone rivers. The Pere Marquette of Michigan, Macan River of Wisconsin, Esopus, Willowemoc, St. Regis, and Trout rivers of New York support good populations. Seasonal occurrence in these waters is from late-June to July, with its hatches appearing at 11 o'clock in the morning.

The nymphs and duns of *E. deficiens* are almost identical in general appearance to those of *E. subvaria,* though comparatively tiny in size. A size 20 version of the pattern recommended for the Dark Hendricksons should be carried astream in case the reader finds that this species is of importance in the waters he normally fishes.

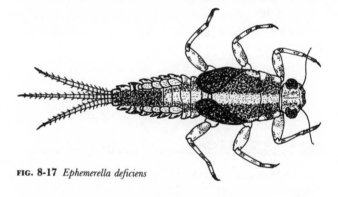

FIG. 8-17 *Ephemerella deficiens*

Little Dark Hendrickson (Ephemerella needhami)

E. needhami shares the same habitats as *E. deficiens,* which resembles it very closely. It is often fairly common in moderate-flowing streams with an abundance of vegetation. The AuSable and Manistee rivers of Michigan, the Yellow Breeches of Pennsylvania, and the Delaware of New York also produce their hatches besides the waters already mentioned for *E. deficiens.* Seasonal emergence of *E. needhami* is usually confined to the last two weeks of June, and it is also a late-morning hatch.

Recognizing the nymphs of *E. deficiens* and *E. needhami* is made easy by the pale cream stripe that

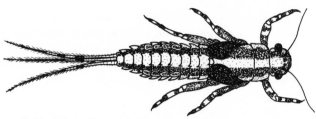

FIG. 8-18 *Ephemerella needhami*

both exhibit along their length, though in the case of *E. deficiens*, the stripe does not extend to the latter half of its abdomen.

Ephemerella deficiens (and related species) Imitations

E. deficiens and *E. needhami* are not as universally common as the *Ephemerellas* covered thus far; nonetheless, the moderate-flowing, weedy sections of eastern and midwestern rivers support them in good enough numbers to warrant a specific pattern for their hatches. The following pattern has proved very effective during their emergences in the last four seasons and is a compromise imitation for the smaller *E. deficiens* and its larger sister *Ephemerella—E. needhami*. Their spinner forms are well imitated by the spinner pattern suggested for *E. lata*.

NATURAL	ARTIFICIAL

Emerging Dun: To be fished *on* the surface and only during actual emergence.

Size: 7mm	Hook: Mustad 94833 #18
Tails: light brown to pale cream	Thread: dark brown prewaxed 6/0
Body: dark reddish brown	Tails: light tan hackle fibers
Wings: dark slate, nearly black in coloration	Body: dark reddish brown
Legs: tannish cream	Wings: two hackles: four turns with a dark, blackish dun hackle; two turns with tan hackle for legs

WESTERN HATCHES OF EPHEMERELLAS

The *Ephemerellas* produce the most important mayfly hatches in the West, and excellent populations of its nymphs are found in slow-moving spring creeks as well as in large rivers of torrential-water conditions. The western angler also gets to enjoy the hatches of the largest *Ephemerellas* in the country, *E. grandis* and *E. doddsi*, commonly known as the Western Green Drakes.

The West is a vast expanse of geography, crisscrossed with a multitude of rivers that are in turn subjected to abrupt deviations in altitudes. Many of its trout streams are also influenced by geothermal extrusions ranging from icy-cold to boiling-hot underground springs. As a result, the water temperatures (which determine emergence of the species) within a

given river system vary extensively and unpredictably. Consequently, predicting the hatches of many river systems is nearly impossible. The emergence dates included here are applicable to trout streams of a constant nature, and they will prove very helpful to the angler who happens to be unfamiliar with the waters he chooses to fish. The chart will give him an idea of where and when he may expect to encounter the most important *Ephemerellas*.

The spinner falls of most western *Ephemerellas* take place in the late afternoons or at dusk; however, when the air temperature drops sharply, the flights are often postponed until the following morning. The best spinner flights occur when the air temperature is in the 70's.

Three important *Ephemerella* species which have not been covered in previous angling texts are *E. margarita*, *E. heterocaudata*, and *E. tibialis*. The first two produce good Blue-Winged Olive hatches during midsummer, and *E. tibialis*, a small Dark Hendrickson, emerges during the month of August. All are indigenous to specific types of waters and are not as universal as *E. inermis* (Pale Morning Dun), *E. grandis* (Western Green Drake), or *E. flavilinea* (Small Western Green Drake). *E. lacustris*, reported to exist in numerous spring creeks in the Yellowstone country of Montana and Wyoming, is found only near Yellowstone Lake (YNP), according to entomological texts and our own findings. The species is almost identical to *E. inermis*, and the erroneous angling reports are most likely the result of mistaken identities.

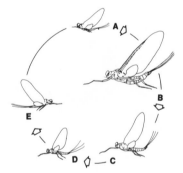

A = Pale Morning Dun (*E. inermis*)
June/August: morning

B = Western Green Drake (*E. grandis*)
June/July: morning

C = Small Western Green Drake (*E. flavilinea*)
July/August: late afternoon

D = Little Western Olive (*E. margarita*)
July/August: morning

E = Small Western Dark Hendrickson (*E. tibialis*)
August/September: midday

FIG. 8-19 Seasonal cycle of western *Ephemerellas* (actual sizes).

Pale Morning Dun (Ephemerella inermis)

The diminutive olive yellow duns of *E. inermis* produce the very best *Ephemerella* and mayfly hatches that take place in western trout waters during the season. The species is quite abundant in every stream and river. When considered together with its sister species, *E. infrequens*, it has an unusually long emergence span, from May through September. Understandably, this impressive mayfly has been well-documented in angling literature throughout the years. It is the most important mayfly hatch to the western angler.

E. inermis belongs to the *E. inermis*, *E. infrequens*, and *E. lacustris* group of closely related and almost identical species. *E. infrequens* is neither as abundant nor as widely distributed as *E. inermis*. Its larger duns make their appearance for the last three weeks during the month of June. *E. lacustris* was originally described only from Yellowstone Lake in Wyoming. Its little duns are visible every morning and evening during the months of July and August off Pumice and Steamboat Points near the West Thumb area. The species can also be found emerging in nearby waters, such as

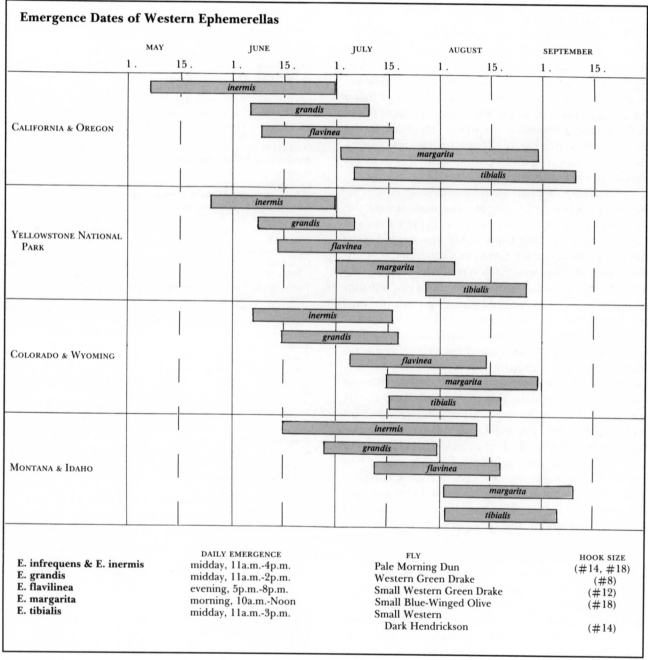

Emergence Dates of Western Ephemerellas

		DAILY EMERGENCE	FLY	HOOK SIZE
E. infrequens & E. inermis		midday, 11a.m.-4p.m.	Pale Morning Dun	(#14, #18)
E. grandis		midday, 11a.m.-2p.m.	Western Green Drake	(#8)
E. flavilinea		evening, 5p.m.-8p.m.	Small Western Green Drake	(#12)
E. margarita		morning, 10a.m.-Noon	Small Blue-Winged Olive	(#18)
E. tibialis		midday, 11a.m.-3p.m.	Small Western	
			Dark Hendrickson	(#14)

Table 8-2

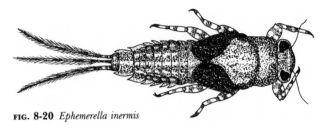

FIG. 8-20 *Ephemerella inermis*

Lewis River in the Park and many of the lakes northward along the Continental Divide, specifically those in the Gravelly Range of Montana.

The best hatches of Pale Morning Duns take place during the months of July and August, with daily emergence occurring between ten and one o'clock in the afternoon. During hot spells, the hatch will begin at nine, last for about an hour, and will emerge again for a short while late in the afternoon. Spinner falls of *E. inermis* and *E. infrequens* are just as important to the angler as the hatch itself. The spinners appear twice a day, in the morning and again at dusk. The females choose the riffles to oviposit their light olive eggs.

Perhaps no other hatch will force the angler to realize the importance of proper presentation and the meaning of drag-free floats as much as the hatches of the little Pale Morning Duns. A few years ago, I once went three fishless days during this hatch in the Madison River of Montana. Each day I had gone to the same spot in a pool. The hatch would begin, a group of fine-sized rainbows would move up from the rapids below me, and my agony would start. I went through a full array of artificial imitations in an effort to match the hatch, and, needless to say, came up with all the usual excuses for my repeated failure. However, on the fourth day, I decided to fish the hatch from the opposite side of the pool. I was totally surprised when, on my third cast, I had a good fish on and managed to land quite a few more before the hatch ended. Not until I had a chance to compare the two different casting angles did I realize that I had previously been placing my casts across a complex maze of mini-crosscurrents that resulted in instantly tightening my leader. This had dragged my artificial imperceptibly about, unlike a perfectly free-floating natural.

There are many ways the angler can protect himself against the hazards of drag. Using a limber or finer tippet helps a lot, especially when combined with deliberate stop casts that cause the artificial to land on the water in a heap, allowing the natural motion of the current to slowly straighten it out. Perhaps, the angler can also try to get a less troublesome casting angle by going to the opposite side of the

stream. However, he then runs the risk of taking a plunge in the water, as I did!

No reliable characteristics are known to separate the nymphs of *E. inermis* from those of *E. infrequens*; however, the latter species is markedly larger in size (8.5mm to 9.5mm) and lacks the pale medium stripe usually exhibited by the *E. inermis* nymphs.

Ephemerella inermis Imitations

The coloration of *E. inermis* and *E. infrequens* is very elusive and does not lend itself to easily being described, though it is an important point for succeeding during the hatches of these two species which are the most common mayflies found in western trout waters. Trout become terribly selective during their profuse emergences. The Conventional Nymph, Emerging Dun, and No-Hackle patterns given for this species and for other *Ephemerella* species included in this section are designed to be fished just under or on the surface of the water during their actual emergence. The choice among the three is really a matter of personal approach and custom, though the Emerging Dun imitation is undoubtedly the most effective. The reader is advised to consult the discussion under the artificial patterns given for *E. subvaria* in the previous eastern section of this chapter. Two sizes are given—the larger for the early-season emergences of *E. infrequens*, usually during the month of June; the second for the more common and midsummer to early fall hatches of *Ephemerella inermis*.

NATURAL	ARTIFICIAL
Conventional Nymph:	
SIZE: 9mm (*E. infrequens*) and 7mm (*E. inermis*)	HOOK: Mustad 94840 #12 and #16
TAILS: banded yellowish amber	THREAD: light olive prewaxed 6/0
ABDOMEN: quite variable, chartreuse and pale yellow the most common colorations	TAILS: dyed wood duck feather fibers
THORAX: same coloration as abdomen; gray wing pads	ABDOMEN: pale yellow dubbing; either Spectrum #21 or Flyrite #25
LEGS: banded yellowish amber	THORAX: pale yellow dubbing; light gray mallard quill for wing cases
	LEGS: dyed yellow wood duck feather fibers
Emerging Dun*:	
SIZE: 7mm and 9mm	HOOK: Mustad 94833 #14 and #18
TAILS: barred pale amber	THREAD: light olive prewaxed 6/0
BODY: pale yellow with olive sheen	TAILS: ginger hackle fibers
WINGS: light bluish gray, folded-back position	BODY: pale yellow dubbing ribbed with olive 6/0 thread (Ex: Flyrite #25)
LEGS: pale tan	WINGS: two hackles: four turns with a light dun hackle for wings; two turns with a light ginger to imitate the legs
No-Hackle:	
SIZE: 7mm and 9mm	HOOK: Mustad 94833 #14 and #18
TAILS: barred pale amber	THREAD: light olive prewaxed 6/0
BODY: pale yellow with olive sheen	TAILS: ginger hackle fibers
WINGS: light bluish gray	

BODY: pale yellow dubbing
ribbed with olive 6/0 thread
(Ex: Flyrite #25)
WINGS: light dun mallard
quills

Spinner*: Spinner falls of both *E. infrequens* and *E. inermis* are extremely important to the western fly fisher and rival the significance of any hatch in western waters.

SIZE: 7mm and 10mm
TAILS: olive brown
BODY: light olive brown
WINGS: translucent (hyaline)

HOOK: Mustad 94833 #14 and #18
THREAD: olive prewaxed 6/0
TAILS: olive brown hackle fibers
BODY: light olive brown dubbing, ribbed pale cream 6/0 thread
WINGS: light dun hen-hackle feather tips or sparse amount of Flyrite #25 fibers

*Most recommended

Western Green Drake *(Ephemerella grandis)*

The hatches of these large, robust flies are a favorite with western anglers, because they usually produce the best dry fly action of the season. *E. grandis* emerges from the latter part of June until the middle of July, when its short seasonal cycle ends as abruptly as it began.

The species is one of the most widely distributed mayflies of the West—from New Mexico to Alaska and from Colorado to California. Excellent populations of its nymphs are found in most cool-water streams and rivers of varied sizes.

Green Drakes are unusually slow and clumsy emergers and, as a result, an Emerging Dun imitation fished dead drift during their hatches is often deadly. The most impressive appearances of this beautiful mayfly will occur during the coldest, darkest days of early summer between the hours of one to four o'clock in the afternoon. Daytime spinner flights are very sparse for such a common species because the

large spinners do not become active until well after nightfall, and ovipositing is accomplished at four o'clock in the morning.

Identification of *E. grandis* nymphs is obvious, since, except for *E. doddsi*, its sister species of fast waters, this is the only *Ephemerella* 14 millimeters or more in length. A dead giveaway is also the toothless fore margins on its legs. Immature *E. grandis* nymphs are, however, easily confused with those of *E. spinifera*, though the difference of size will separate these two species when handling mature specimens.

E. grandis nymphs exhibit age and geographical variations, and consequently, entomologists have had to revise the status of this species over the years. The changes have unfortunately confused angling authors, and they have listed many of the *E. grandis* subspecies as distinct hatches of importance to anglers. In 1962, Dr. George Edmunds and Richard Allen clarified the *E. grandis* complex in their systematic *A Revision of Subgenus Drunella in North America*. Their clarifications are as follows: *E. grandis* is divided into three subspecies—*E. grandis grandis* (= *E. glacialis* Carsona) is found in southern Idaho and Wyoming south to Arizona and New Mexico; *E. grandis ingens* (=*E. glacialis* Traver, = *E. proserpina* Traver, =*E. yosemite* Traver) is indigenous to the trout streams that flow through the Sierra Nevada and Cascade Ranges as well as in northern Idaho and Montana; and *E. grandis flavincta* found along the Pacific Coast from Oregon to Alaska. Since the subspecies are practically identical in size and color, it serves little purpose for the fly fisher to make the distinctions. Some of the subspecies do intergrade in some of the most popular trout areas of the West.

Ephemerella grandis (and *related* species) Imitations

The following patterns are very effective imitations for the hatches of both the Western Green Drake, *E. grandis*, and the Small Green Drake hatches caused by its closely related but smaller sister species *E. flavilinea* which is discussed in the pages that follow. Except for size, both are nearly identical species.

NATURAL   ARTIFICIAL

Conventional Nymph: The following can be tied in heavy-hook versions (Mustad 3906 #8 and #10) to imitate *E. grandis* and *E. flavilinea*, respectively, and are good patterns to use during nonhatch periods during the Green Drake time of the season. The light-wire hook suggested is recommended with the intention of using the imitation during the actual emergences of this relatively large *Ephemerella*, just under the surface. Again, an Emerger and No-Hackle pattern is included for those who prefer to use dry fly imitations during the hatches.

SIZE: 15mm (*E. grandis*) and 11mm (*E. flavilinea*)
HOOK: Mustad 94840 #8 and #10

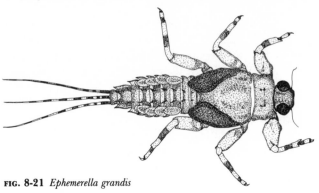

FIG. **8-21** *Ephemerella grandis*

TAILS: dark brown faintly banded
ABDOMEN: dark olive brown; olive brown gills
THORAX: olive brown; black wing pads
LEGS: mottled dark amber

THREAD: olive prewaxed 6/0 or 3/0 monocord
TAIL: dark brown partridge hackle fibers
ABDOMEN: dark olive brown dubbing; olive ostrich herl for gills ribbed with fine gold wire
THORAX: olive brown dubbing blend tied very fuzzy; dark gray goose quill segment for wing cases
LEGS: dark brownish amber partridge fibers or mottled hen pheasant fibers

Emerging Dun*:
SIZE: 15mm and 11mm
TAILS: blackish brown
BODY: dark olive
WINGS: dark slate or gray
LEGS: mottled yellow with brown

HOOK: Mustad 94831 #10 and 94833 #12
THREAD: brown prewaxed 6/0
TAILS: dark moose hairs
BODY: dark olive dubbing ribbed with bright yellow floss or monocord thread 3/0
WINGS: two hackles: four turns of dark dun for wings; two turns of grizzly dyed chartreuse for legs

Dry Flies*: Because of the large size of E. grandis, it is best tied in the Paradrake style, while E. flavilinea is tied in the No-Hackle method.
SIZE: 15mm and 11mm
TAILS: blackish brown
BODY: dark olive
WINGS: dark slate or gray

HOOK: Mustad 94833 #12 and #14
THREAD: yellow prewaxed monocord 3/0 or 6/0
TAILS: dark moose hairs
BODY: E. grandis—dark olive dyed elk hair; E. flavilinea—dark olive dubbing
WINGS: E. grandis—dark gray deer hair with a grizzly saddle hackle dyed bright chartreuse and tied in parachute style; E. flavilinea—dark slate mallard quill segments

Spinner: The spinner swarms of E. grandis take place in the very early hours of the morning and rarely are their falls of importance to anglers. Those of E. flavilinea are another matter, and the following pattern is specifically recommended for them.
SIZE: 11mm
TAILS: pale cream
BODY: medium reddish brown
WINGS: clear (hyaline)

HOOK: Mustad 94831 #14
THREAD: olive prewaxed 6/0
TAILS: pale cream hackle fibers
BODY: medium reddish brown dubbing
WINGS: light dun hen-hackle tips

*Most recommended

Western Green Drake (Ephemerella doddsi)

E. doddsi is a second *Ephemerella* which produces good Green Drake hatches in cold, fast-flowing sections of freestone rivers of varied sizes, the *only* type

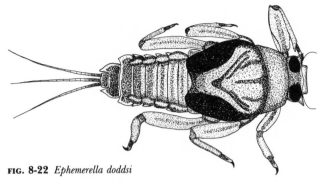

FIG. 8-22 *Ephemerella doddsi*

of waters in which the species is found. It often emerges with *E. grandis*, which makes it unnecessary to have a special artificial imitation for the species.

The geographical range of *E. doddsi* is similar to that of *E. grandis* and follows it in seasonal emergence. It is also a midafternoon hatch. Trout waters like the Bitterroot River in Montana, the Shoshone River in Wyoming, and Roaring Fork of Colorado produce good concentrated emergences.

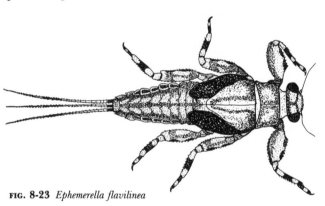

FIG. 8-23 *Ephemerella flavilinea*

Small Western Green Drake (*Ephemerella flavilinea*)

Small Western Green Drakes begin to emerge in the wake of the prolific *E. grandis* and *E. doddsi* hatches and offer the angler continuous dry fly sport. Its habitat extends from cold streams to the slow, flat sections of very large rivers.

Its seasonal occurrence is during the months of July and August, with daily appearances between late-afternoon and evening. Spinner flights take place in the riffled sections of water, and as is often the case, the slightest wind causes the delicate spinners to fall helplessly on the water, enticing the feeding activity of trout.

E. coloradensis and *E. spinifera* are closely related species and also emerge at the same time of year. The nymphs and duns of both of these species are almost identical to those of *E. flavilinea*, and the three species can certainly be treated as one by the angler. *E. flavilinea* is identified by the *rounded* spines on its abdominal segments, distinctly differing in configuration from the sharp, pointed spines exhibited by *E. coloradensis* nymphs.

For artificial imitations of *Ephemerella flavilinea* and related species, see the fly tying instructions given for *E. grandis*.

Small Western Green Drake (*Ephemerella coloradensis*)

The nymphs and duns of this species and that which follows are quite close to the stages of *E. flavilinea*. Their populations are found in rather small, rapidly flowing streams that traverse the high-altitude meadows of western mountains. Because their nymphs cannot survive in waters that exceed the 60-degree mark during the summer months, their distribution, and simultaneously their importance to the angler, are considerably limited. (See Fig. 3-6.)

Emergence of *E. coloradensis* is in late afternoon, during the months of July and August. Spinner swarms gather daily ten feet over the stream at dusk and will fall on the water just before nightfall. Rivers like the Gallatin in Montana and Big Wood of Idaho are suitable habitats for its populations.

Small Western Green Drake (*Ephemerella spinifera*)

E. spinifera is fairly important to the angler who fishes the colder streams and rivers of the Pacific states. Occasionally good populations of its nymphs are found in the trout streams of Idaho, Montana, and Wyoming. Seasonal emergence is in August and September, and daily occurrences are during late afternoon. Spinner flights are at dusk and much too sparse to be of any significance to anglers. I have encountered this species only twice, in the South Fork of Bishop Creek in California and upper Williamson

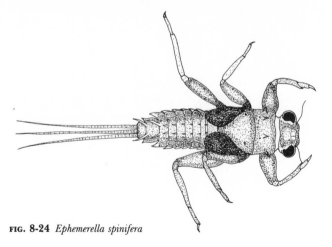

FIG. 8-24 *Ephemerella spinifera*

in Oregon. Seine tests have divulged their presence in Rock Creek and Gardiner River in the general area of southwest Montana. Its nymphs are instantly recognizable by the exaggerated, long spines on the last two segments of their abdomen.

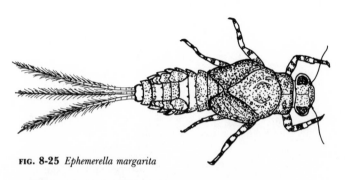

FIG. 8-25 *Ephemerella margarita*

Little Western Blue-Winged Olive (*Ephemerella margarita*)

This is a hatch in the West that has received only brief mention in angling texts. The species, however, is found in very good numbers in rather large, cold, sluggish creeks and rivers, waters where trout can afford to be very selective. Waters like Hat Creek in California and Henry's Fork in Idaho produce fishable hatches.

It is a morning hatch and is important to the angler who is willing to be on the stream by nine o'clock in the morning during August. Trout will usually concentrate on the struggling nymphs during these hatches, making the nymph fished on the surface a killing method when employed during actual emergence. *E. margarita* hatches are also prone to the "still-born" phenomenon (the case when duns become stuck to nymphal shucks) that Doug Swisher and Carl Richards wrote about in their useful book, *Fly Fishing Strategy* (New York, Crown Publishers, Inc., 1975).

The spinner flights take place just before nightfall and induce the instant feeding of trout. Male spinners are black, except for their whitish abdomen and wings. Similar colors are exhibited by *Baetis* imagoes.

A similar *Ephemerella* species, though not taxonomically related, is *E. heterocaudata*, which can produce fair hatches in fast-flowing streams and also emerges during the month of August at midday. It is easy to detect in the stream by its different tail lengths, the middle one being twice as long as the two outer ones. Its lighter Blue-Winged Olive duns have striped abdomens, unlike those of *E. margarita* (see drawing in Nymph section in Appendix II).

Ephemerella margarita Imitation

E. margarita is occasionally encountered in very good numbers, though only in very slow-flowing waters, while the hatches of another Blue-Winged Olive, *E. heterocaudata*, take place in faster waters. The following Emerging Dun pattern compromises their slight difference in size and coloration. It is quite effective for both of their emergences.

NATURAL	ARTIFICIAL
Emerging Dun:	
SIZE: 7mm	HOOK: Mustad 94833 #18
TAILS: barred olive brown	THREAD: light olive prewaxed
BODY: light olive brown	6/0
WINGS: medium gray or slate	TAILS: light brown hackle
LEGS: mottled olive brown	fibers
	BODY: light olive brown
	dubbing, unribbed
	WINGS: two hackles: four turns
	of medium dun hackle for
	wings; two turns of grizzly
	dyed olive brown for legs

Small Western Dark Hendrickson *(Ephemerella tibialis)*

This species is the last *Ephemerella* to emerge for the fishing season, appearing weeks after the *Ephemerella* "greats"—*E. grandis*, *E. inermis*, and *E. flavilinea*—have disappeared for the year. It chronologically follows the emergence of the Little Western Blue-Winged Olives. (See Fig. 8-5.)

Good populations of *E. tibialis* nymphs can be found at *any* altitude in most streams and rivers throughout the West; they demonstrate a remarkable ability to adapt to a wide variety of habitats. I have encountered good hatches from the Yellowstone River in the Park to the Deschutes River in Oregon.

Daily emergence takes place at midday, and the hatches are brief, lasting only one to two hours in duration. They are at their best during the months of August and September. Spinner falls do not appear to be concentrated enough to be of significance to fly fishers.

Another *Ephemerella* whose duns look very much the same as those of *E. tibialis* (though they are conspicuously larger, being nearly the size of Western Green Drakes) is *E. hecuba*. Its flattened nymphs inhabit slow-moving, slightly silted rivers, water that also supports good populations of Tricos (see illustration in Chapter 3). The species, however, is never very abundant wherever it is found and emerges over a long period of time—throughout the entire summer months. As a result, *E. hecuba* hatches are usually too sparse and often barely manage to induce the feeding activity of trout. If the reader suspects that this hatch may be of importance to him, a number-eight version of the pattern given for the eastern *Ephemerella subvaria* dun, tied in a Paradrake style, will match it perfectly.

No specific pattern will be given here for *E. tibialis* for the sole reason that the imitations recommended for the *Paraleptophlebias* would be exactly as the one for this species. The only difference would be that the wings of *E. tibialis* are a bit darker; however, in all other respects including size, the two types are very similar. Ironically, the most important *Paraleptophlebia* in the West is *P. debilis*, which emerges late in the season. Its seasonal emergence happens to coincide with that of *Ephemerella tibialis*.

CHAPTER 9: Mid-Season Drakes of Placid Waters (Family *Ephemeridae*)

IMAGINE arriving at your favorite stretch of water and, upon gazing at the water surface, you see hundreds of gigantic duns fluttering about; it appears as if every trout in the stream is frantically feeding on them. To your pleasant surprise, even those large holdover rainbows and nocturnal browns—that you suspected existed but felt no longer would be interested in satisfying their ravenous appetites during insect hatches—are now wildly chasing emerging nymphs and even rising freely to floating duns! The spectacular, blizzard-like hatches of the members of the mayfly families covered in this chapter can, upon emerging, easily transform this idealistic spectacle into a reality for the angler.

The noted Eastern Green Drake, Yellow Drake, Great Lead-Winged Drake, and Brown Drake hatches are produced by the burrowing-mayfly types discussed here. All are extremely large mayfly species, in fact, the very largest in North America. When their hatches are taking place, they cannot help but convert tranquil pools and sections of our trout streams into arenas of lively action. Surprising as it may first seem, it does not follow that the mere size of these flies, their concentrated emergence, and their consistency in managing to entice the feeding activity of trout are in any way a guarantee that anglers will attain absolute success during their hatches. As is often the case, they prove very frustrating for anglers because when they take place, the trout gorge themselves rather quickly with the large morsels and then either become ultra-selective or stop feeding entirely. It is imperative for the fly fisherman to be in total preparation before the daily hatches begin and to act fast when they are actually taking place. The information in the pages that follow is intended to help the reader to be better prepared to make the most of the hatches of the burrowing mayflies that include some of the most celebrated and important ones of the entire fishing season.

Mayflies of the Super Family *Ephemeridae*, whose nymphal forms burrow in the bottom of streams (with the exception of *Potamanthus* nymphs), are found in the best numbers in tree-lined, slow-moving waters of a fine gravel or silt substrate. The East Branch of the Delaware and West Canada Creek in New York, Big Springs and Yellow Breeches of Pennsylvania, and the AuSable River in Michigan are fine examples. One species alone, *Hexagenia limbata*, popularly known as the Great Lead-winged Drake, has over the years produced a distinct subcult of midwestern anglers. These anglers' every fishing strategy, artificial imitations, and even streamside jargon center entirely around this hatch. Western anglers should think of the smooth stretches of the upper Gibbon in Yellowstone National Park, the Beaverhead River in southwestern Montana, and the slower section of Henry's Fork of the Snake River as the western homegrounds for the excellent hatches of the Brown Drake, the only burrowing mayfly of general importance to those who fish the trout waters west of the Great Plains.

The faster freestone streams and rivers that drain the eastern mountain ranges—from the Great Smokies to the Green Mountains of Vermont—also contain burrowing mayflies in the silt and debris that collect around large rocks and boulders in the faster sections. Even better populations will be found in the placid flats of large pools and back eddies that are created by those streams that decrease in elevation in stepladder fashion. The perfect microhabitat for burrowers can also be artificially formed by man or beavers. Their engineering endeavors forcibly reduce

FIG. 9-1 Brown Drake action on a spring creek.

manthus nymphs are a notable exception: their gills extend laterally; they are free swimmers (at least in their mature stages); and they do not burrow like the other "tuskers." Ironically, they choose to live in the same type of microhabitat.

Upon actual emergence, the nymphs swim with exaggerated, vermicular movements during their journey to the surface. These movements are enticing to the trout, but they are difficult for anglers to imitate. Once on the surface film, they momentarily hover before the entrapped duns quickly slip out of the nymphal shucks. Although so far they accomplish their emergence function quite rapidly, the duns may take some time before leaving the water, thus offering anglers a chance at some exciting dry fly action. Naturally, when weather conditions are optimal for the duns to leave the surface of the water immediately, using a nymph imitation during the entire hatch remains the most effective approach to catch your quarry. When the duns are compelled to flutter frantically about before their wings dry enough to permit them to get airborne, they become the focus of the trout's attention. The trout will take them with explosive, almost startling, rises. As with most mayfly hatches, the angler should play his game "by ear." Imitating the streamside behavior of the natural, according to how the trout respond to it, remains his best approach in dealing with these and all hatches.

the bedload-carrying capacity of the current enough to allow the otherwise sustained sand and silt particles of the water to settle along the bottom.

Four kinds of burrowers or tusk-bearing mayflies are customarily found in trout streams; by far, the members of genera *Ephemera* (Eastern Green Drake, Yellow Drake, and Brown Drake) and *Hexagenia* (Great Lead-Winged Drake) are the most abundant and influential to the fly fisherman. The hatches of the other two genera, *Potamanthus* and *Ephoron*, are not as important because either they are not as profuse and take place during those of genus *Ephemera* or, in the case of *Ephoron*, are known to occur only in certain localities. Consequently, few anglers have reason to be concerned with their hatches.

Burrowing nymphs exhibit double, branchlike gills that are held straight back and, when in motion, give a wavy appearance. The propulsive action of their gills is what generates the amount of current (and oxygen) that flows through the U-shaped burrows that the nymphs make in the bottom substrate. *Pota-*

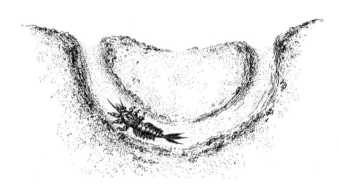

FIG. 9-2 The U-shaped underground houses of burrowing mayflies.

The members of the four genera discussed here differ greatly in their seasonal emergence, geographical range, and general taxonomy, thus making it necessary to treat each one separately. This offers the writer the opportunity to acquaint the reader with the different genera which will facilitate his streamside identifications.

FAMILY EPHEMERIDAE

Genus Ephemera (*West: common in Rocky Mountain waters; Midwest: fairly common; East: abundant*)

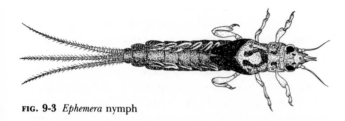

FIG. 9-3 *Ephemera* nymph

This genus produces the great Green Drake (*E. guttulata*) and Yellow Drake (*E. varia*) hatches, which are found in the East and the Midwest, respectively. A third species, *E. simulans*, is found commonly in midwestern lakes. Its range extends to western states where it's responsible for the excellent Brown Drake emergences that take place during the month of July in Rocky Mountain watersheds.

Ephemera nymphs are fairly large and easily recognizable even by a neophyte on the subject of entomology. They exhibit curved tusks and forked-frontal processes which protrude from their heads as shown in the illustration. They have chisel-like legs that are well designed for the type of microhabitat the nymphs choose to burrow in.

The dry forms have unique, blotchy markings on their wings and three tails of equal lengths, making it hard to confuse them with those of any other mayfly similar in size.

Genus Hexagenia (*West: common in certain localities; Midwest: abundant; East: common in certain localities*)

Though the range of genus *Hexagenia* is known to extend from Maine to California, its hatches are paramount to those who fish the trout waters of the Midwest. Populations of *Hexagenias* can also be found in certain eastern and western waters, but, in general, not all anglers from these areas need be preoccupied with their hatches, unless they have preknowledge of a local population.

Hexagenia nymphs are the largest mayfly nymphs found in our North American trout streams and, when fully mature, may reach up to 1½ inches in length; however, since growth to maturity of most species takes up to two or three years, nymphs will be found in various sizes at any time of the season. Recognizing them is rather straightforward; they have

straight tusks and *round-frontal* processes, unlike the forked extensions exhibited by *Ephemera* nymphs. (See Fig. 3-4.)

The large, unicolorous duns have only two tails and no other mayflies are similar in size or color. Except for their translucent wings, *Hexagenia* spinners closely resemble them.

Genus Potamanthus (*West: nonexistent; Midwest: fairly common; East: fairly common*)

Potamanthus nymphs are usually found in the same type of waters that support populations of *Ephemera* nymphs—the gravelly runs of slow- to medium-current rivers of varied sizes. They scurry about in the accumulations of detritus that collect in these sections and along the bottom of deep pools and back eddies of fast freestone rivers.

They are large and handsome and easily recognized by their sickle-shaped tusks and gills that protrude sideward. Unlike the nymphs of the other genera included in this chapter, *Potamanthus* nymphs are not burrowers, and they move about freely.

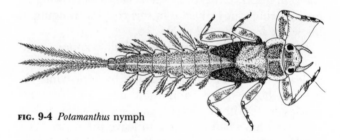

FIG. 9-4 *Potamanthus* nymph

The duns have cream-colored bodies and bright, golden yellow wings. They are a beautiful sight in our streams at a time of the year when the streamside flora is a dull, sun-scorched color. (*Potamanthus* is Latin for riverflower.) Their wings have a multitude of very fine, dark cross veins, unlike the blotchy markings on the wings of *Ephemeras*. Their middle tails are distinctly shorter than the outer ones. Both characteristics are dead giveaways for streamside identification.

Genus Ephoron (*West, Midwest, and East: extremely abundant where found*)

The nymphs of this genus have an inexplicable distribution and are found only in certain waters. Some examples of trout rivers that support their populations are: the Yellowstone, Big Hole (Melrose), Jefferson (Twin Bridges to Three Forks), and Missouri rivers of

Montana, as well as some eastern waters like the Yellow Breeches in Pennsylvania, upper Potomac in Maryland, and the West Branch of the Delaware in the Catskill Mountains. Last year I discovered them in five more locations: the Oswegatchie and West Canada Creek of northern New York, the Lower Tomorrow in Wisconsin, and the main Snake River below Idaho Falls, Idaho. All these waters have slow to medium currents and a clay or fine-silt bottom, soft enough for the nymphs to burrow in.

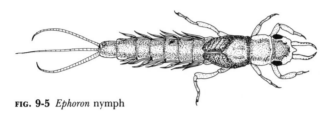

FIG. 9-5 *Ephoron* nymph

Ephoron nymphs have inward-curved tusks that almost touch at their apical ends. Their gills resemble those exhibited by the nymphs of *Ephemera* and *Hexagenia*. In general, these are the smallest burrowing or tusk-bearing types covered in this chapter, ranging in hook size from No. 12 to No. 16.

Ephoron nymphs are unique in their taxonomy and streamside behavior. The hatching of the two-tailed males precedes that of the females by approximately half an hour. They soon molt into spinners and quickly mate with the freshly hatched females before they even have had a chance to leave the water. The hatch, mating, and ovipositing process take place within the hour, the mass confusion usually enticing the frantic feeding of trout.

Fishing Facts and Artificial Imitations

After a hatch, the water will literally remain covered with the empty nymphal shucks of the emerging burrowing species. It is usually at this time that fly fishermen take the opportunity to appreciate the impressive numbers in which these species emerge. The thought that the same fly may continue to hatch for weeks in such daily concentrations will undoubtedly add to an angler's sense of wonderment.

When the hatch begins, trout will take positions in the stream and begin to leisurely intercept the ascending nymphs as they helplessly drift into their area of coverage. The angler, in turn, should concentrate on a single fish and refrain from the natural tendency to fish randomly. A series of rises that takes place in the same spot in the water usually means that at least that particular trout is holding his position. Placing your imitation directly upstream, letting it sink, and lifting it in short retrieves toward the surface when it is within the trout's range will usually cause him to strike at it.

In most cases, the angler will find that fishing a nymph imitation during the entire hatch will prove to be the most effective method for catching fish consistently. The use of a Wiggle Nymph artificial will further improve his chances for success. When in the water, this type of imitation closely resembles the undulating motion of the swimming natural. Its effectiveness during a hatch is demonstrated by the good results the angler attains by employing it.

When the duns have trouble leaving the water and the trout are aware of their difficulties, it is time for the dry fly. Careful streamside observation will tell the angler whether the duns are riding the surface

FIG. 9-6 The wiggle nymph

FIG. 9-7 The Paradrake

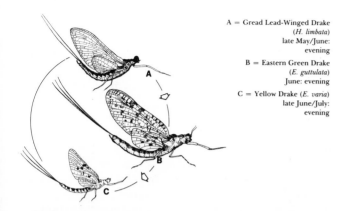

A = Gread Lead-Winged Drake
(*H. limbata*)
late May/June:
evening

B = Eastern Green Drake
(*E. guttulata*)
June: evening

C = Yellow Drake (*E. varia*)
late June/July:
evening

FIG. 9-8 Seasonal emergence cycle of eastern and midwestern *Ephemeridae* (actual sizes).

while their wings dry or are attempting to get airborne prematurely. Mimicking their behavior adds the necessary credibility to the angler's artificial that will cause trout to mistake it for a natural. Two practical patterns used to imitate these large duns are the parachute-style and Paradrake imitations, with the latter having the edge when dealing with selective trout.

The imagoes do not become active until dusk or the early hours of night. A Double Hen-Winged Spinner is an excellent artificial version of the natural that lands flush on the water to extrude its eggs.

Identification

Determining specimens of the burrowing or tusk-bearing types past the generic level is in most cases unnecessary, since usually only one species of each genera is dominant in the trout streams of a given area of the country. Furthermore, the species within each genus are almost identical to each other, thus precluding the necessity of carrying specific artificial patterns for each. Members of genus *Ephemera* are an exception; they produce two distinct hatches in the East, and the species differ in appearance, biology, and seasonal emergence. Those who wish to identify the species of a specimen are advised to consult the keys that are provided in Appendix II of this book.

The emergence of these large flies can indeed be one of the highlights of the fishing season and can even cause old lunkers to respond. The reader will notice, however, that when they first begin for the season, anglers will attain better results than after these flies have been emerging for a few days. The trout quickly become accustomed to the presence of these nymphs and begin to feed on them whenever

they are active and available, usually an hour before the actual hatch. As a direct result, the trout may already be stuffed with the nymphs and ignore the hatch when it actually takes place, to the bewilderment of anglers prepared for fishing action. It is to the angler's advantage to anticipate the seasonal occurrences of the particular species influential to his fishing and to begin to drift a nymph imitation before the daily emergences actually commence.

EASTERN AND MIDWESTERN HATCHES OF EPHEMERIDAE

The months of June and July, considered by most eastern and midwestern anglers as the midseason, signal the seasonal commencement of the large mayfly hatches. Eastern anglers can depend on the Green Drake (*E. guttulata*) and Yellow Drake (*E. varia*) emergences in most slow to moderate sections of their trout streams. In the meantime, midwesterners can expect the legendary hatches of the most important aquatic insect in that part of the country—*Hexagenia limbata*. The Yellow Drakes (*E. varia* and *Potamanthus myops*) also constitute important hatches for them.

About 7 p.m., anglers will begin to notice the conspicuous spinners of these large flies flying straight upstream. They are apparently only concerned with reaching some preconceived destination and are oblivious to the merciless attacks from winged predators. At dusk, nuptial flights and mating occur high above the stream, and occasionally some of the spinners descend to the water to rest momentarily. Anglers should not confuse this respite from the activity of mating for the actual fall of the spinners, which does not take place until almost nighttime. At such time, the spinners land flush on the water surface and wriggle their egg-filled abdomens to extrude the eggs into the water. When one stops to consider the time of day of these spinner falls, the size of the naturals, and their manner of ovipositing one can understand why they manage to entice the furious feeding of rapacious trout with such a marked degree of regularity.

Many of the species included in this chapter are already known to anglers; others, like *Ephemera varia*, have only recently received the notoriety they deserve. Species of genus *Ephoron* (*E. album* and *E. leukon*) remain to be discovered in more trout streams than are included here for the first time.

Great Lead-winged Drake (*Hexagenia limbata*)

H. limbata is the unquestionable king of this genus, producing the bulk of the Great Lead-winged Drake hatches in the Midwest that take place from the latter part of May through the month of June. Later in the season, its hatches are replaced by those of other *Hexagenias*, none of which approaches the density or importance of *H. limbata*. The species is genotypical of the six *Hexagenias* (and *Litobranchas*) found in North America.

In the Midwest, excellent populations of *H. limbata* exist in the slower stretches of streams and rivers of varied sizes as well as in most ponds, lakes, and reservoirs that maintain cool enough water temperatures throughout the year. The type of microhabitat in these waters is also an important factor that influences the distribution and abundance of these nymphs. Substrates of a soft, muddy character appear to be the most suitable for their propagation. The astute observer will notice the small holes made by these nymphs along the margins of streams that, at first glance, appear to be made by worms.

By no means does the Midwest have an absolute monopoly on *Hexagenias*, but the area does contain the most abundant populations that produce very dependable hatches. Penn's Creek, Bald Creek, and Falling Spring Run in Pennsylvania are known for their *Hexagenia* hatches, and Ernest Schwiebert reports them from Maryland streams like the Big Hunting and Antietam. My first encounters with these hatches were in the Fir Brook headwater section of the Willowemoc, the Muddy Brook inlet of Cranberry Lake in the Adirondacks, and some of the cold lakes in Baxter State Park in northern Maine. Western anglers have a slim chance to meet *Hexagenia* hatches for they are known to occur only in isolated localities. Flathead Lake in Montana, Hayden Lake in Idaho, and the San Joaquin and Sacramento River system of California support populations of these large critters. Its hatches are becoming a favorite among California fly fishers who frequent the bends of the Fall River. Last year, I also encountered a fair hatch in the upper Williamson of Oregon.

Expect *Hexagenia* hatches to commence at twilight, and their two- to three-hour hatches may continue through the early hours of the night. Fishing a nymph deep is the most effective approach, and occasionally raising it toward the surface will usually turn the odds in the fisherman's favor. During the hatch, the nymph to dun transformation is very fast, but, like most of the species discussed in this chapter, they may have some difficulty in leaving the water. At such times, the trout may aggressively respond to their flutterings, and anglers should then quickly make use of their dry fly imitations.

Only five *Hexagenia* species and one of genus *Litobrancha* (=*H. recurvata* has been assigned this genus because of the single gills on its first abdominal segment) are presently recognized by entomologists to exist in North American waters. *H. limbata* is the most abundant and widespread, its range extending from Maine to California and as far south as Texas. The eastern half of the country also contains other *Hexagenias* that emerge throughout the summer months. *L. recurvata* appears in May and June and accompanies the hatches of *H. limbata*. Another species, *H. atrocaudata*, follows it in the late-summer months of July and August. Both species are of local importance to eastern and midwestern anglers. *H. munda* (=*H. carolina* and =*H. malicanda*), on occasion, is significant to anglers who fish the streams and rivers of the Great Smokies, Cumberland, and Pocono mountains, though the range of this species encompasses most of the states east of the Mississippi River.

The density in which these large flies are found in trout streams, specifically those of the Midwest, is often incomprehensible; up to 500 nymphs have been known to inhabit a single, square-foot section of bottom substrate. Their size and concentrations are unbeatable, and, as a result, no other aquatic insect stands in the way of their eminent importance when they are emerging. Anglers should remember that within a short time after one of these hatches begins, the trout quickly become fully gorged with them, making it imperative for anglers to be totally prepared before it actually begins.

Hexagenia limbata Imitations

NATURAL	ARTIFICIAL

Streamlined Nymph*: Imitations for the elongated and large nymphs of *Hexagenia* and other burrowers in this chapter can be tied either in a single hook, the Streamlined Nymph, or a jointed, swiveling two-hook combination, the Wiggle Nymph. The hook required for both ties is given here.

NATURAL	ARTIFICIAL
SIZE: 22-35mm (a 27mm artificial is given here)	HOOK: *Streamlined:* Mustad 9672 #4 of the natural
TAILS: light olive brown	*Wiggle:* Abdomen—ring-eye hook cut to 15mm;
ABDOMEN: olive brown ringed with yellow bands; dark slate gills	Thorax—Mustad 3906 #12
	THREAD: tan monocord 3/0 (weighted with 1 amp lead wire)
THORAX: olive brown; mottled brown wing pads	
LEGS: light olive brown	TAILS: tan mini ostrich herl, three strands approximately

half the length of hook shank
ABDOMEN: olive brown dubbing blend and dark slate ostrich herl for gills tied down with fine gold wire
THORAX: olive brown dubbing, dark mottled turkey tail segment for wing cases
LEGS: light brown partridge hackle fibers

Paradrake*: Due to the large size of *Hexagenias* and other burrowers in this section, the optimal artificial pattern is one that floats well and is durable in construction. The Paradrake, which employs elk hair in its construction, is highly recommended. The lightest hook for its length is Mustad 94831. All dry fly imitations take into consideration the bottom coloration.

SIZE: 27mm
TAILS: black
BODY: olive brown
WINGS: dark gray or slate
LEGS: yellowish tan, slightly mottled

HOOK: Mustad 94831 #8 (shank equals only ⅔ total length of body of imitation)
THREAD: yellow monocord 3/0
TAILS: two dark moose hairs
BODY: olive brown dyed elk hair ribbed with yellow monocord 3/0 (tying thread)
WINGS: dark gray deer hair clump; a grizzly saddle hackle dyed yellowish tan tied around wing clump in parachute style for legs

Spinner*: The spinner activity of *Hexagenias* and all burrowers rivals, if not exceeds, the importance of their own hatches. The pattern given is for *Hexagenia* females.

SIZE: 27mm
TAILS: black
BODY: yellowish tan
WINGS: light dun, little pigmentation

HOOK: Mustad 94831 #4
THREAD: brown monocord 3/0
TAILS: two black moose hairs
BODY: yellowish tan dubbing ribbed with brown monocord 3/0 thread
WINGS: light dun hen body feathers tied spent; a few turns of a grizzly hackle dyed to yellowish tan for legs and clipped top and bottom is optional

*Most recommended

Eastern Green Drake *(E. guttulata)*

This June hatch is considered by many eastern anglers to be the climax of their fishing season. The time of the Gordon Quills, Hendricksons, Pale Evening Duns, and March Browns has either already expired for the year or is just about to. Only those of a sister species, such as morning *Ephemerellas* and late-season Tricos, are left to provide concentrated emergences of mayflies. This belief may be an exaggeration on their part, but it does contain a certain degree of validity. (See Fig. 9-3.)

Most fine-gravelled streams that run at a slow to medium tempo support good *E. guttulata* populations, but they are also found in good numbers in the flat pools of faster-running rivers. Their hatches are important only to fishermen who fish the trout waters of the Appalachian Range from Tennessee to New Hampshire.

Ephemera guttulata hatches take place at dusk and are rather brief, lasting from one to two hours. The nymphs are quick swimmers and, upon emergence, reach the surface of the water without unnecessary delay. Though the duns escape the nymphal shucks almost instantaneously, they customarily struggle for some time before finally getting airborne. This makes them a favorite with surface-feeding trout and with anglers hoping to fish successfully with dry flies. Spinner falls are at dusk, usually right after a hatch, and are often of equal importance to the angler as the hatch itself. The well-known Coffin Fly was designed to imitate the imago stage of *E. guttulata*.

It appears that the once stupendous Green Drake hatches of yesteryear will forever remain a memory because of pesticides, organic pollution, and the adverse effects of the clearing of forests along the margins of our trout streams. Nonetheless, excellent hatches are still to be enjoyed in many trout streams of Maryland, Pennsylvania, and New York. One evening last season, *E. guttulata* spinners were so numerous above a stretch of the Ausable River just above the town of Wilmington that their collective density obstructed much of the dwindling twilight from the surface of the stream. A similar spectacle occurred in the Schoharie the previous season. Many localities support Green Drake populations in numbers which still provide great sport for the same creatures who have carelessly caused this mayfly's general decline.

Ephemera guttulata Imitations

This mayfly species is prone to variations in color, ranging from pale cream to strongly olive brown. The patterns choose the coloration most common in the great majority of trout waters.

NATURAL	ARTIFICIAL

Streamlined Nymph: See comments under *H. limbata*.

SIZE: 17–20mm (an 18mm artificial is given here)
TAILS: dark brown
ABDOMEN: light olive brown; medium gray gills
THORAX: light olive brown; mottled dark brown wing pads
LEGS: light brown slightly marked

HOOK: *Streamlined*—Mustad 9672 #8; *Wiggle Abdomen*—ring-eye hook cut to 12mm length; *Thorax*—3906 #16 weighted with 1 amp lead wire
THREAD: tan monocord 3/0
TAILS: three mini ostrich herls of brownish coloration

ABDOMEN: light olive brown
dubbing blend and gray
ostrich herls ribbed with fine
gold wire

THORAX: light olive brown
dubbing, brown mottled
turkey tail segment for wing
cases

LEGS: light brown partridge
hackle fibers

Paradrake*:
SIZE: 18mm
TAILS: brown
BODY: pale cream
WINGS: mottled dark brown
and yellow
LEGS: mottled dark brown and
yellow

HOOK: Mustad 94831 #12
(hook shank constitutes only
⅔ total length of body of
imitation)

THREAD: olive monocord 3/0

TAILS: three brown or black
moose hairs

BODY: cream or tannish elk
hair ribbed with olive
monocord (tying thread)

WINGS: grayish brown deer
hair clump; grizzly hackle
dyed brownish olive tied at
base of clump in parachute
style for legs

Spinner*: Known popularly as the Coffin Fly.
SIZE: 18mm
TAILS: dark brown
BODY: pale cream
WINGS: translucent with dark
blotches

HOOK: Mustad 94831 #8

THREAD: yellow monocord 3/0

TAILS: three moose hairs

BODY: creamy white ribbed
with olive monocord thread

WINGS: light dun hen body
feathers tied spent,
preferably feather with any
kind of markings

*Most recommended

Yellow Drake (*Ephemera varia*)

This is a second *Ephemera* of consequence to those anglers who fish the waters that produce Green Drake hatches. They emerge from late June through the month of July and will preempt the importance of another summer mayfly emergence that may already be taking place.

E. varia is consistently a dusk emerger, and its brief hatches last about an hour. Like Green Drakes, Yellow Drakes also demonstrate difficulty in leaving the water and are compelled to ride the surface of the water for a long time before getting in flight or being seized by trout. The spinners return the following day after the hatch and materialize over the stream just before dark. They are so similar to the duns in size and color that anglers can usually manage without a special imitation for this stage. They only need to make the necessary modifications of the dry fly pattern to achieve the silhouette of the down-winged spinner.

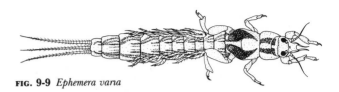

FIG. 9-9 *Ephemera varia*

Michigan waters like the White, Muskegon, Big Manistee, and AuSable rivers produce Yellow Drake hatches. This species appears to be more tolerant of high water temperatures than *E. guttulata*, and consequently, it is more geographically widespread. It is found in the lower-altitude sections of large eastern and midwestern rivers. In many waters it equals, or even surpasses, the abundance and importance of its sister species.

E. simulans is a third *Ephemera* that anglers who fish the waters east of the Mississippi waterway will find in their streams. Generally it is seldom found in sufficient numbers in trout streams to constitute a good hatch. The species, however, emerges in excellent numbers in midwestern lakes and in the smooth-flowing sections of some rivers, such as certain sections of the Delaware River (Hancock to Lordville) in New York. Brown Drakes, or *E. simulans*, are of primary importance to western anglers. For this reason I have placed it in that section and do not propose it as a hatch of *general* consequence to those who fish the waters on the opposite side of the country.

Ephemera varia (and related species) Imitations

E. varia is as often encountered as its sister species, *E. guttulata*; thus the following pattern which differs markedly from that recommended for the latter species is important. It simultaneously serves well for the hatches of *Potamanthus distinctus*, and the midwestern species, *Potamanthus myops*. Though, admittedly, it is slightly larger than that required for the hatches of yet another member of this family, *Ephoron album* or *leukon*, it is close enough in coloration to be adequate during their hatch-spinner fall combination. Dry fly patterns take into consideration only the coloration of the bottom side of the naturals.

NATURAL	ARTIFICIAL

Streamlined Nymph:
SIZE: 13–14mm
TAILS: pale cream
ABDOMEN: yellowish tan; light
brown gills
THORAX: yellowish tan; light
olive brown wing pads
LEGS: pale cream

HOOK: *Streamlined:* Mustad
9672 #12; *Wiggle:*
Abdomen—ring-eye hook
cut to approx. 9mm;
Thorax—7948A #16
weighted with 1 amp lead
wire

THREAD: cream prewaxed 6/0

TAILS: pale cream hen
pheasant feather fibers

ABDOMEN: yellowish tan
dubbing and light brown

ostrich herl ribbed with fine
gold wire

THORAX: yellowish tan fuzzy
dubbing, light brown hen
pheasant or turkey for wing
cases

LEGS: pale cream hen pheasant
feather fibers

Paradrake*:
SIZE: 13mm
TAILS: light olive brown,
barred
BODY: pale cream
WINGS: pale yellowish tan
LEGS: mottled brown and
yellow

HOOK: Mustad 94833 #14
(hook shank only constitutes
⅔ total length of imitation)
THREAD: yellow prewaxed 6/0
TAILS: light brown deer hairs
or moose hairs
BODY: pale cream elk or deer
hair
WINGS: creamish yellow deer
hair for wing clump; grizzly
hackle dyed yellow tied
around base of clump in
parachute style for legs

Spinner*:
SIZE: 13mm
TAILS: yellowish tan, barred
BODY: creamish white
WINGS: whitish with small
blotches

HOOK: Mustad 94831 #12
THREAD: beige prewaxed 6/0
TAILS: light ginger hackle
fibers
BODY: pale cream dubbing, no
ribbing
WINGS: speckled or marked
hen body feathers tied in
spent position

*Most recommended

Yellow Drake (Potamanthus distinctus)

The large, pale yellow flies of *Potamanthus* are evident during the months of July and August and are part of the midsummer aquatic fauna of trout streams. By far, the hatches of *P. distinctus* are the most common and important to eastern anglers, *P. myops* being the principal species in the Midwest. None are found in western waters. (See Fig. 9-4.)

Potamanthus are late-evening emergers. They often hatch with *Ephemera varia*, a very similar species in size and color, thus precluding the necessity for anglers to carry a specific artificial imitation to match this hatch.

White Drakes (Ephoron album and Ephoron leukon)

Ephoron hatches take place in the fall, during the months of September and October. Upon emergence, the nearly white duns form dense clouds over the water just before dark. Anglers familiar with these hatches feel they are just "too good" since the flies literally carpet the water, greatly reducing the possibilities of a trout picking their imitation among so many naturals. (See Fig. 9-5.)

The reader should bear in mind that populations of *Ephoron* are found only in certain localities, and few anglers have reason to be concerned with their hatches. To date, neither this nor any other angling author has been able to come up with a rational explanation for the reason for such a spotty distribution.

In case these flies exist in the waters the reader customarily fishes, look for their exciting hatches in the fall months and count on large fish becoming active during their evening hatch/spinner combination which barely lasts an hour.

WESTERN HATCHES OF EPHEMERIDAE

Comparatively speaking, the West has very few hatches of the burrowing mayflies. Of the three species found in this region, only one, *Ephemera simulans*, produces predictable and fishable emergences. The species is known to many anglers as the Brown Drake and emerges from meandering, smooth-flowing streams during the months of June and July in most Rocky Mountain states. *H. limbata*, the same species that produces the unexcelled Great Lead-Winged Drake hatches in the Midwest, is also found in western waters though only in certain lakes and river systems. As in the East, *Ephoron album* causes the concentrated White Drake hatches in the fall, but, in the West, they are indigenous to big, often unwadable rivers like the Missouri, Jefferson, and Yellowstone (below its junction with the Mussleshell River). The latter two mayflies are then of limited importance to westerners and have already been discussed in the preceding pages; however, *Ephemera simulans* or Brown Drake is an important western hatch and merits more elaboration.

FIG. 9-10 Brown Drake (actual size).

Brown Drake (*Ephemera simulans*)

The Brown Drakes cause impressive summer hatches in certain western waters and customarily begin to appear at the end of the seasonal cycle of the better known Green Drake (*Ephemerella grandis*). Occasionally the two species will be found emerging within a given day, but never at the same time. Consequently, they provide fly fishermen with a double opportunity at the good-sized trout that their hatches consistently manage to put into feeding action. (See Fig. 2-1k.)

E. simulans nymphs are indigenous to slow-moving, meandering streams of a fine-gravel substrate and margins of a soft character. The Big Hole (below the town of Melrose), Beaverhead, and Odell Creek of Montana are optimal waters for their populations, as are larger rivers like the Henry's Fork of the Snake River, Clark's Fork of the Columbia, and even the mighty Yellowstone River below Livingston.

Customarily *E. simulans* emerges for only three to four weeks during the season from late June to the middle of July, or when the water temperature permanently reaches the high 50's. Daily emergence is always in the evening about 8 p.m. (except for the very first hatches in their seasonal cycle). Nymphs are exceptionally fast swimmers and Brown Drake duns, unlike their eastern counterparts, leave the water surface almost instantaneously.

Spinner swarms begin to formulate in nearby woods around dusk, and their semicircular rotations occur but a few feet from the ground. At twilight, the males appear high over the stream and begin to descend into the swarms of waiting females, the connected pairs falling to the water surface before disjoining when females begin to oviposit their eggs. The actual fall of both sexes does not take place until just before or at nighttime.

During these hatches, trout will invariably prefer the nymphal stage over the dry form and after a hatch, though the contents of their stomachs may not contain a single dun, it is usually cramped with as many as 100 large Brown Drake nymphs. Anglers are advised to fish a nymphal imitation deep the hour *before* the actual hatch and, during actual emergence, work it a foot or two below the surface, bringing it up when it is within range of their objective.

Ephemera simulans Imitations

This mayfly is of principal importance in western waters, though it is often common and profuse in certain midwestern lakes and eastern rivers. In the West, it is confined to Rocky Mountain watersheds, while *Hexagenia limbata* is an important burrower and hatch in the Sierras and Cascade mountain ranges (see eastern section of this chapter for its artificial imitations). As in all burrowers, artifi-

cial imitations for their nymphs can be tied with the Streamlined or Wiggle tying procedures, and hook types and sizes are given for both nymph patterns. Dry fly patterns below take into consideration the bottom coloration of the natural.

NATURAL	ARTIFICIAL

Streamlined Nymph*:

SIZE: 17–20mm (an 18mm artificial is given here)
TAILS: light brown olive
ABDOMEN: light yellowish tan; gray gills
THORAX: light yellowish tan; mottled brown wing pads
LEGS: slightly mottled olive brown

HOOK: *Streamlined*—Mustad 9672 #8; *Wiggle* Abdomen—ring-eye hook cut to 12mm; Thorax—3906 #16 weighted with 1 amp lead wire
THREAD: tan monocord 3/0
TAILS: light brown mini ostrich herl fibers, three strands
ABDOMEN: light yellowish tan dubbing, and gray ostrich herls ribbed with fine gold wire
THORAX: light yellowish fuzzy dubbing blend, mottled brown turkey for wing cases
LEGS: grouse or partridge hackle fibers preferably of an olive brown coloration

Paradrake: This type of tie is the most practical and effective for the large duns of all burrowing mayflies.

SIZE: 18mm
TAILS: medium olive brown
BODY: yellowish tan
WINGS: mottled brown
LEGS: light olive brown, mottled

HOOK: Mustad 94831 #12 (hook shank should only constitute ⅔ total length of artificial or natural)
THREAD: brown monocord 3/0
TAILS: three moose hairs
BODY: elk hair dyed yellowish tan and ribbed with brown thread (tying thread)
WINGS: medium brown deer hair clump for wings; grizzly hackle dyed olive brown tied in parachute style at base for legs

Spinner*:

SIZE: 18mm
TAILS: dark brown
BODY: reddish tan
WINGS: light brown to tan, mottled

HOOK: Mustad 94831 #8
THREAD: tan monocord 3/0
TAILS: three moose hairs
BODY: reddish tan ribbed with brown monocord
WINGS: light tan hen body feathers or brown partridge tied in spent style

NOTE: No pattern is given here for the pale *Ephoron* species of importance in certain waters during the month of September because the artificial recommended for *H. simplicoides* in Chapter 6 is exactly what would be required for the hatch-spinner combination of *Ephorons* which also occurs in the fall.

*Most recommended

CHAPTER 10: All-Summer Hatches of Great Lead-Winged Coachmen and Gray Drakes (Family *Siphlonuridae*)

THIS family contains two types of mayflies that are important to the fly fisher throughout the entire second half of the fishing season, from late June through the month of September. They are large handsome flies known to anglers as Great Lead-Winged Coachmen and Gray Drakes, whose hatches are produced by genera *Isonychia* and *Siphlonurus*, respectively.

Isonychia and *Siphlonurus* are long and minnow-like in configuration in their nymphal stages and thus should be thought of as the large swimmers and represented by long and slender artificial imitations. A third type, *Ameletus*, is also occasionally found in trout streams, but its emergences do not in any manner compare with those of its sister genera. Its species have been undoubtedly misidentified by enough angling authors in their works to warrant some mention in this work. *Ameletus*, *Isonychias*, and *Siphlonurus* thrive in different types of waters and, consequently, not all three types will be found, or are of equal importance, in the same stretch of a trout stream. Moreover, each type is of greater importance on one side of the country than the other. *Isonychias* thrive in the East and Midwest, while the western states support impressive populations of *Siphlonurus*.

The large members of this family have traditionally been placed by angling authors with the tiny swimmers covered in Chapter 5 in this book. This is probably because of the resemblance between the two types in the basic configuration of their nymphs. However, the similarities end there; *Siphlonuridae* members differ in physical characteristics and, most importantly, in their manner of actual emergence.

The reader should bear in mind that the separation of mayfly families by entomologists takes into consideration not only morphological structure but also the common biology of their members. Unlike the tiny mayflies of *Baetidae*, the members of *Siphlonuridae* migrate en masse toward the margins of the water as they reach full maturity. Upon actual emergence, the nymphs will crawl out of the water, like stoneflies, before the duns escape the nymphal exoskeletons. Impressive collections of their discarded and empty nymphal shucks can often be seen just above the watermark on stones, logs, and other permanent, protruding fixtures in a stream containing their numbers. The implications of their unique biology will make these mayflies in the nymphal stage important to the fly fisher because the nymphs are perpetually on the move and available to trout. Only on occasion are they of significance as duns. In Chapter 1, this type of mayfly was used to illustrate how a little knowledge of the biology of a family type can be immensely helpful to the fly fisher.

Though *Siphlonuridae* mayflies are exemplified by sporadic emergences of up to two to three hours, their spinner flights are more dense in comparison and the imagoes fall on the water in great concentrations. The spinner activities of *Isonychias* and *Siphlonurus* take place at dusk. *Isonychias* are known as the White-Gloved Howdy in the spinner stage, and *Siphlonurus* as the Gray Drake Spinner. In typical fashion, the female will hover ten to twenty feet above the surface of the water and will drop down to the water to extrude a few eggs at a time. Occasionally, as is the case with *Isonychias*, their females may release the eggs from a distance above the water. Regardless of the manner of ovipositing, the fall of the spinners is inevitable, as is the frenzied feeding of trout on these large mayflies.

Identification

Nymphal stages of *Siphlonuridae* are conspicuously large and streamlined and exhibit other characteristics that serve well for streamside recognition. These will be pointed out below. Adults are two-tailed, like *Baetidae* members, but have, in addition, large visible hind wings, unlike the minute or entirely absent ones of *Baetidae* members.

FAMILY SIPHLONURIDAE

Genus Ameletus (*East, Midwest, and West: fair populations in certain localities*)

The nymphs and duns of *Ameletus* are most often confused with those of *Baetis*, and consequently, they have been offered as examples of this smaller mayfly in angling texts. *Ameletus* are markedly larger, and the distinction between its nymphs and those of *Baetidae* members is a routine matter once the angler knows what to look for. They thrive, often profusely, in the rapidly flowing headwaters of trout streams, whose shallow sections consist of a bottom substrate of pebbles and small rocks.

The identification of *Ameletus* nymphs is accomplished by determining their approximate size (10 to 12mm), which is a size between the small members of Family *Baetidae* and the larger ones of *Siphlonuridae*. Furthermore, the majority of their species found in eastern and western trout streams exhibit conspicuous color patterns on their abdomen, with one or more abdominal segments being pale cream in color. Their tails usually have a dark medium band. The bottom side of their abdomen (sternites) has a color pattern usually arranged in a manner that resembles three longitudinal stripes. Taxonomically, they are identified by entomologists by their oval, round gills which have a thin and conspicuous dark line near one or both of their margins.

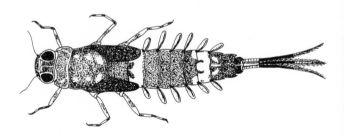

FIG. 10-2 *Ameletus* nymph

The dry forms of *Ameletus*, like all members of this family, have two tails. Those of *Ameletus* in particular exhibit a point or angulation on the fore margin of their hind wings, which serves to distinguish them from those of *Isonychias* and *Siphlonurus*. Duns of many species are dark blackish gray in general tone, and if a common name were to be given to them, the Dark Gray Quills would be the most appropriate.

In the East, *Ameletus ludens* produces fair to good hatches in many of the upper stretches of freestone rivers, especially those throughout central New York and Pennsylvania. Catskill streams like the Esopus and the West Branch of the Delaware have fair populations. Most hatches are in late spring during the late afternoon and are best on cloudy days.

Western waters contain better numbers of *Ameletus* by comparison. I have encountered fishable hatches of *Ameletus connectus* in Rock Creek, Bitterroot, and the Clark's Fork rivers of Montana, lower stretches of Henry's Fork in Idaho, and good hatches of *Ameletus sparsatus* in the Little Firehole in Yellowstone National Park. The most impressive hatch that I encountered during my research was on the Owens River near Bridgeport, California, where the widely distributed and large species *Ameletus velox* produced a good hatch during late May and early June two seasons ago. A second southwestern *Ameletus*, *A. validus*, emerges during September and October every afternoon. The Truckee River experiences sporadic emergences.

Ameletus species are not included here for the purpose of presenting them as a hatch of general consequence to all anglers, but simply to make the reader aware of their existence in trout streams. The frequency in which they are encountered makes *Ameletus* hatches of lesser importance. It is doubtful that they are profuse enough to warrant specific imitations on the part of anglers. In the majority of cases, their nymphs and duns are well duplicated by the artificials required for the much more important *Siphlonurus* hatches, which are certainly encountered more consistently. Eastern *Ameletus* happens to be well matched by the popular Gordon Quills recommended to imitate the abundant species of *Epeorus pleuralis*.

Genus Isonychia *(West: found in fair to good numbers only in certain localities; Midwest: abundant; East: abundant)*

Isonychia hatches are important to anglers on the eastern side of the country and to a lesser extent in the West. Their best numbers are supported by the faster sections of streams, their nymphs being strong swimmers and able to forage about in moderate- to fast-water environments. They are active and carnivorous mayflies, feeding on the minute larvas of midges and blackflies, as well as on the immature stages of other mayfly nymphs.

Isonychia nymphs are dark reddish-brown in color and usually exhibit a pale medium stripe along their backs, making them easy to be recognized at streamside even without the aid of a magnifying glass. However, the long hairs on the inner margin of their forelegs differentiate them taxonomically from the nymphs of all other mayflies. These long hairs serve as catching "baskets" for passing particles of food which the nymphs intercept drifting in the moving currents of their microhabitats. (See Fig. 1-2.)

Adults have two tails, are dark, and their middle and hind legs are distinctly pale. The latter characteristics make *Isonychias* perhaps the easiest mayfly duns and spinners to identify at streamside. Entomologists have utilized the distinctive bi-coloration of their legs to name the species. Dr. J. G. Needham classified the first *Isonychia* species as *I. albomanica*, meaning the white handed. The rounded foremargin of their hind wings separates them from those of *Ameletus*, and their dark reddish to purplish brown coloration from the Gray Drakes of *Siphlonurus*.

Eastern and midwestern trout streams are undoubtedly endowed with the best *Isonychia* populations found in North American waters. They are June to September emergers, with *I. sadleri* being the principal species and *I. bicolor* complementing its hatches throughout the season. The latter undoubtedly has been given much of the credit for hatches that in actuality are those of its more abundant sister species. Both of these species are late-afternoon to early-evening emergers, and their spinner flights always have their occurrence at dusk.

Generally speaking, western waters support poor populations of *Isonychias*—except the coastal rivers of the Pacific states like Oregon and California. In these steelhead waters, the claret-colored *I. velma* species produces fair hatches that cause up to "five-pounders" to feed on them during the summer and fall. Swifter stretches of rivers like the Chetco, Redwood, Pit, and Trinity rivers experience fair hatches. A second western *Isonychia* which I have also witnessed emerging is *I. sicca* (species divided into subspecies, *I. s. campetris* being one of them). Its geographical range encompasses the inland waterways of the West. Rivers like the lower Yellowstone in Montana support them, as do many of the large rivers that drain both sides of the Rockies all the way south to the Verde River in Arizona.

Isonychias, regardless of species, resemble each other closely in general appearance and size and exhibit a similar preference for the same type of habitats and general biology. All species will migrate toward the shallows prior to emergence, and the nymphs will leave the water before they hatch. Spinner flights take place 20 to 30 feet above the riffles, and many of the females will release their eggs from a distance above the water.

Isonychias are of principal significance to anglers on the eastern side of the country, and consequently, few western anglers need to be concerned with their hatches. However, the pattern suggested in this chapter for the important *I. sadleri* species would be the same needed by those anglers in the West who discover *Isonychia* populations in the streams they customarily frequent or who are in the habit of fishing the aforementioned western rivers.

Genus Siphlonurus *(West: common; Midwest: locally abundant; East: uncommon)*

Unlike *Isonychias*, the hatches and spinner falls of *Siphlonurus* are of principal importance to western anglers, and unlike *Isonychias* they occur in the slow to moderate stretches of large rivers and lakes, preferably those rich in aquatic vegetation. In weedy environments their nymphs are guaranteed natural hiding places and are less susceptible to predators. *Siphlonurus* nymphs also have a long seasonal duration—from June through September. Their hatches occur in the mornings, though their spinner falls again take place in the evenings as those of all genera in Family *Siphlonuridae*.

The most striking characteristics of *Siphlonurus* nymphs are their large size and grayish body, which is much paler than those of *Isonychias*. They lack the conspicuous long hairs on their inner margins, but in turn, exhibit large double gills with conspicuous branches or trachea. Their tails customarily have a dark brown band near their apex. Western species have striking coloration—rows of inverted horseshoe-shaped markings on the bottom or ventral side of their abdomen. (See Fig. 1-1, page 17.) *Siphlonurus* nymphs can only be confused with those of *Callibaetis*, which also inhabit the weedy, slow areas of rivers and lakes in the West. However, the short antennas in *Siphlonurus* nymphs are a dead giveaway for distinguishing them from those of the smaller ones of

FIG. 10-3 The Beaverkill River in New York—excellent habitat for the *Isonychia* hatch. *Photograph by Austin M. Francis.*

Callibaetis, who have antennas as long as half of their total body length.

The dry forms of *Siphlonurus* are two-tailed and conspicuously long and slender. Most of their species preserve much of the striking color patterns from the nymphal stage, and in conjunction with their large size, they stand as a unique type among the mayfly order.

In the East and Midwest, *Siphlonurus* are only of local significance, and waters that afford them slow-flowing currents rich in aquatic vegetation often support their population. The AuSable and Saranac rivers of New York have fair to good hatches of *S. quebencis*, which emerge from mid-June to August, as do those in the Battenkill and Otter in Vermont. Many Pennsylvania waters are reported to contain them, though I have never encountered *Siphlonurus* hatches in the streams in that state. The Lower Tomorrow River in Wisconsin produces good fishable and dependable hatches during the latter part of June, and in typical *Siphlonurus* fashion they occur in the morning or early afternoon, with spinner falls in the evening. It should be remembered that *Siphlonurus* emergences on the eastern side of the country often coincide with those of the more abundant *Stenonemas* that closely resemble their color in the spinner stage, and preclude the need for specific artificial patterns for their spinner falls. If the reader suspects that he may require a more exacting imitation for locally important spinner falls of *S. quebencis* or *S. alternatus*, the artificial suggested for the common western species *S. occidentalis* is a nearly exact imitation for its eastern counterparts.

The West, in comparison, has a virtual monopoly of *Siphlonurus* populations, and excellent numbers of the abundant and widespread species *S. occidentalis* and *S. columbianus* are found from the trout streams of the Black Hills of South Dakota to those of California. Their importance is, of course, as all the generic types covered in this chapter, in the nymphal and spinner stages. These two *Siphlonurus* species will be covered in more detail in the pages that follow.

Fishing Approach and Artificial Imitation

The general biology of these mayflies, the fact that they will migrate prior to actual emergence and will leave their aquatic habitat before their duns will emerge out of their nymphs, has many implications on the approach that anglers should adopt in fishing their hatches. Both *Isonychia* and *Siphlonurus* are large species, and their nymphal stages are best imitated by slender, streamer-like artificials, referred to in this work as the Streamlined Nymphs. When fishing these patterns the approach should be one of making the

cast three-quarters upstream, allowing them to sink to the bottom before starting to work them with eight- to ten-inch sudden retrieves toward the shore. The naturals of *Isonychia* and *Siphlonurus* nymphs are perpetually on a mini-exodus toward the bank during summer months, and anglers aware of this biology stand to do well with opportunistic trout capitalizing on the nymphal migration.

Hatches of *Siphlonuridae* are not as important as the spinner falls of its members for no other reason than if all goes as planned by nature, the duns will not escape the nymphs while they are still in the water. However, exceptions will inevitably occur, such as during unusually high-water conditions when the duns will involuntarily have to escape the nymphs while they are still riding the surface film. At such times, imitations for the dun stages are applicable. Exceptionally windy weather also causes the duns clinging to the streamside vegetation, rocks, and logs along the margins of streams to be blown onto the water. Moreover, some rivers have steep banks lacking boulders and do not provide natural emergence sites for the nymphs. The nymphs often exhibit an emergence that deviates from the more customary ones of Family *Siphlonuridae*. Whatever the reasons, the duns of *Isonychias* and *Siphlonurus* are occasionally of importance to the fly fisher, and no better pattern probably exists for mayflies of such large size than the Paradrake (also recommended for the species in the last chapter). It is a very buoyant imitation, well suited for the types of water that support *Isonychias*. It

FIG. 10-4 Weedy margins of slow-flowing rivers and cold lakes are optimally suited for the propagation of *Siphlonurus* nymphs.

is also a very credible artificial in the placid, clear-water environment where *Siphlonurus* hatches usually take place, a type of ambient where trout can afford to study closely what the angler is offering them as an alternative to the natural.

The spinner forms of both types occur at dusk, and their large imagoes are welcomed by the trout. The Hen-Winged spinner type is the most practical and effective artificial to fish the concentrated falls of their spinners.

EASTERN AND MIDWESTERN HATCHES OF ISONYCHIA

As said before, most of the hatches of *Isonychias* in the East and Midwest are, in all likelihood, those of *I. sadleri*, though historically *I. bicolor* has received most of the credit for the emergences of its sister species. (See Fig. 1-2, page 17.) The majority of *Isonychia* hatches take place during the months between June and September, with the best hatches occurring at the very beginning and end of their seasonal cycle. Daily occurrences are from late afternoon to evening. The seasonal commencement of their hatches is signaled by the collections of their dried-out shucks that can be seen just above the water level on the rocks along the margins of streams.

Spinner flights are at dusk, and their swarms will occur high above the stream. Eventually groups of females will come down within five to ten feet above the water and perpetually drop down, barely touching the water, to extrude a few eggs at a time. Both sexes will fall spent by nightfall with trout responding to them eagerly.

The differentiation of *I. sadleri* nymphs from those of its sister species *I. bicolor*, which also accompanies it during the very beginning of the *Isonychia* seasonal cycle, is accomplished by detecting to what extent their dorsal pale stripes extend along the body. *I. sadleri* nymphs usually exhibit a stripe along their entire body, while those of *I. bicolor* will be found on the head, thorax, and only on the first few abdominal segments. This characteristic is only a general one for streamside identification, but it often proves to be unreliable for a precise determination of the species.

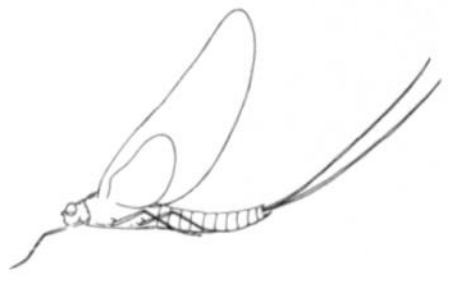

FIG. 10-5 *Isonychia* dun (actual SIZE).

During the fall, the hatches of *I. sadleri* will be replaced by those of *I. harperi*, a species that produces good hatches during the months of September and October in many eastern trout streams. They will emerge at midday in the open currents of the stream. The artificial nymph given below works superbly during their hatches.

Isonychia sadleri (and related species) Imitations

NATURAL	ARTIFICIAL
Streamlined Nymph*: Weighted version to be used during non-hatch periods and fished deep.	
SIZE: 15mm	HOOK: Mustad 3906 #8 or 9671 #10 weighted with 1 amp lead wire
TAILS: light reddish, banded	THREAD: brown monocord 3/0
ABDOMEN: dark reddish brown; gills purplish brown	TAILS: dark brown hen pheasant feather fibers, banded
THORAX: dark reddish brown; black wing pads	ABDOMEN: dark reddish brown dubbing, purplish brown ostrich herl for gills ribbed with fine gold wire
LEGS: heavily mottled brown and yellow	THORAX: dark reddish brown dubbing, black goose quill segment for wing cases
	LEGS: brown partridge hackle fibers
Paradrake:	
SIZE: 15mm	HOOK: Mustad 94833 #12 (hook shank constitutes only ⅗ total length of imitation)
TAILS: dark brown	THREAD: brown monocord 3/0
BODY: medium reddish brown	TAILS: three moose hairs
WINGS: dark slate	BODY: medium grayish brown elk hair ribbed with brown tying thread
LEGS: reddish brown (forelegs)	WINGS: dark slate or gray deer hair for wing clump; reddish hackle tied around clump in parachute style for legs
Spinner*:	
SIZE: 15mm	HOOK: Mustad 94833 #8
TAILS: medium gray	THREAD: brown monocord 3/0
BODY: dark reddish brown	TAILS: light dun hackle fibers
WINGS: translucent (hyaline)	BODY: dark reddish brown dubbing ribbed with brown monocord
	WINGS: light dun hen-hackle tips tied in spent position

*Most recommended

WESTERN HATCHES OF SIPHLONURUS

Siphlonurus occidentalis is the omnipresent *Siphlonurus* of western waters, an impressive mayfly that produces dependable spinner falls during the months of July to

September. It is one of the few large mayflies found in the West and along with *E. grandis*, *H. limbata*, and *E. simulans* makes up the four members of the big mayfly group. (See Fig. 1-3.)

Siphlonurus occidentalis nymphs, and those of related species *S. columbianus*, thrive in excellent numbers in the slow, weedy margins of barely moving rivers as well as in lakes, ponds, and reservoirs rich in aquatic vegetation. Some western rivers that produce their hatches are: the Bitterroot, Big Hole, Yellowstone, Hebgen Reservoir, Henry's Fork of the Snake River in Idaho, South Platte in Colorado, and upper Sacramento in California. Other species like *S. spectabilis* will supplant their importance along the Pacific states; however, *S. occidentalis* is neotypical of all *Siphlonurus* found in western waters, and the recommended pattern is a very exacting one for all western *Siphlonurus* species.

FIG. **10-6** *Siphlonurus* dun (actual size).

Though the seasonal emergence of *S. occidentalis* encompasses the summer months, its importance to anglers surges during the fall months when their populations reach a peak at a time of the fishing season when there is little competition for the trout's attention from the hatches or spinner falls of other mayflies. During such times, daily occurrences are from late morning to early afternoon. Prior to the 11 o'clock hatch, an artificial nymph cast close to the bank, allowed to sink to the bottom and retrieved approximately a foot, and then allowed to settle again to the bottom is a very effective approach. This will deceive good-sized trout that forage for these nymphs close to the shore. The actual hatch, however, often proves to be of little value to the angler; on the other hand, the evening spinner falls are excellent producers by comparison.

Species differentiation is really unnecessary, for the majority of *Siphlonurus* are quite identical in general appearance among each other, overlap in seasonal emergence, and the great majority of their emergence is caused by the single species *S. occidentalis*.

Siphlonurus occidentalis (and related species) Imitations

The following imitations serve very well to match the hatches of other *Siphlonurus* species found in western waters, as well as some of the larger *Ameletus* which frequent many of the Sierra and Cascade trout streams of California.

NATURAL	ARTIFICIAL
Streamlined Nymph*:	
SIZE: 15mm	HOOK: Mustad 3906B #8 or 9671 #10 weighted with 1 amp lead wire
TAILS: grayish, unbanded	
ABDOMEN: tannish gray; light gray gills	THREAD: gray monocord 3/0
THORAX: tannish gray; dark slate wing pads	TAILS: three gray mini ostrich herls
LEGS: mottled gray	ABDOMEN: tannish gray dubbing, with gray ostrich herl fibers for gill and ribbed with brown monocord
	THORAX: tannish gray dubbing or gray peacock herl; barred mallard flank dyed dark gray for wing cases
	LEGS: dark gray partridge hackle
Paradrake: *S. occidentalis* in its dun stage is of limited value; this is an optional pattern.	
SIZE: 15mm	HOOK: Mustad 94833 #12 (hook shank constitutes only ⅔ of total length of imitation)
TAILS: medium gray	
BODY: medium gray	
WINGS: gray	THREAD: brown monocord 3/0
LEGS: medium gray, slightly mottled	TAILS: medium gray moose hairs
	BODY: medium gray elk hair ribbed with brown monocord 3/0
	WINGS: gray deer hair clump for wings; grizzly tied around clump in parachute style for legs
Spinner*: Represents the most important stage of *Siphlonurus* species.	
SIZE: 15mm	HOOK: Mustad 94833 #8
TAILS: gray	THREAD: gray monocord 3/0
BODY: dark reddish gray	TAILS: medium gray hackle fibers
WINGS: translucent (hyaline)	BODY: dark reddish gray dubbing ribbed with brown monocord
	WINGS: light or pale dun hen-hackle feathers tied in spent style

*Most recommended

CHAPTER 11: The Late-Season Tiny White-Winged Tricos and *Caenis* Flies (Families *Tricorythidae* and *Caenidae*)

THE members of these two closely related families are important to all anglers during the summer months when the emergences of larger aquatic insects are either already in full progress or, in many cases, have expired for the season. Their species are extremely small; in fact, they are the smallest mayflies found in North American waters. Whatever they lack in size, however, they certainly make up for in numbers, since during their emergence and more specifically during their spinner falls, they can literally carpet a stretch of water. Their impressive density has caused entomologists to refer to them as the "Snowflake Mayflies," and fly fishers from both sides of the Atlantic to call them "angler's curse." Regardless of the description, the spinner falls of these little mayflies are of great significance to the sport of fly fishers and are synonymous with good-sized though very selective trout.

Of the three types constituting these two mayfly families (*Tricorythodes*, *Caenis*, and *Brachycersus*), by far the hatches and spinner falls caused by the "Tricos" are the most important and are commonly known as the White-Winged Blacks to anglers. They thrive in a wide variety of trout waters varying greatly in dimension and composition, though the little nymphs are found most profusely in any trout stream microhabitat that offers them a thin cap of silt along the bottom as of midsummer. Good examples of Trico waters are the tail ends of large pools of freestone rivers and meandering limestone or western spring creeks. *Caenis* is of limited importance to anglers; however, when encountered, it can parallel the intensity and the importance of its sister genus. In general, *Caenis* nymphs are indigenous to more silted and warmer environments which are often inhospitable to any species of trout. *Brachycersus* is only occasionally of

consequence to fly fishermen, since of the three types it is the one that gravitates toward the warmest and most stagnant aquatic environment.

FIG. 11-1 Male *Trichorythodes* spinners descending from streamside flora to gather into swarms.

116

FIG. 11-2 The most effective way to fish a heavy hatch is straight upstream, placing the fly a few inches upstream from a rising trout.

FIG. 11-3 Female spinner in flight still with dun exoskeleton attached to its abdomen.

The biology of these mayflies is unique and a true exception to that of any other type of mayfly. In the case of Tricos, the males will emerge throughout the night and the females during the early hours of morning. Yet both sexes will have molted into spinners by nine o'clock in the morning, and mating will begin soon after. Within the hour they will form into low-flying "clouds," and the spent males will have literally covered the surface of the water with their bodies. This latter stage is the one of principal importance to the fly fisher, for it is when these little mayflies will attain their greatest concentration, providing the necessary impact to set tro' on a feeding activity. *Caenis* mayflies also exhibit a similar biology, though in their case, emergence and spinner activity take place in the evening. Before the spinner falls of both types, anglers will be pre-warned of their impending availability on the water by their obvious formations just over the banks. From far away they resemble a slow-moving white cloud of dust.

In most angling texts, the repeated claim is made that the transition from dun to spinner by these little mayflies takes place in the air. I, myself, have witnessed their veil-like dun exoskeletons descending from their spinner swarms. The mechanics of a dun metamorphosing to a spinner would undoubtedly require that it must do so at rest and certainly before heading to join mating companions, as is the case with all other mayflies. However, it is quite apparent

that, in the case of *Tricorythodes*, the females—that emerge hours after the males—often take flight prematurely. Before they become fully detached from the dun exoskeleton, they join the awaiting males with it still trailing from their abdomens. Eventually, the dun veil will detach itself and fall gently toward the surface, causing the streamside observer to believe they have indeed molted in the air. When considering the physical mechanics that all mayflies must undergo to slip out of one and then another wing to become spinners, the fact that members of these two families can do so *in the air* is obviously a physical impossibility.

Streamside identification of these little mayflies is difficult to accomplish with the naked eye because even when their nymphs are mature they approach only three to seven millimeters in length or No. 20 to No. 28 hook sizes. With the aid of a ten-power hand lens, those of all three types can be identified as to genus more easily. They exhibit conspicuous enlarged abdominal gills on their second segment which are either triangular or square in shape. As explained in Chapter 3, the physical characteristic of an enlarged protective gill is an important one for survival in all mayflies that are sprawlers in silted microhabitats. It acts as a protective shield to prevent those gills on segments 3 to 7 from choking on the fine particles of silt that are perpetually settling to the bottom in their basically currentless environment. Other mayflies exhibit a similar adaptation. The best examples are *Ephemerella simplex*, the Small Blue-Winged Olive of eastern states, and *Ephemerella hecuba*, the large western species that produces sporadic hatches of Large Western Dark Hendricksons in slightly silted meandering streams throughout the Pacific Northwest and Rockies.

Dry forms of these mayflies have three tails and a single pair of wings conspicuously oversize in comparison to their body. The wing coloration lacks discernible pigmentation, and thus, even as duns, they appear at first glance to have already molted into spinners. In the latter stage, which is most important to the fly fisher, Tricos have a black to gray body coloration, and *Caenis* are mahogany to tan.

Of the three kinds of mayflies constituting families *Tricorythidae* and *Caenidae*, the members of the former family are the most important to trout anglers for no other reason than that they are indigenous to a cool, clean-water environment, ideally suited to support species of trout. The three are now discussed in more detail in the order of their preference for water quality; this happens to coincide with their order of importance to the trout angler.

FAMILY TRICORYTHIDAE

Genus Tricorythodes

Tricos are indigenous to a clean-water environment and cause excellent fishing activity in eastern, midwestern, and western trout waters during the months of July through September, with the morning spinner falls often producing some of the best results of the season. Their principal importance, as well as all the types given here, is in the spinner stage.

Nymphs of *Tricorythodes* are differentiated by their enlarged triangular-shaped gills, unlike those of *Caenis* and *Brachycersus*. Its nymphs are short and robust and are of a beige-to-tan color, except for the conspicuous black wing pads on mature nymphs. Some species exhibit thin black lines running laterally on their abdomen. (See Fig. 2-1o.)

Trico duns exhibit the same dissimilarities among the sexes as do the males and females of Family *Ephemerellidae*, which are closely allied to *Tricorythidae*. Males have whitish-tan bodies often with minute black lateral markings on their abdominal segments. Females exhibit the *Ephemerella*-like olive tones and likewise are markedly larger than their respective mates. The differences between the two often cause

anglers at streamside to presume they are seeing two different species emerging simultaneously. Spinner forms of Tricos are commonly referred to as Tiny White-Winged Blacks, the males having black bodies though the females are grayish in general tone.

The biology of *Tricorythodes* is quite unlike that exhibited by any other mayfly. The males emerge throughout the night, and the females in the early hours of morning. Both sexes are ready to mate and fall spent on the water about ten o'clock. However, after mating, females must first return to the streamside flora to "pump" their fertilized eggs out of their abdomen into a ball which they carry at the base of their abdomen when in flight. They follow the falls of the spent males by approximately half an hour.

Most *Tricorythodes* species resemble each other very closely throughout the country, and few differences among them are noticeable. Eastern Trico activity is produced by *T. minutus* in the waters from the Maritime Provinces south to Tennessee. In that part of the country, their spinner falls occur between eight and ten o'clock in the morning, with their size ranging between No. 22 and No. 24 hook sizes. Midwestern species *T. stygiatus* and *T. stratus* also barely reach a No. 24 hook size. Western waters support excellent populations of *T. minutus* nymphs, but in that half of the country they are conspicuously larger than their eastern brethren. Of the samples collected for this work, 142 hatches of this common species were encountered over six years and exhibited an incredible size deviation—from 3mm to 8mm. Hook sizes of No. 18 to No. 20 approximate the average size of the great majority of collected naturals. Their excellent spin-

FIG. 11-4 Good Trico waters— the Firehole in Yellowstone National Park.

FIG. 11-5 Belly tube fishing for trout during spinner falls of *Tricorythodes* in a western lake.

ner falls were met in many trout waters from the Black Hills in South Dakota to the coastal rivers of California, their range extending south well into Mexico. Most western Trico hatches are caused by *T. minutus*. Species like *T. fallax*, *T. explicatus*, and *T. fallacina*, which have been included in angling texts as separate species, are tentatively considered by entomologists as species synonymous with *T. minutus*.

FAMILY CAENIDAE

Genus Caenis

Caenis nymphs are indigenous to warmer and slower waters than those of Tricos, though their population range in a given river system occasionally overlaps that of its sister genus. They are evening emergers, and when found in stretches that also support Tricos they offer a second chance for fly fishers to connect with the "Snowflake Mayflies." They are all but omnipresent in lakes, ponds, and sluggish areas. They also can be found in the dead-flow sections of large rivers whose bottom substrate consists of liberal deposits of silt—similar types of water that also support and produce the thick hatches of such other warm-water mayflies as *Ephoron*, *Centroptilums*, and *Traverellas*. However, generally speaking, these mayflies are of limited importance to the average angler. Only in marginal areas where the nymphal populations and the range of trout coincide are they of significance. In such circumstances there will be a rare combination of good-sized browns and other fish rising enthusiastically to

these sulphur-colored mayflies that upon emergence can carpet the surface of the water.

Caenis nymphs are separated from those of *Tricorythodes* by their square-shaped second gills, unlike the triangular one found on Tricos. They are often even smaller in size than the latter type; however, with a ten-power hand lens the differentiation between the two is rather simple.

Dry forms of *Caenis* also exhibit the clear hyaline wings in all stages and a single pair of wings. Their coloration is markedly more pale than those of Tricos, ranging between brown and tan, depending on species.

C. simulans is the species of this genus most often found in North American trout waters, and its range encompasses the entire country from Maine to California south to Mexico. In the East and Midwest, it precedes the hatches of Tricos, making its seasonal appearance during the month of June and often lasting sporadically until August. The Ausable River in New York and the Battenkill in Vermont produce fair to good hatches. Western waters like the lower Hat Creek (Burney) and upper Sacramento (Dunsmuir) offer fair hatches for California anglers.

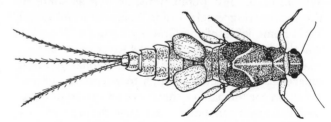

FIG. 11-6 *Caenis simulans* nymph

The importance of *Caenis* does not compare to that of the much more common and widespread *Tricorythodes*. Therefore, it is questionable whether anglers, in general, have need for a specific artificial pattern to match their infrequent hatches. In case *Caenis* prove to be of significance to the reader, he is strongly advised to prepare himself with the patterns suggested. The minute size of these mayflies is the quickest way that trout can make a distinction between the tiny natural and the overly big pattern that unaware anglers tempt trout with during their spinner falls.

Genus Brachycersus

Brachycersus is even more limited in its significance to anglers, preferring environments that may be unable to support trout. Its general biology resembles that of Tricos, which also emerges in the morning.

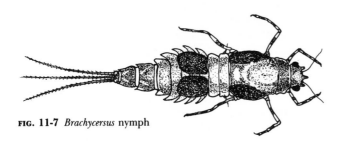

FIG. 11-7 *Brachycersus* nymph

Brachycersus nymphs are quite conspicuous by their square gills in conjunction with the three prominent projections in the shape of a little crown that they exhibit on their heads. When collected in the streams they will move about very slowly and hold their tails over their abdomen like miniature scorpions. Their general configuration is slightly more slender than *Tricorythodes* or *Caenis* nymphs. Mature specimens are very dark in color.

Brachycersus has constituted a very small percentage of the hatches that I have encountered throughout the years. The Macan and Kinnickinnick rivers o Wisconsin support populations, as well as some of the meandering creeks inside Yellowstone National Park. Some lakes of the Gravelly Range in Montana and the main branch of the Snake River near Payette, Idaho, also produce their hatches. None of these emergences was dense enough to warrant a specific imitation for them since they were so sparse in numbers that trout remained unselective during their actual emergence or spinner falls.

EASTERN, MIDWESTERN AND WESTERN HATCHES OF TRICORYTHODES

Fishing *Tricorythodes* imitations is a demanding game and perhaps no other mayfly will necessitate implementing the concepts of presentation covered in Chapter 4 to the degree in which their dense spinner falls will. The streamside scenario is customarily one of fishing to rising trout. They are either feeding in place as is the case in waters with natural drift lanes or cruising about and rising in a nearly predictable pattern, consuming as many as ten naturals with each gulp. The waters are usually crystal clear. In order to attain exact deliveries at the right time and place, close positioning should be accomplished through careful wading and by keeping a low profile. The trick is to intercept rising trout in place or in time and forget about trying to attract them. Light fly lines, long leaders, and fine tippets in the 6 to 8X range will also contribute decidedly. Regardless of the circumstances, the spinner falls of these little mayflies demand the best in anglers, and those individuals who may feel that any artificial or approach will do are destined for disappointment.

In western lakes, Tricos are producers of some impressive catches. In such habitats, Westerners choose to fish their spinner falls from belly tubes, which allow them to get close to their targets and to maneuver about in order to intercept schools of cruising, surface-feeding trout.

T. minutus is neotypical of the *Tricorythodes* species found in North American trout waters. With the exception of size, its artificial pattern will do very well during the hatches and spinner falls caused by other species found in different parts of the country. The two optimal patterns for it are the No-Hackle and Hen-Winged Spinner. Both artificials are the most credible at a time of the season when the waters are clear and as smooth as glass, and when trout are already well aware of the presence and treachery of anglers for the season.

Tricorythodes Imitations

No pattern is offered here for the nymph since hatches of *Tricorythodes* take place so early in the morning as to be of little practical value to the angler. The No-Hackle imitation takes into consideration the coloration and size of the female which will often be found emerging sporadically up to an hour before the important morning spinner flights of *Tricorythodes*. The spinner artificial, on the other hand, is specifically designed for the sizes and colors of the *males* which customarily fall all at once and serve to put trout on a feeding activity.

NATURAL | ARTIFICIAL

No-Hackle Dun:

SIZE: 4mm (East and Midwest), 6mm (West)
TAILS: pale gray
ABDOMEN: grayish olive
THORAX: grayish brown
WINGS: pale slate or whitish gray, slightly longer than body length

HOOK: Mustad 94859 #22, 94833 #20, respectively
THREAD: olive prewaxed 6/0
TAILS: light dun hackle fibers
ABDOMEN: grayish olive dubbing
THORAX: grayish brown dubbing
WINGS: pale dun mallard quill segments, or post of light dun poly in an upright position

Spinner*:

SIZE: 4mm (East and Midwest), 6mm (West)
TAILS: dark gray
BODY: dark gray, almost black
WINGS: translucent (hyaline)

HOOK: Mustad 94859 #22, 94833 #20, respectively
THREAD: black prewaxed 6/0
TAILS: dark dun hackle fibers
BODY: very dark gray dubbing
WINGS: light dun hen-hackle feather tips

In those localities of the country in which *Caenis* are known to cause good and dependable spinner falls, the following pattern may make the difference between success and total failure. The main problem and principal concern of anglers in tackling their spinner activity is to offer the trout an artificial tiny enough to approximate the size of these minute mayflies.

Caenis spinner*:

SIZE: 3mm
TAILS: whitish
BODY: tannish
WINGS: translucent (hyaline)

HOOK: Mustad 94859 #26
THREAD: tan prewaxed 6/0
TAILS: pale dun hackle fibers
BODY: pale cream or light tan dubbing
WINGS: very pale gray hen-hackle feather tips or light dun fibers of dubbing, tied extremely thin

*Most recommended

FIG. 11-8 Tiny White-Winged Black (actual size).

APPENDIX I: Fly Tying Instructions

IT is often difficult to attain a level of proficiency in all aspects of fly fishing simultaneously. I would be less than candid if I did not admit that my greatest limitation in fly fishing lies in the art of fly tying. Fortunately, I befriended Mike Lawson a few years ago, before he began his own fly shop in Last Chance, Idaho, on the very banks of Henrys Fork of the Snake River. We have not only become good friends throughout the years, but with time I have come to realize that Mike has outright genuine ideas and innovations that the fly fishing fraternity, up to now, have been deprived of. I consider him an asset to this book, and hope that the reader will recognize his expertise and make full use of his instructions and recommendations concerning fly tying.

Mike's philosophy of imitation and fly tying is a simple yet perceptive one. Anglers should use materials that are readily available and of affordable quality. They should also employ only materials whose texture gives *movement* to their artificials, since they are intended to imitate the structural qualities of a *living* insect. Lastly, artificial imitations should not just match the size and color of a natural but also its configuration. The latter is best accomplished through the employment of specific fly-tying procedures for each type of mayfly. Since all mayflies are not similar in shape and size and do not thrive in identical types of waters, no single pattern will suffice to imitate their numbers in general. The patterns recommended here, then, are based on the biological and emergence realities discussed in the previous family chapters.

As pointed out numerous times throughout this book, the members composing *each* family or "type" of mayfly exhibit common structural similarities and biological tendencies and thus are best imitated with the same kind of artificial imitation. Optimally, it should be one that imitates the most vulnerable stage of their emergence, *and* it also should be of a construction best suited for the type of water environment in which they are found. Good examples are the Floating Nymph artificial for members of Family *Baetidae* (composed of *Baetis*, *Pseudocloeon*, and *Callibaetis* species) and the Emerging Dun which is a killing pattern during all *Ephemerella* hatches. In so far as construction is concerned, the Paradrake is not only a buoyant artificial well suited for the type of waters in which the large *Isonychias* will be found, but also an extremely deceptive pattern to handle picky trout during the hatches of the big burrowing mayflies.

In some cases, options as to hook types are offered to the reader, for instance, in the case of the Conventional Nymph. The heavy-hook version tied in Mustad 3906B is designed to be fished deep *before* the hatch. A second type, employing a dry fly hook, is designed to cause the artificial nymph to float at or near the surface. Two distinct types of tying procedures are given for the nymphs of the burrowing mayflies— the Streamlined and Wiggle nymph patterns—and the choice of the reader between the two is, of course, a matter of personal preference.

Size is one of the most important aspects of an effective imitation. The exact measurement of small insects, such as mayflies, is not accomplished by reference to hook sizes but to the millimeter system of measurement. It's a simpler and more precise system and one which all anglers will undoubtedly prefer once they become acquainted with its rationale. However, to those not yet accustomed to it, it may at first prove vague and confusing. This is probably why most past angling authors have avoided it and have utilized hook sizes to convey the sizes of the naturals in their coverage. Unfortunately, a system utilizing hook sizes as a reference can be detrimentally inexact

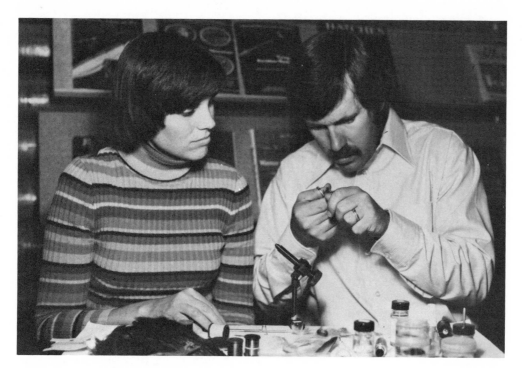

Mike and Sheralee Lawson,
of Henry's Fork Anglers

and can undermine the very purpose of exact imitation. For example, a hook size of No.16 in Mustad hook style 7948A is 6mm, while type 9671—another very popularly used hook—is 9mm, exactly one-third larger. When comparing the two lengths for a given hook type, this would be a two hook-size difference, a Mustad 7948A not reaching a length of 9mm until one is picked of that type in a No.12 hook size. Because of the inexactness and inconsistency of hook-type numbers and styles, a chart is provided at the end of this section. It will enable the reader to make the correct size substitutions if he does not own the hook types recommended in the fly tying procedures given under each "super species" throughout this book.

I have asked Mike to list the five most common mistakes made by beginners when they first tie their own flies. He reminds me, however, that on many occasions he finds that he also makes some of them himself.

1. Do not clamp the barb of the hook in the vise since that will weaken it.
2. Use the smallest size thread possible; size 6/0 will suffice for most imitations.
3. When dubbing bodies, use *only* the amount needed to achieve a neatly tapered body.
4. Always leave plenty of room for a neatly tapered and well-finished head.

5. While constructing a fly, avoid excessive turns of thread; a uniformly and firmly applied pressure on two turns is better than ten turns applied loosely and in an arbitrary fashion.

All hook-style numbers given here are of Mustad brand, unless otherwise noted.

NYMPH PROCEDURES

The pre-blended, synthetic materials available on the market today are quite adequate for tying and imitating the bodies of the natural nymphs; however, for optimal *translucency*, a ⅓ seal, ⅓ acrylic Orlon wool yarn, and ⅓ soft natural fur, such as Australian opossum, mixed to attain the color recommended under the nymphs of the principal species is superior to that of an all-synthetic composition.

Conventional Nymph
Family Baetidae (Chapter 5)
Family Leptophlebiidae (Chapter 7)
Family Ephemerellidae (Chapter 8)

These nymphs are tied on hook type 94840 and are designed to be fished during the hatches either on the surface or just under the surface film. A heavier hook version, tied on 3906, would be more appropriate for an imitation to be fished deep, close to the holding places of trout, and *before* the hatch.

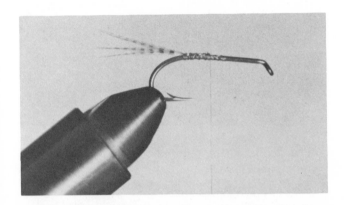

1. Secure tail fibers at the bend of the hook. These should be equal to the length of the hook shank.

2. Spin dubbing on the tying thread. Wrap the body approximately halfway up the hook shank. The body should be neatly tapered.

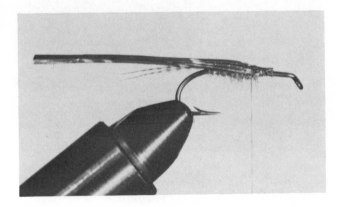

3. Tie quill segment on the top of the hook shank.

4. Spin dubbing to form thorax. Thorax should be twice the thickness of the body.

5. Tie in a soft hackle and make one or two turns with it to form the legs.

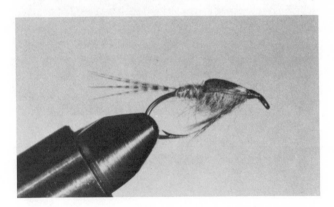

6. Pull the wing quill forward to form the thorax. Whip finish and cement head.

Floating Nymph
Family Baetidae (Chapter 5)

The merits of this pattern are that it can be seen, since it is designed to simulate the small nymphs of *Baetis*, *Pseudocloeons*, or *Callibaetis* when on the surface and the dun is struggling to escape out of them. It is tied with a light dry fly hook such as 94833. It is an alternative pattern for the Conventional Nymph pattern for the members of Family *Baetidae*.

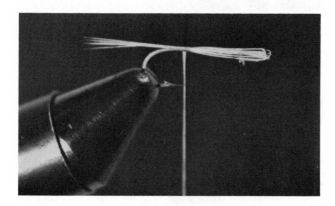

1. Tie in four to six hackle fibers at the bend of the hook for the tails.

2. Wind the thread back to the bend of the hook and under the base of the tail fibers. Lift the thread up and forward to cause them to splay and give a fan-like appearance.

3. Dub a fine, neatly tapered abdomen ⅔ of the way up the hook shank.

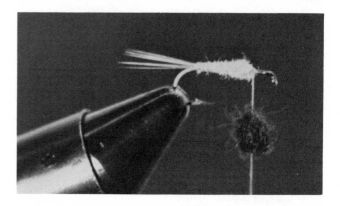

4. Spin a fat ball of tightly wound dubbing on the tying thread. Its color should match the wings of the dun.

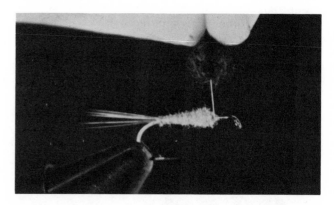

5. Hold the thread straight up so that the ball of dubbing is above the thorax portion.

6. Now push the ball of dubbing down tightly against the hook shank. Make two tight turns of thread in front and behind the ball of fur.

7. Tie in four or five hackle fibers on each side of the ball of dubbing to form the legs. These legs act as little outriggers to help the fly float upright. Add a drop of cement to the base of the ball and allow it to flow back under it.

8. Spin a small amount of dubbing on the tying thread for the thorax. Wind this dubbing a couple of times behind the ball of dubbing and the legs and in front to form the thorax.

9. Whip finish and cement head.

Flat-Body Nymph
Family Heptageniidae (Chapter 6)

This pattern matches the side and top configuration of the clingers. It is to be fished deep before and during the hatch. Hook type—3906B.

1. Secure three tail fibers at the bend of the hook. These should be equal to the length of the hook shank.

2. Tie in four strands of ostrich herl at the bend of the hook. Also tie in one strand of fine gold wire for ribbing.

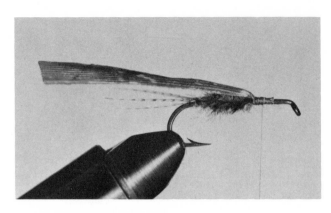

5. Tie in quill segment for wing case.

3. Spin a finely dubbed body halfway up the hook shank.

6. Spin dubbing to form the thorax. Dubbing should be very fuzzy. Clip dubbing top and bottom to flatten the thorax.

4. Pull two strands of ostrich herl on each side of the body and tie in. Rib *through* the herl with the fine gold wire and tie in.

7. Tie in several soft hackle fibers on each side of the thorax to form the legs.

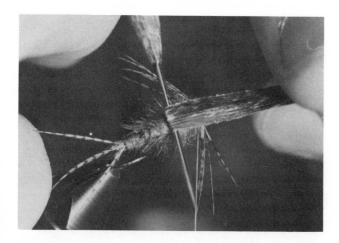

8. Pull wing quill forward to form the case. Tie off.

9. Whip finish and cement head.

10. Pick out herl fibers between the ribbing with a dubbing needle to form the quills.

Streamlined Nymph

Family Ephemeridae (burrowers; Chapter 9)
Family Siphlonuridae (large swimmers; Chapter 10)

An easy-to-tie imitation that closely duplicates the long and elongated bodies of the large burrowing and swimming mayflies. Hook type: 9672 3X Long.

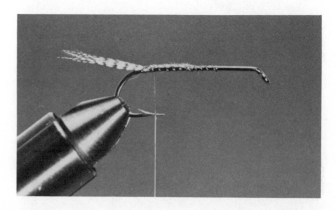

1. Tie in tail fibers at the bend. These should be of a very soft texture such as grouse or ostrich herl.

2. Spin a small amount of dubbing in front of the tails, and attach two or three strands of ostrich herl on each side of the hook, and one strand of fine gold wire.

3. Spin a slender tapered abdomen. This should extend two-thirds of the way up the hook shank. The dubbing used on this nymph should be very fuzzy.

6. Tie in quill segment for the wing case.

4. Pull the ostrich herl forward on each side of the body and tie in. Rib the gold wire forward through the ostrich herl.

7. Spin fuzzy dubbing to form the thorax. Also make two turns with a soft hackle to form the legs.

5. Pick out the ostrich herl fibers from the gold wire ribbing with a dubbing needle to form the gills. The gills are very important on this type of nymph.

8. Pull the quill segment forward and tie in at the head to form the wing case. Whip finish and cement head.

Wiggle Nymph
Family Ephemeridae (burrowers; Chapter 9)

This is an alternative pattern for the imitation of the burrowing mayfly nymphs. It is an extremely effective one during nonhatch and hatch times in the type of waters that support the populations of these mayflies. Once the pattern is mastered it should be incorporated for the imitation of other mayflies that are of an adequate size, since it simulates the undulating movements of the nymphs of many types of mayflies. The front portion should be weighted slightly which will cause it to move with greater motion than when tied without any weight. Hook types: thorax—Mustad 3906 or 7948A; abdomen—Thunder Creek Hook Series of any length provided it is long enough for the abdomen. Size No. 6 (3XL ring-eye hook) should be sufficient for all burrowing species.

3. Tie in quill segment. In front of the quill section tie in a philo flume (base feather found at the base of a pheasant's main feather). This flume feather is excellent for the gills. Tie in a fine gold wire for the ribbing.

1. Tie in tail fibers.

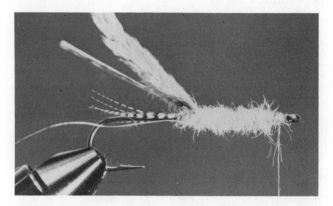

4. Spin dubbing to form a finely tapered abdomen all the way to the hook eye.

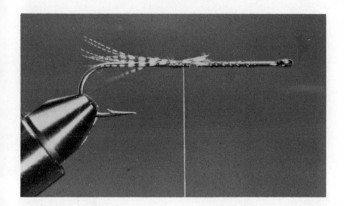

2. Dub a small section of dubbing at the base of the tails.

5. Pull the philo feather forward over the top of the abdomen and tie off at the eye of the hook.

6. Pull the quill segment over the top of the philo feather and tie off at the hook eye. Now rib the fine gold wire through the philo feather and tie off. Pick out the gills with a dubbing needle. Cement the head and snip the hook shank at the base of the tails with side cutters. This completes the wiggle portion of the fly.

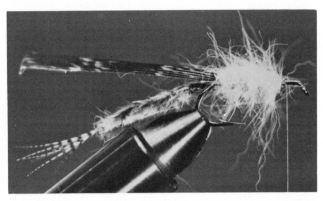

9. Spin dubbing to form the thorax. Dubbing should be fuzzy. Wind two turns of soft hackle for legs. Grouse or partridge is best.

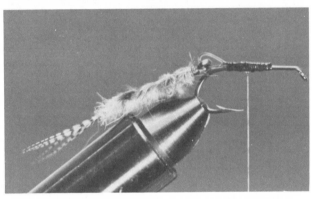

7. Tie in piano wire or 15 1b. monofilament at the bend of the thorax hook. Pass the wire through the eye of the wiggle section. Form a round loop and tie off. This loop should be bound down firmly and cemented so it won't pull out on a short strike.

10. Pull the quill segment forward over the thorax and tie off.

8. Tie in a quill segment at the bend of the hook.

11. Whip finish the head and cement.

12. Top view of finished fly.

DRY FLY INSTRUCTIONS

Emerging Dun
Family Ephemerellidae (sprawlers; Chapter 8)

This pattern is designed to imitate an intermediate stage between a nymph and a fully developed dun. It is an extremely effective pattern for the important and very prolific hatches of *Ephemerellas*, which are customarily accompanied by very selective trout. Its effectiveness no doubt lies in the fact that it simulates a helpless floating dun trying to get its wings in an upright position, the most vulnerable interim of dun development. The imitation is intended to be fished *on the surface*, thus tied with a light-wire hook such as 94831.

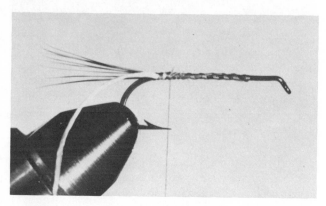

1. Tie in six or eight cock hackle fibers at the bend of the hook for the tails. Tie in a strand of floss for the larger sizes, monocord on the smaller sizes for the ribbing.

2. Dub the body. This should be neatly tapered, thin in the abdomen, and made progressively thicker toward the thorax.

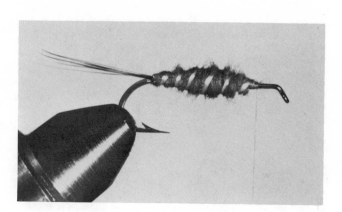

3. Rib the body.

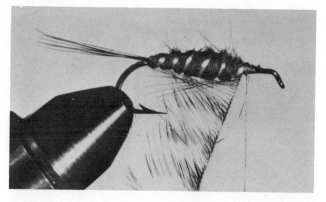

4. Fold a cock hackle that matches the color of the legs of the dun to be imitated. Tie in place. The hackles should always be tied in reverse, from tip toward butt.

5. Make approximately two turns with it and clip the rest off.

6. Tie in a second folded cock hackle that is the color of the wings of the natural dun to be imitated. Make three to four turns with it and tie off.

7. Whip finish and cement head.

The No-Hackle Fly

Family Baetidae (Chapter 5)
Family Leptophlebiidae (Chapter 7)
Family Ephemerellidae (Chapter 8; except Western Green Drake)
Family Tricorythidae (Chapter 11)

This is probably the most effective and true to life dry fly imitation ever devised for the imitation of a natural mayfly dun. The pattern is very durable when tied properly, and it is an excellent floater when the natural buoyancy of the mallard quill wings *are not* hampered by coating them with any kind of solution. After some use the wings may split; however, if originally positioned correctly, it will do so with a uniform fashion, preserving the optimal configuration of the wing like the natural. It remains just as effective with or without split wings. Tying the No-Hackle requires a certain amount of practice and patience, but once mastered, it will undoubtedly prove the most effective dry fly imitation an angler will have in his fly box. Mustad 94833 3X Fine is recommended, with 94840 as a substitute for those tied with a double wing.

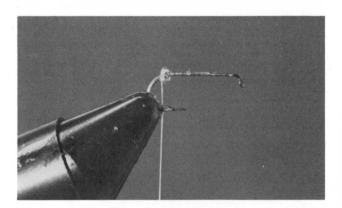

1. Spin a very tiny amount of dubbing to form a small ball at the bend of the hook. This is an important step to maintain the tails separated at a 90-degree position to each other.

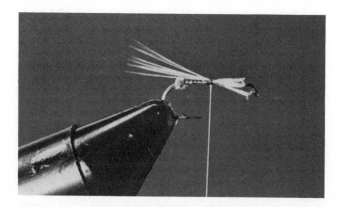

2. Tie in six to ten stiff hackle fibers at the center of the hook shank. These should be extended beyond the hook bend to approximately the length of the hook shank, as shown.

5. Cut a matched pair of mallard quills to a width about half that of the hook shank. Beginners should try narrower wings to start. Use only lower third of quill (upper part is too coarse).

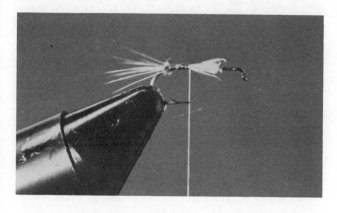

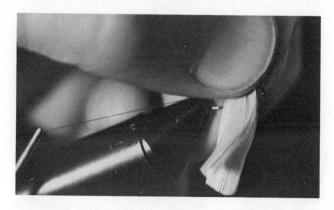

3. Now wind the thread back toward the ball of dubbing, forcing the hackle fibers to divide in half and to be 90 degrees to each other.

6. Hold the quill segments by the tips over the thorax area. *Do not pinch the quills against the hook shank;* fingers should barely feel the hook shank but not press against it. Thread should be in the straight down position, between the wings. While holding the wings in place, bring thread straight back between them. Now bring it loosely all the way around in front of both wings and on top of hook shank. Do not tighten thread until it is in the straight back position, as shown. Tighten snugly.

4. Wind the thread forward to the thorax area. There should be a good solid base of thread on the hook shank to prevent the wings from rotating on it.

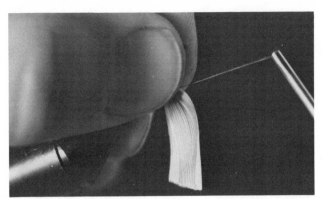

7. Bring the thread around behind the wings loosely. Slowly tighten it, pulling it forward toward the eye of the hook. The tension again should be applied parallel to the hook shank. Repeat steps six and seven two or three times, tightening only when thread is in the straight back or forward position.

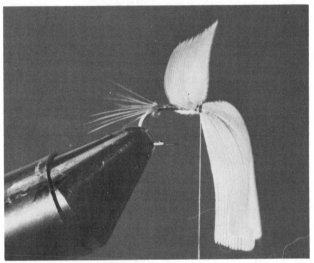

8. The wings should now be in an upright position, as shown. Carefully cut butts of the wings as closely as possible to the hook shank. Make two or three turns with the thread to further secure the wings in their position. At this point, the wings should be pushed forward and spread with the left thumb to prevent the positioned quills from doubling onto themselves during subsequent steps.

9. To divide the wings the thread should be brought forward between them, forcing the near wing forward and anchoring the tension of the thread with a few turns in front of the wing.

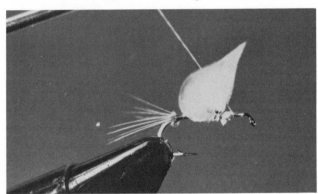

10. The thread should now be brought back between the wings on the far side of the hook shank. Carefully, pull the far wing forward and anchor it by making several tight turns in front of it with the tying thread. A touch of vinyl cement only on the base of the wings is recommended at this point.

11. Wind the thread back toward the tails and dub a finely tapered body. Take the dubbing up to just behind the wings as much as possible, then skip over to the front of the wings. *Do not* figure eight between the wings with the dubbing.

12. Whip finish and cement the head.

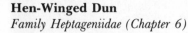

Hen-Winged Dun
Family Heptageniidae (Chapter 6)

Members of Family *Heptageniidae* cause the majority of mayfly hatches of importance to anglers in the faster stretches of streams and rivers; thus a strong and high-floating artificial is the best suited for such waters. Hook types: 94831 in sizes up to No. 14, 94840 for sizes No. 16 and smaller.

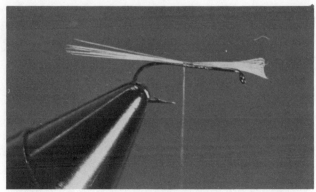

1. Tie in stiff hackles for tails. The amount of fibers depends on the size of the fly; however, it should not be overdone.

2. Tie in two matched hen-hackle tips for the wings. These should be *body* feathers not the neck hackles of a hen. Their color should be that of the wings of the natural to be imitated.

3. Stand up the wings and divide them.

4. Dub a fine-tapered body of dubbing to just behind the wings. Leave a little room for the hackle.

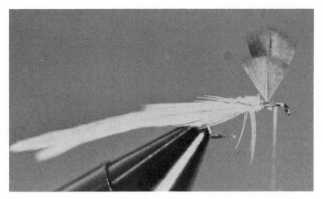

5. Tie in two matched cock hackles by the butts behind the wings. They should be the same color as the legs of the natural.

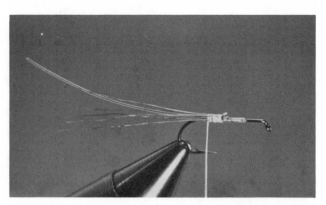

1. Secure a long strand of 15 lb. monofilament at the center of the hook shank. Tie in about five moose hairs for tails. These should be about twice the length of the hook shank.

6. Wrap the hackles by making at least two turns behind and in front of the wings with each hackle. Whip finish and cement the head.

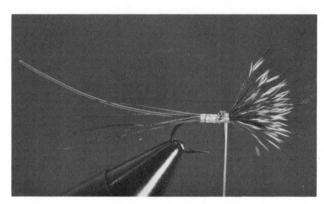

2. Tie in a clump of elk hair for the wing, at the center of the hook shank.

Paradrake

Family Ephemeridae (Chapter 9)
Family Siphlonuridae (Chapter 10)
Family Ephemerellidae (Chapter 8; only the Western Green Drake)

The members of these two families (and *E. grandis* or Western Green Drake) are large and elongated mayflies best imitated with Paradrakes, a good floater for the construction of artificials in such sizes. The Paradrake is a very deceiving pattern for selective trout which are the rule, not the exception, in slow to medium waters that also support the large burrowers of *Ephemeridae*. Hook type: Mustad 94831.

3. Stand the wing up with the tying thread and wind the thread a couple of turns around the base of the wing to bunch up the fibers.

4. Tie in a clump of long dyed elk hair forward in front of the wing and clip the butts.

7. Tie in a high quality saddle hackle by the tip on the front of the wing.

5. Pull the elk hair back over the hook shank. Make sure the hair covers all of the shank. Tightly wind the thread back over the body forming a rib.

8. Make five or six turns of the hackle in a parachute style around the wing. These turns should be made counterclockwise. The fly should be whip finished at this point and cemented.

6. Continue the ribbing back past the bend of the hook until the total body length is 1½ times the length on the hook shank. Make several tight turns of the thread at the tail. Now reverse the procedure and rib the thread tightly forward up to the front of the wing.

9. The elk hair now should be carefully cut at the tail. Be very cautious so that you do not clip the moose tail fibers. Leave three fibers for the tails. Spread the tails into position and add a drop of cement at the tail to hold them in that fixed angle. Another option is to bring the back end slightly and also add a touch of cement on the underside of the body at the hook bend.

Poly or Hen-Winged Spinner
All mayflies

Mayfly spinners, regardless of species or type, should be imitated with the following pattern. It is optional whether poly or a soft, webby body feather of a hen should be used; however, hen-winged spinners undoubtedly give a better and more realistic silhouette in comparison to those tied with liberal amounts of coarse poly yarn. Since few artificial materials are able to imitate the perfectly clear wings of a mayfly spinner, the selection of a neutral color for the wings, such as light gray, is recommended. This tone will minimize contrast between the sky and the wing of the artificial, an important aspect of a credible and deceiving spinner imitation. Hook type: 94833 for all sizes down to No. 12; Mustad 94831 for larger mayflies.

3. Dub a slender tapered body. Whip finish and cement the head.

1. Tie in three to six stiff hackle fibers for the tails. Run thread under them and pull up and forward to cause them to splay in a fan-like effect.

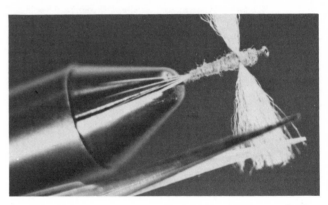

4. Cut the wings off so that they each equal the length of the body.

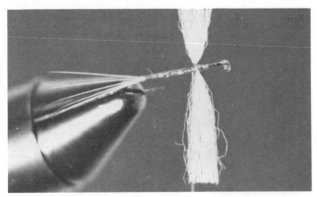

2. Tie in with a figure eight motion a *small amount* of poly yarn, Flyrite dubbing, or hen gills at the thorax in a spent position. Get excess out of your way by clipping it off at this point. (Both dubbing material and hen hackles are recommended over poly yarn.)

5. Shape them to resemble the configuration of a natural mayfly.

Millimeter to Hook Type and Size Chart

(Length includes exact measurements from just behind the ring-eye to the beginning of the hook-gap bend.)

NYMPHS

MILLIMETERS	#3906; Regular shank; heavy wire; Conventional Nymph, weighted version	#3906B; Sproat Bend; 1X Long; Flat-Body Nymph; Thorax of Wiggle Nymph	#9671; Turned-down eye; 2X Long; Good substitute for either #3906B or #9672	#9672; Same as #9671 except 3X Long; Large Streamlined Nymphs
3mm				
4mm	#20			
5mm	#18	#18*		
6mm	#16			
7mm	#14	#16*	#18	
8mm				#18
9mm	#12	#14*	#16	
10mm				#16
11mm	#10	#12*	#14	
12mm				#14
13mm		#10	#12	
14mm	#8			#12*
15mm		#8*	#10	
16mm				#10*
17mm			#8	
18mm				#8*
19mm		#6		
20mm			#6	
22mm				#6
24mm			#4	
27mm				#4
30mm			#2	
33mm				#2

*Critical Size Range

* Critical size range: Naturals whose lengths are below 10mm should be imitated in size as closely as possible. The smaller-sized mayflies cause the most profuse emergences and thus offer trout an uninterrupted size comparison between the numerous naturals and an angler's occasional passing artificial.

Table 11-1

Millimeter to Hook Type and Size Chart

(Length includes exact measurements from just behind the ring-eye to the beginning of the hook-gap bend.)

DRY FLY

MILLIMETERS	#94859; Ring-eye type; Recommended for flies in the 3mm to 5mm range	#94840; Turned-down eye; standard; (#94845 barbless); Smaller Hen-Winged or Hackle Duns; Conventional Nymph	#94842; Turned-down eye; Xtra Fine; Good substitute for #94840 or #94833	#94833; Super fine; 3X Long; Floating Nymphs; No-Hackles; Spinners	#94831;Turned-down eye; 2X Long; Conventional Nymphs; Emerging Duns; Large Hen or Hackle Duns; Paradrakes
3mm	#26–#28*	#24–#26	#26	#26	
4mm	#22–#24*	#22	#24	#24	
5mm	#20*	#20	#22	#22	
6mm		#18	#20	#20*	
7mm		#16	#18	#18*	
8mm		#14	#16	#16*	
9mm		#12*	#14	#14*	
10mm			#12	#12*	
11mm		#10*			#14*
12mm			#10	#10	
13mm		#8			#12*
14mm			#8	#8*	
15mm					#10*
16mm		#6		#6	
17mm					
18mm				#4	#8*
19mm		#4			
20mm					
22mm					#6
24mm					
27mm					#4*
30mm					
33mm					

* Hook sizes are those specifically recommended for the tying of the exact imitations given in this book. Substitutions can be made, but the reader should bear in mind the relationship of length to weight when making a substitution.

Table 11-2

APPENDIX II: Advanced Entomology and Research

DOING YOUR OWN RESEARCH

THE purpose of this section is to provide the reader with practical and simplified keys to enable him to identify the hatches he will encounter throughout each season. With experience he will become so familiar with them that he will be able to recognize them even at a glance. From the recognition of an emerging insect, a lot can be derived as to its nymph's underwater behavior, the manner in which it transforms into a dun, the stage most vulnerable to the trout, and the type of artificial that should be employed to match it. It is then important that an angler catch a natural when meeting the hatches in the stream—preferably before each hatch is already in full progress, in order to get the full benefit from any deductions he can make. During any hatch, duns and nymphs are easily obtained by holding a small portable aquarium net in the first few inches of the surface film. Collections of empty floating nymphal shucks, available during hatches, are also useful for family, generic, and even species determination. The naturals can be stored in a collecting vial filled with regular 70 percent alcohol, which is available in any drugstore. The duns will lose their coloration quite rapidly; unfortunately, to date there are no reliable solutions to maintain these colors. I have experimented with many different formulas recommended in angling and scientific texts, but have found their ingredients hard to obtain, expensive, and in the long run useless. Regular alcohol will preserve the general coloration of nymphs, and this stage—not the duns—should be the one used by fly fishermen to classify mayflies.

The imago or spinner stage is the most dependable stage for the determination of the species. Consequently, that was the stage used for the identifications in this volume. This stage, however, is hard to work with, especially for an individual lacking such essential equipment as a microscope of high magnification. It also requires some expertise in mounting the genitalic parts of a male spinner on slides. For the average angler, this whole process may well prove overly involved and complicated, and as the keys to the nymphs are easier and more applicable, they are provided in this book.

Those who wish to raise duns to their spinner stage can do so by capturing a few males at streamside during a hatch (see Key to Adults for determining males from females) and place them in a small plastic box, making sure that they are kept in a cool and shaded place at all times. Providing they are properly kept, they will molt into spinners or imagoes approximately 24 hours after being collected. In the spinner stage, determination as to family and genus classification is then simple, though identification as to species requires the study of its genitalic characteristics under high magnification.

Obtaining specimens during nonhatch periods can be accomplished by closely scrutinizing the streamside flora, which often reveals the insects presently emerging from a stream. The vegetation provides the natural molting sites for the conversion of duns to spinners, and both can be found in the shaded areas near the margin of the water. Entomologists, unlike fly fishermen who spend most of their time in the stream instead of in a laboratory, obtain the bulk of their collections by passing a large butterfly net through the bushes along the banks encircling streams. Anglers can often find mayflies clinging to the bottom (shaded) side of bridges or other man-made structures, and in such places large collections

FIG. AII-1 During the actual hatches is the best time to obtain samples of naturals.

of spinners which are waiting for the right time to return to the stream and complete their life cycle can be found. Regardless of individual approach and method, collected specimens will show the angler what species are presently emerging in a specific stream and at what point it is in the seasonal emergence cycle. It will, moreover, reveal what hatches he can expect at certain times of the day and which will take place in the weeks to come.

Examining a few rocks picked out of a stream will reveal some of the organisms common to it. Most such organisms will, however, be immature and the information derived by such informal inspection serves only to show what types inhabit that stream. Still, the presence of nymphs with nearly black wing cases will mean that they are either ready to emerge or very close to maturity; the observer can then expect their hatches shortly.

A seine net constructed with a regular piece of fine screen and fastened at both ends to posts or handles is a useful tool for the collection of the mayfly biota indigenous to specific stretches of water. Seine testing makes collecting very simple; however, it should be noted that it is illegal in many states, in order to prevent the selling of nymphs and larvas for commercial purposes. Streams subjected to this method may also suffer damage. When used with consideration, however, seining will aid the interested angler in

finding out what organisms inhabit his local streams and will enable him to determine what hatches they will produce the coming season. Seine tests should be done before the season so as not to encroach upon the enjoyment of others. Place the screen downstream from yourself and gently overturn the rocks along the bottom; this will dislodge many nymphs and larvae. Take the entire collection to the bank and with a pair of tweezers select a few members of each type and you will have a representative sample of that stream's biota. This exercise should be done quickly, to minimize the loss of those nymphs that are to be returned to the stream. Tests conducted in early spring will yield the nymphal forms of the mayflies that will emerge during the first half of the season; late-season emergers will be too small to be trapped by the screen and too minute to be detectable with the naked eye. For such reason, a second test during mid-season is advisable and will reveal the coming hatches of the latter half of the year. It should be remembered that many aquatic forms cannot be collected satisfactorily by this method, since some are too fast and agile and will escape from the net; other types cling too tightly to the rocks along the bottom, so as to not be dislodged by the force of the current. Specific examples of these types are the clinging members of mayfly Family *Heptageniidae*, as well as many caddises, namely the case builders of *Glossoso-*

FIG. **AII-2** Streamside vegetation provided a natural molting site for this thick group of *Callibaetis* mayflies.

matidae and *Leptoceridae*, and the immature stages of the common *Hydropsyches*. These types are best obtained by taking them from the rocks by picking them off with a pair of tweezers.

FIG. **AII-3** Seine testing a moving-current stream.

EQUIPMENT

Equipment could range from the most simple tools to expensive and very sophisticated paraphernalia. Because of the charts provided in this work, on rare occasions will the reader need anything more than a 10X and 15-20X pair of hand lenses, though they should be of a very high quality. The price of both need not exceed $20. These lenses can easily be carried in one of the pockets in your vest, and be put to use at streamside to determine the family or "type" of an emerging mayfly. For more precise identification, and classification as to the genus and species of a specimen, it could be reexamined back at home; the use of a strong light and a glass petri dish, when placed against a black-colored background, will undoubtedly reveal the features for more specific determination. The accumulation of data from such exercises will prove valuable in the long run, since it will give the angler accurate notes as to the time of seasonal emergence, daily occurrences, trout response, and pattern that worked best during the hatches of principal importance in the waters in which he customarily fishes. There is no substitute for first-hand information, and the ability of the reader to be able to draw his own conclusions and form his own opinions based on personal experiences is the purpose of this Appendix.

FIG. AII-4 Gathering representative samples from the diverse and abundant biota of a western stream.

NYMPH IDENTIFICATION

The most important consideration in identifying a specimen is that the angler exercise some degree of discipline in his approach. Just randomly trying to spot a telltale characteristic that will reveal the identification of a specimen will lead only to confusion and frustration. When examining a mayfly nymph, which in the majority of cases will exhibit three tails—unlike the two-tailed stoneflies which are similar in general configuration—the optimal approach should be one of scrutinizing its head first, then thorax, abdomen, and finally its tails. If its head is flattened, as wide as its body, and the eyes are on the dorsal (top side) of it, then it could belong to no other family than that of *Heptageniidae*. All other types have their eyes protruding from the sides (lateral margins). Moreover, if conspicuous tusks or "horns" are evident, the nymph is a member of Super Family *Ephemeridae*—with the possible exception of its being one of the four western *Paraleptophlebia* species which also exhibit such "horns" on their heads. During family determination, legs should be tentatively overlooked. The bottom half of the nymph is the abdomen and all mayflies have respiratory gills attached to the abdominal segments. At the family level, gills with filamentous-like extensions resembling threads or tuning-fork gills are members of *Leptophlebiidae* (presumably the nymphs of *Ephemeridae* have already been eliminated—they also have bifid gills). Small, plate-like gills lying on the

dorsal of the abdomen separates the common *Ephemerellidae* members, but if little plate gills stick out towards the side, the specimen is a member of either of two families constituting the "swimmers." These latter forms are streamlined in general configuration and resemble wiggling minnows when they are picked up from the stream; Family *Siphlonuridae* includes the larger swimmers which have short antennas; *Baetidae* is comprised of comparatively tiny mayflies whose nymphal forms have long antennas, three to four times the width of their heads. The tiny nymphs of families *Tricorythidae* and *Caenidae* are given away by their minute dimensions, and their conspicuous, enlarged second gill, resembling a shield.

In entomology, practice may not make perfect, but it does reduce certain identification exercises to a routine level, eventually allowing the researcher to place his specimens in their family type just by configuration and size. In the Nymph Chart in this chapter, the naturals are drawn according to the size relationship of their mature species in the nymphal stage, with the burrowers of Family *Ephemeridae* presented as the largest mayflies, followed by those of *Siphlonuridae*, and so on. Size relationship is also preserved in the color plates of this book to convey to the reader differences of lengths of the different mayfly types, which should help him in becoming acquainted with them more quickly and aid in streamside identifications.

DRY FORM IDENTIFICATION

It should be noted that mayflies have two dry forms, the dun and the spinner, and that specimens of the former are not as easily identified as many angling texts have led readers to believe. When working with this stage, therefore, extreme caution should be exercised in any classification to any level. Many features are available for the differentiation of duns as to their family designation; unfortunately, in the majority of cases this is the furthest that they can be taken, though some types can be safely determined to their genus by the comparison of size and coloration. When working with both dry forms—duns and spinners, the latter being a specimen the wings of which lack general pigmentation—the number of tails it possesses instantly serves to place it into either of two four-family groups. Moreover, the presence or absence (or near absence) of hind wings, and their general shape if present, will reduce its possible classification to only one or at most two possibilities.

Identification as to genus and species of either a nymph, dun (quite limited), or spinner would, in turn, demand the detection of added specific characteristics pointed out in the charts of this Appendix.

RAISING MAYFLIES

The method used for this book for procuring mayflies was to raise them at streamside in half-submerged wire cages. This had many advantages, since water temperature and current flow—so critical for the emergence of certain types—were provided by the mayflies' natural environment. Most importantly, when the nymphs emerged, their discarded shucks were able to be directly identified with the newly formed dun and, approximately twenty-four hours later, with the spinner. Many of the keys to identification in this book were able to be composed because of these positive and reliable correlations among the stages of the life cycle of specific mayfly species. Such a method, of course, is time-consuming, and certainly not for the weekender or the individual with a few precious days in a given locality. However, an alternative approach for the angler curious to rear a mayfly in order to witness its transition from nymph to dun is to gather a few mature nymphs from the stream (those with black, compressed wing pads) and place them in a container in a cool, shaded area. Within one or two hours the dun will emerge.

Home aquariums are a much more interesting venture and a fascinating way to learn about mayflies. The home unit should be of ten gallons' capacity or larger and provided with aeration devices at two separate corners. This will create maximum current flow and a diversity of mini-habitats so as to offer the introduced nymphs one which they would have preferred in the real stream. The bottom should be filled with two inches of pebbles and silt and be all set up before stocking. The type of mayflies best suited for this type of artificial environment are those that are naturally tolerant of slow-water environments such as *Leptophlebias*, *Tricorythodes*, any of the large burrowers of *Ephemeridae*, or the versatile *Ephemerellas*. When actually introducing them into the tank, fill at least half of it with the water of the stream in which you got them from; this will serve to reduce climatic shock. Regardless of the amount of precautions, you can expect at least 50 percent mortality; but when specimens are gathered late in the year, you can still count on their hatches in your basement during the winter, well before they will emerge in their natural state.

PHOTOGRAPHY

Raising mayflies in captivity is not only fascinating, but makes it handy for making the dry forms available for home photography. As with scientific equipment, photographic implements vary extensively in quality

FIG. AII-5 A 35mm SLR fixed with a 10X close-up lens—an inexpensive, fast-to-handle, and reliable set-up for outdoor photography of mayflies.

and expense. Many choices are available, depending on personal needs and finances. An excellent unit—and the most versatile—is the popular 35mm SLR camera, which when fixed with a bellows and a 135mm lens makes an unbeatable combination for the photography of anything relatively small, such as mayflies. It allows you to get a 1:1 magnification ratio when taking photographs as much as two feet away from the fly. Indoor lighting can either be provided by electronic flash or by two 3400K tungsten lamps. For field photography, use the same type of camera and lens but replace the bellows with an equivalent K-tube extension. This makes the unit less cumbersome and faster to handle. Again an electronic flash can be used, but so can natural sunlight. When working outdoors, place the naturals in the desired position (while protecting them from the sun), and when ready to shoot, expose them to the sun to provide the requisite lighting. A less expensive unit would be a regular 35mm SLR with a 50mm lens, and adding a *single* close-up lens of 8X or 10X magnification. Pictures with this set-up will not be quite so good as those attained with the bellows or tube extensions, but for all practical purposes they are quite adequate for most uses.

Entomology is another fascinating aspect of the sport of fly fishing, and when approached practically and analytically, it can be an added source of enjoyment for the fly fisher. The reader should not be surprised if he becomes personally captivated by it. However, it is not a subject that is easily grasped overnight—it takes a season or two to become acquainted with its intricacies. The first year, perhaps, the reader could concentrate on identification down only to the family and genus levels, and eventually narrow his findings to the species level the following season. At any rate, he will undoubtedly be intrigued with the microcosmic world of the mayfly which exhibits the same interplays of the forces of physical and behavioral adaptations, competition and struggles for survival as do all other macrocosms in the natural order.

NYMPH IDENTIFICATION

The following illustration serves to point out the principal characteristics employed by entomologists and utilized in the keys that follow, for the separation of the families, genera, and species of mayflies. All features are readily visible with the aid of a 10X hand lens. On smaller specimens (less than 8mm), one of 15X would prove more practical. Nymph example given is *Ephemerella grandis*.

NYMPHAL PARTS

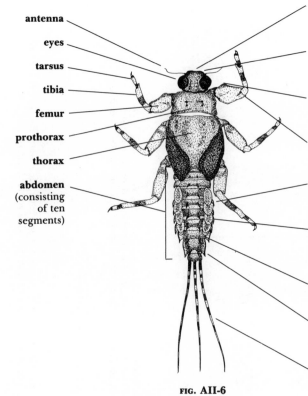

antenna

eyes

tarsus

tibia

femur

prothorax

thorax

abdomen
(consisting
of ten
segments)

FIG. AII-6

IDENTIFYING FEATURES

Frontal tusks: Long projections extending from mouthparts exhibited by burrowing members of Family *Ephemeridae*; also by four western species of genus *Paraleptophlebia*. None are shown here.

Head Projections or "Horns": Some eastern mayflies of family *Ephemerellidae* (subgenus *Drunella*) are separated from each other by the size and shape of their horns. None shown here.

Anterior Margin of Forelegs: The absence or presence of these teeth separate subgenus *Drunella* of Family *Ephemerellidae* from other species in the same family.

Femoral Flange: Shape of minute extension of femur at apex is a useful characteristic for the separation of *Epeorus* species.

Abdominal Color Pattern: Relatively reliable feature for the differentiation of nymphs belonging to many families. No pattern shown.

Gills: In which segments they are present, their configuration, size, and whether they exhibit visible branches (trachea) are the principal determinors of the family, genus, and, in many cases, species classification.

Abdominal Tubercles: Characteristic employed to distinguish species of Family *Ephemerellidae*.

Postero-lateral Spines: Their presence or absence, and on which segments they are found, are frequently used characteristics to determine family, generic, and species classification.

Tails: Their relative lengths to each other is a helpful feature to separate certain types. The presence or absence, and relative length of the middle tail to outer ones, are the characteristics that separate genera of families *Baetidae* and *Heptageniidae*.

DEFINITIONS
COMMONLY USED IN ENTOMOLOGY

anterior frontal edge (or top)
lateral toward the sides
posterior rear edge (or bottom)
projection small process extending beyond body
tubercle small process often resembling a sharp spine
tarsi plural for tarsus
tibiae plural for tibia
femora plural for femur
dorsal top side
ventral bottom side

NOTE: One of the most important concepts to keep in mind for identification is that all mayfly nymphs have *ten* abdominal segments. Moreover, that abdominal gills and tubercles or spines *always originate from the bottom* or posterior edge of an abdominal segment. Whenever the feature of a specific segment is referred to, the segment is best found by counting backwards from the last one. Last segment, that which holds the tails, is always number 10, next one up being number 9, and so on.

FAMILY EPHEMERELLIDAE

Identifying characteristic: oval-shaped gills attached to top of abdomen

EAST/MIDWEST/WEST

EAST/MIDWEST

WEST

subgenus
Ephemerella
(=Invaria Group)

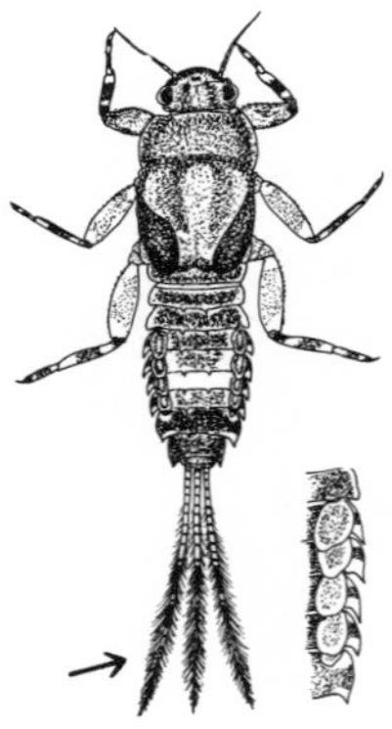

subgenus
Drunella
(=Fuscata group)

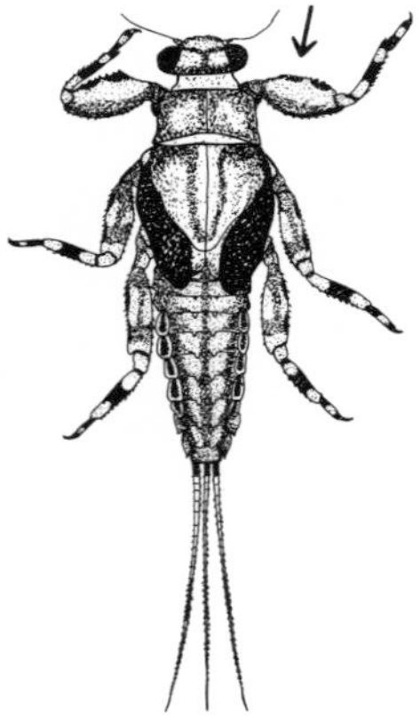

subgenus
Attenella
(=Simpex Group)

subgenus
Serratella
(=Serrata Group)

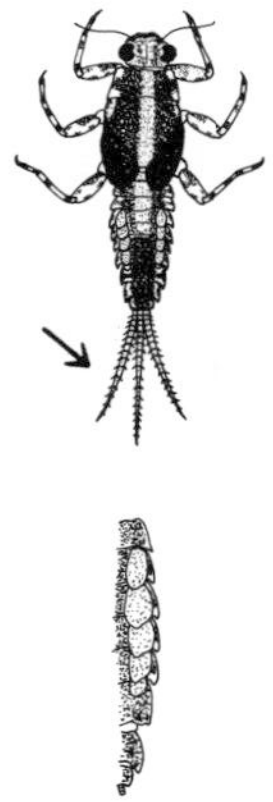

subgenus
Eurylophella
(=Bicolor Group)

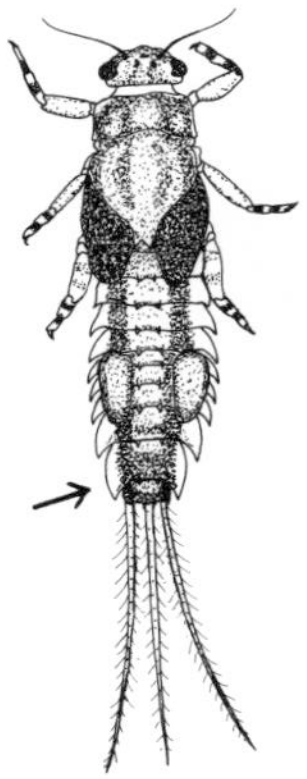

subgenus
Danella
(=Simplex Group)

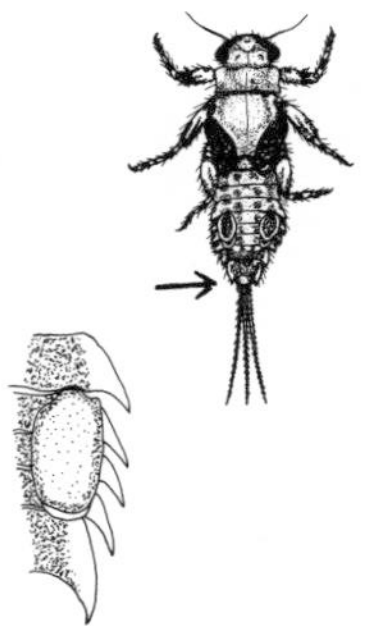

subgenus
Timpanoga
(=Hecuba Group)

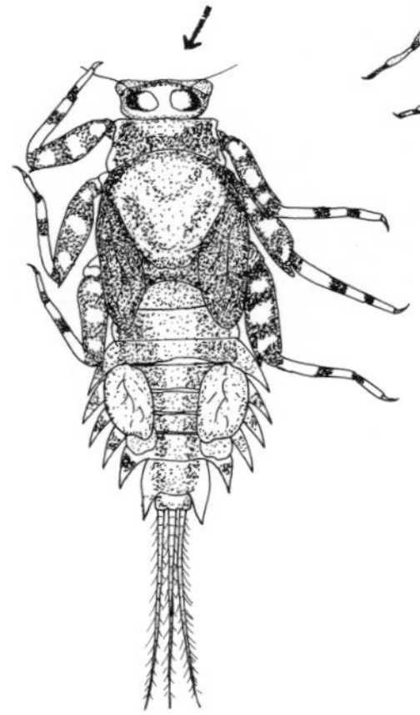

subgenus
Caudatella

East: (April-June)
E. subvaria
E. rotunda
E. dorothea

West: (June-August)
E. infrequens
E. inermis

East: (June-July)
E. cornuta
E. cornutella

West: (June-July)
E. grandis
E. flavilinea

East: (April-June)
E. attenuata

West: (July-August)
E. margarita

East: (June-July)
E. deficiens

West: (July-August)
E. tibialis

East: (June)
E. funeralis

East: (June-July)
E. simplex

West: (July-August)
E. hecuba

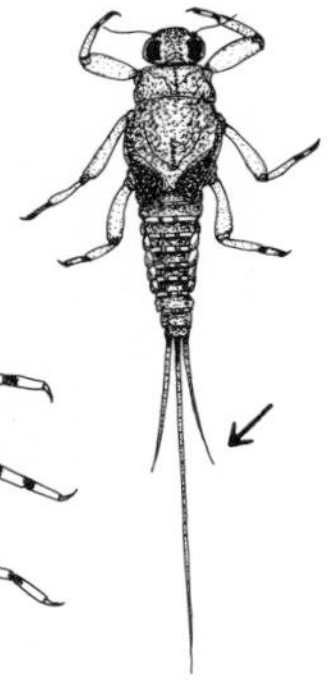

West: (July-August)
E. heterocaudata

FIG. 7   FIG. 8   FIG. 9   FIG. 10   FIG. 11   FIG. 12   FIG. 13   FIG. 14

Key to Subgenera

Gills on abdominal segments 3-7:
Forefemora broad and with teeth on anterior margins; abundant ....subgenus *Drunella*
Last 2/3 of tails with fan-like row of coarse and fine hairs (setae); most common and usually over 8mm in size ....subgenus *Ephemerella*
Entire tails with only minute, black hairs; usually with medium pale stripe; species under 8mm in size; fairly common ....subgenus *Serratella*

Gills on abdominal segments 4-7:
Small species usually 7mm or smaller; uncommon in East: common in West ....subgenus *Attenella*

Additional eastern genera:
(enlarged fourth gill)
Well-defined abdominal tubercles; abdominal segment 9 longer than 8: species average 9mm; slow-water dweller; uncommon ....subgenus *Eurylophella*
No abdominal tubercles; species average 7mm; abdominal segment 8 longer than 9; slow-water dweller; fairly common ....subgenus *Danella*

Additional western genera:
Head with a complete frontal shelf; lack abdominal tubercles; very large species; uncommon ....subgenus *Timpanoga*
Outer tails shorter than middle one; 7mm–11mm; fairly common ....subgenus *Caudatella*

150

FAMILY HEPTAGENIIDAE

Identifying characteristic: Flattened head as wide as body; eyes on dorsal surface of head

g. *Epeorus*	g. *Stenonema*	g. *Heptagenia*	g. *Rhithrogena*	g. *Cinygmula*

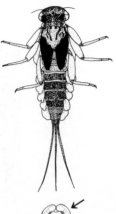

East: (April-August)
  E. pleuralis
  E. vitreus
West: (June-August)
  E. longimanus
  E. albertae

FIG. 15

East: (June-August)
  S. vicarium
  S. fuscum
  S. interpunctatum

FIG. 16

East: (July-Sept.)
  H. hebe
West: (June-Sept.)
  H. elegantula
  H. simplicioides

FIG. 17

West: (April-August)
  R. morrisoni
  R. hageni
  R. undulata

FIG. 18

East: (May-June)
  C. subequalis
West: (July-August)
  C. ramaleyi
  C. reticulata

FIG. 19

Two tails; found abundantly specifically in medium to fast waters . . . . genus *Epeorus*
Gills on abdominal segment 7 slender, unlike those on 1-6; very common in all eastern waters . . . . genus *Stenonema*
Similar gills on all segments, 7th gill may be slightly smaller; slow-water dweller . . . . genus *Heptagenia*
First and last gills enlarged and usually meet beneath abdomen; very abundant only in the West . . . . genus *Rhithrogena*
Mouthparts visible when head is viewed from the top; only fairly common in certain localities . . . . genus *Cinygmula*

FAMILY BAETISCIDAE

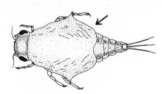

FIG. 20 Thorax enlarged forming a shield . . . genus *Baetisca*

FAMILIES CAENIDAE AND TRYCORYTHIDAE
(Enlarged second gill)

Tricroythodes	*Caenis*	*Brachycersus*

FIG. 21	**FIG. 22**	**FIG. 23**

Triangular second gill . . . genus *Tricorythodes*
Square second gill . . . genus *Caenis*
Head with three prominent tubercles . . . genus *Brachycersus*

SUPER FAMILY EPHEMERIDAE

Identifying characteristic: Head with large tusks protruding from its mouthparts

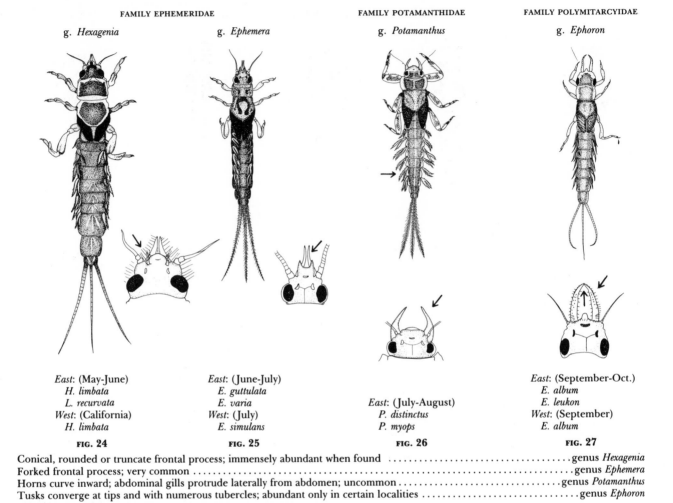

FAMILY EPHEMERIDAE

g. *Hexagenia*   g. *Ephemera*

FAMILY POTAMANTHIDAE

g. *Potamanthus*

FAMILY POLYMITARCYIDAE

g. *Ephoron*

East: (May-June)
  H. limbata
  L. recurvata
West: (California)
  H. limbata

FIG. 24

East: (June-July)
  E. guttulata
  E. varia
West: (July)
  E. simulans

FIG. 25

East: (July-August)
  P. distinctus
  P. myops

FIG. 26

East: (September-Oct.)
  E. album
  E. leukon
West: (September)
  E. album

FIG. 27

Conical, rounded or truncate frontal process; immensely abundant when found . . . . .genus *Hexagenia*
Forked frontal process; very common . . . . .genus *Ephemera*
Horns curve inward; abdominal gills protrude laterally from abdomen; uncommon . . . . .genus *Potamanthus*
Tusks converge at tips and with numerous tubercles; abundant only in certain localities . . . . .genus *Ephoron*

FAMILY LEPTOPHLEBIIDAE

Identifying characteristic: Filamentous gills

Leptophlebia

Paraleptophlebia

FIG. 28
Double gills with threadlike extensions . . . genus *Leptophlebia*

FIG. 29
Tuning fork gills on segments 2–7 . . . genus *Paraleptophlebia*

FAMILY SIPHLONURIDAE

Identifying characteristic: Streamlined configuration; postero-lateral spines on segments 8 and 9; relatively short antennas

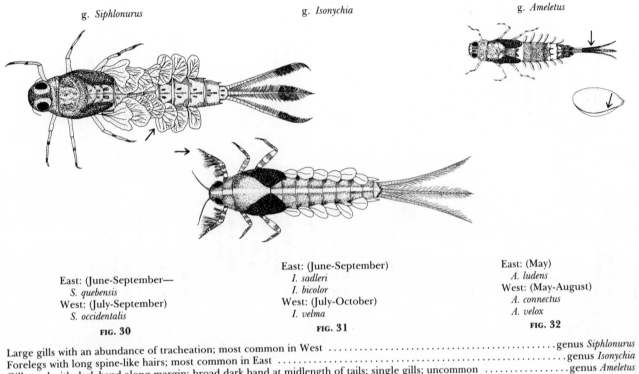

g. *Siphlonurus*

g. *Isonychia*

g. *Ameletus*

East: (June-September—
  S. quebensis
West: (July-September)
  S. occidentalis
FIG. 30

East: (June-September)
  I. sadleri
  I. bicolor
West: (July-October)
  I. velma
FIG. 31

East: (May)
  A. ludens
West: (May-August)
  A. connectus
  A. velox
FIG. 32

Large gills with an abundance of tracheation; most common in West . . . . genus *Siphlonurus*
Forelegs with long spine-like hairs; most common in East . . . . genus *Isonychia*
Gills oval with dark band along margin; broad dark band at midlength of tails; single gills; uncommon . . . . genus *Ameletus*

FAMILY BAETIDAE

Identifying characteristic: Streamlined configuration; postero-lateral spines; conspicuously long antennas

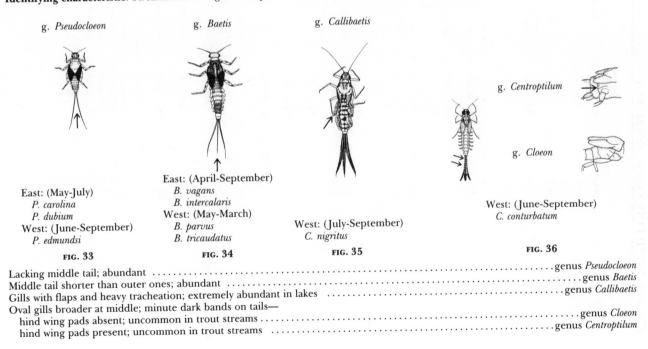

g. *Pseudocloeon*

g. *Baetis*

g. *Callibaetis*

g. *Centroptilum*

g. *Cloeon*

East: (May-July)
  P. carolina
  P. dubium
West: (June-September)
  P. edmundsi
FIG. 33

East: (April-September)
  B. vagans
  B. intercalaris
West: (May-March)
  B. parvus
  B. tricaudatus
FIG. 34

West: (July-September)
  C. nigritus
FIG. 35

West: (June-September)
  C. conturbatum
FIG. 36

Lacking middle tail; abundant . . . . genus *Pseudocloeon*
Middle tail shorter than outer ones; abundant . . . . genus *Baetis*
Gills with flaps and heavy tracheation; extremely abundant in lakes . . . . genus *Callibaetis*
Oval gills broader at middle; minute dark bands on tails—
  hind wing pads absent; uncommon in trout streams . . . . genus *Cloeon*
  hind wing pads present; uncommon in trout streams . . . . genus *Centroptilum*

FAMILY SIPHLONURIDAE (NYMPHS)

Genus Isonychia

SPECIES	DIST.	SIZE	GILL COLOR	BASAL JOINT OF ANTENNA	REMARKS
I. sadleri	E,M	13–16mm	yellowish brown	pale	Usually with conspicuous dorsal stripe (Fig. 37)
I. bicolor	E,M	13–14mm	purplish	light brown	Dorsal stripe on head, thorax, and only first few abdominal segments
I. harperi	E,M	13–15mm	—	—	A Fall emerger; September and October
I. sicca campetris	W	10–12mm	—	—	Warmer waters of rather large western rivers
I. velma	W	15–19mm	grayish brown	—	Thin dorsal stripe on its head, thorax, and abdomen; abdominal pattern (Fig. 38)

Genus Siphlonurus

SPECIES	DIST.	SIZE	GILLS	ABDOMINAL MARKINGS (BOTTOM SIDE)	REMARKS
S. quebencis	E,M	10–13mm	single	As in Fig. 39	Indigenous to large rivers
S. alternatus	E,M	11–14mm		As in Fig. 40	Found in slow-moving warm rivers
S. occidentalis	W	14–18mm		Usually as in Fig. 41	Most common western Siphlonurus species
S. columbianus	W	12–15mm		Very faint markings often resembling Fig. 41	Very difficult to separate its nymphs from those of S. occidentalis
S. spectabilis	California	13–15mm		Faint, often resembling those in Fig. 39	A southwestern species

Genus Ameletus

SPECIES	DIST.	SIZE	BANDS ON TAILS	ABDOMINAL MARKINGS (BOTTOM SIDE)	REMARKS
A. ludens	E,M	9–12mm	middle	As in Fig. 42	Only Ameletus species found in northeastern trout waters
A. lineatus	M	11–14mm	middle	As in Fig. 42	Last abdominal segment mostly pale, crossbarred
A. sparsatus	W (NW)	12mm	middle	variable	Usually top side of abdomen (Fig. 43)
A. connectus	W (NW)	10–12mm	middle	faint markings	Abdominal 5 & 6 unicolorous brown
A. oregonensis	W (NW)	11–14mm	alternately banded	—	Early spring emerger
A. velox	W (NW,SW)	12–14mm	unicolorous brown	variable	Top side of abdomen (Fig. 44)

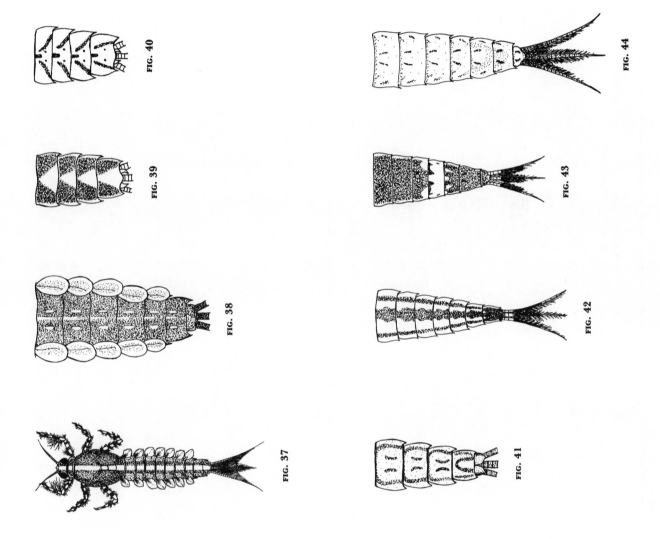

FIG. 40

FIG. 39

FIG. 38

FIG. 37

FIG. 44

FIG. 43

FIG. 42

FIG. 41

FAMILY BAETIDAE (NYMPHS)

SPECIES	DIST.	SIZE	BANDS ON TAILS	ABDOMINAL MARKINGS	GILL VEINLETS	REMARKS
Genus Baetis						
B. vagans	E,M	7–8mm	none	5,9–10 pale (Fig. 45)	indistinct (Fig. 49)	Rounded oval 7th gill (Fig. 49); common spring emerger
B. rusticans	E	5mm	none	5,9–10 pale (Fig. 45)	indistinct	Pointed, slender 7th g (Fig. 51)
B. hiemalis	M	9–10mm	none	1–10 brown	indistinct	A fall emerger in MW
B. brunneicolor	M	7–8mm	at base & tip	1–10 brown; faint pale stripe (Fig. 46)	indistinct	June emerger
B. intercalaris	E,M	5mm	at base & middle	5 & 9 paler, 10 pale (Fig. 47)	conspicuous (Fig. 50)	Rounded 7th gill (Fig. 50)
B. phoebus	M	5–6mm	at middle & tip	5 & 9 often pale (Fig. 48)	indistinct	Summer emerger
B. levitans	E,M	4mm	at middle & tip	5,9–10 pale	conspicuous	Rounded, oval 7th gill (Fig. 50)
B. pygmaeus	E,M	4mm	at middle & tip	1–10 brown	conspicuous	Pointed, slender 7th gill
			NUMBER OF TAILS			
B. insignificans	W	6–7mm	2	Fig. 52	indistinct	Fairly common species
B. bicaudatus	W	4–5mm	2	4–5, 9–10 often pale	indistinct	
B. intermedius	W	6–7mm	3 with middle one ½ length of others	Fig. 53	indistinct	Small to med. sized streams
B. parvus	W	6–7mm	3 with middle over ¾ length of others	Fig. 54	indistinct	Most common western Baetis
B. tricaudatus	W	8–9mm	3	4–5, 9–10 pale	visible	A profuse winter emerger; Oct. to March
				Fig. 55, faint stripe		
Genus Pseudocloeon			**BANDS ON TAILS**			
P. carolina	E	5mm	none	1–8 brown (Fig. 56)		Stout, and chunky configuration
P. dubium	E,M	3–5mm	at middle	3–4, 8–10 pale (Fig. 57)		Summer emerger
P. anoka	M	4–5mm	at middle	Faint stripe (Fig. 58)		Abdominal sternites with black dots
P. parvulum	M	5–6mm	alternately banded their entire length	—		Uncommon
P. edmundsi	W (NW)	6mm	—	Fig. 59		Bright chartreuse color
P. turbidum	W (SW)	5–6mm	—	—		Usually found with B. insignificans
Genus Centroptilum						
C. album	M	5mm	—	7–10 brown	visible	Warm water mayfly
C. elsa	W (NW)	6mm	—	1–10 pale	indistinct	Most common western Centroptilum
C. bifurcatum	W (NW)	7–8mm	at middle & tip	Fig. 60	visible	Summer and fall emerger
C. venosum	W (NW,SW)	7–8mm	none	Fig. 61	visible	Found in large rivers
C. convexum	W (SW)	5–6mm	at middle	3–5 brown; 7–10 pale	visible	Found in California

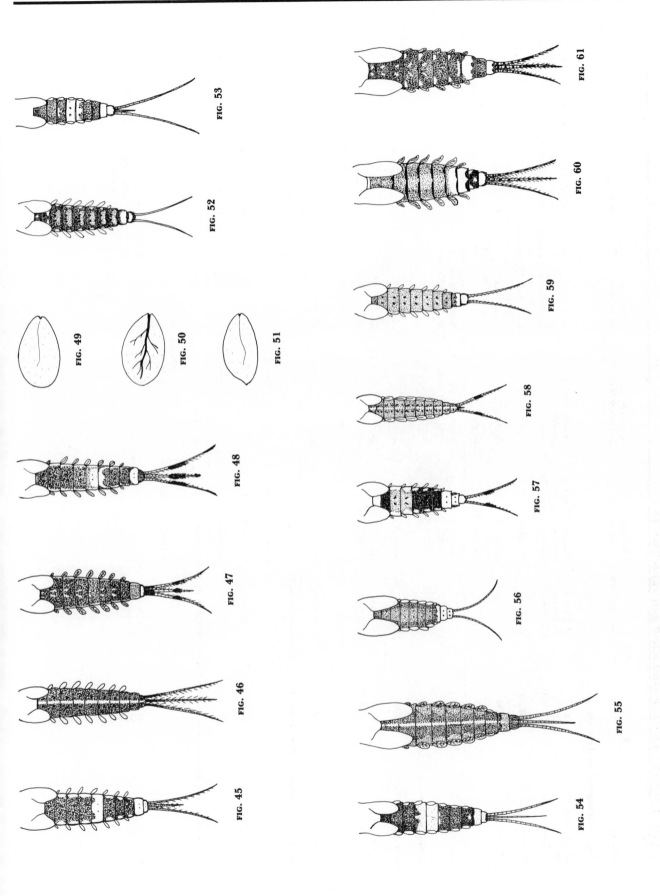

FIG. 45
FIG. 46
FIG. 47
FIG. 48
FIG. 49
FIG. 50
FIG. 51
FIG. 52
FIG. 53
FIG. 54
FIG. 55
FIG. 56
FIG. 57
FIG. 58
FIG. 59
FIG. 60
FIG. 61

FAMILY EPHEMERIDAE (and allied genera) NYMPHS

SPECIES	DIST.	BODY LENGTH	FRONTAL PROCESS	GILLS ON 1ST SEGMENT	LENGTH OF TUSKS	REMARKS
Genus Hexagenia (& Litobrancha)						
H. atrocaudata	E,M	18–26mm	truncate (Fig. 62)	double (Fig. 62a)	—	Abundant in beaver-impounded waters
H. rigida	E,M	22–29mm	conical (Fig. 63)	double	—	Widespread but only fairly common
H. limbata	E,M,W	19–35mm	rounded (Fig. 64)	double	Less than 1½ length of head	Extremely widespread and abundant; tarsal claws (Fig. 65)
H. bilineata	SE,M	18–25mm	rounded	double	Less than 1½ length of head	Common in larger rivers; tarsal claws (Fig. 66)
H. munda	E,M	17–30mm	rounded	double	More than 1½ length of head	Of principal importance in Southwest
L. recurvata	E,M	20–36mm	angular (Fig. 67)	single	—	Usually accompanies H. limbata hatches
Genus Ephemera			ABDOMINAL MARKINGS	MARKINGS ON FORE WING PADS	MARKINGS ON HIND WING PADS	
E. guttulata	E,SE	15–26mm	none (Fig. 68)	—	—	Known as the Green Drake in dun stage; June emerger
E. varia	E,M	13–17mm	yes (Fig. 69)	yes	no	Emergence follows that of E. guttulata
E. simulans	E,M,W	17–21mm	yes (Fig. 70)	yes	yes (Fig. 71)	Uncommon in East, but an abundant lake species in the Midwest; very common in slow-moving rivers of Rocky Mountain states
E. blanda	SE	12–16mm	—	no	no	Known from N.C., S.C., and Georgia
Genus Potamanthus (classified in Family Potamanthidae by entomologists)			GENERAL COLOR		ABDOMINAL PATTERN	
P. distinctus	E,SE	12–16mm	reddish brown		As in Fig. 73	Most abundant Potamanthus species in East
P. myops	M	13–18mm	cinnamon brown		As in Fig. 72	Fairly common midwestern species
Genus Ephoron (classified in Family Polymitarcyidae by entomologists)			TRACHEA ON GILLS		NUMBER OF SPINES ON TUSKS	
E. leukon	E,M	10–13mm	yes		28–39	Found in streams of rocky bottoms
E. album	M,W	12–14mm	no		16–25	Prefers microhabitats of a soft clay character

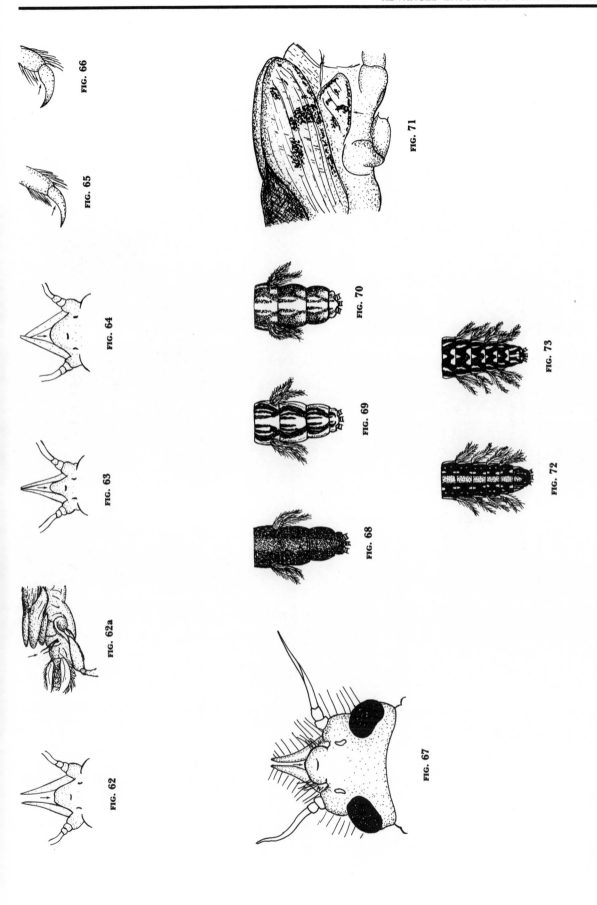

FIG. 66

FIG. 65

FIG. 64

FIG. 63

FIG. 62a

FIG. 62

FIG. 71

FIG. 70

FIG. 69

FIG. 68

FIG. 73

FIG. 72

FIG. 67

FAMILY LEPTOPHLEBIIDAE (NYMPHS)

Genus *Leptophlebia*

SPECIES	DIST.	BODY LENGTH	GENERAL COLOR	REMARKS
L. cupida	E,M	11–13mm	medium yellowish brown	Found in good numbers only in slow-moving streams
L. gravastella	W	10–12mm	mottled yellowish brown	Emerges during the months of June and July

Genus *Paraleptophlebia*

SPECIES	DIST.	BODY LENGTH	TRACHEA ON GILLS	POINT WHERE GILLS FORK	ABDOMINAL SPINES	REMARKS
P. adoptiva	E,M	8–10mm	present (Fig. 75)	approx. midway (Fig. 74)	—	An abundant species; April to June emergence
P. mollis	E,M	6–7mm	present	approx. ⅓ from base (Fig. 75)	—	Follows *P. adoptiva* in seasonal emergence
P. guttata	E,M	7mm	absent (Fig. 76)	approx. ⅓ from base (Fig. 76)	Seg. 9	Abdominal segments with small black dots
P. strigula	E,M	7mm	absent	approx. ⅓ from base	Seg. 9	Abdominal segments with dark streak along their margins
P. debilis	E,M,W	9–10mm	absent	approx. ⅓ from base	Segs. 8, 9	Principally a September/October emerger
P. bicornuta	W	9–11mm	absent	—	—	Exhibits conspicuous tusks (Fig. 77)
P. packii	W	9–10mm	present	—	—	Has similar sickle-shaped horns as *P. bicornuta* (Fig. 77)
P. heteronea	W	7–8mm	—	approx. ⅓ from base	Seg. 9	Fairly common; June/July emerger; abdominal pattern (Fig. 78)
P. memorialis	W	6–7mm	—	approx. ⅓ from base	Segs. 8, 9	Principally a July/August emerger; abdominal pattern as in Fig. 78;
P. gregalis	W	7–8mm	present	approx. ⅓ from base	—	Best populations found in Pacific states

Genus *Traverella*

SPECIES	DIST.	BODY LENGTH	REMARKS
T. albertana	mostly western	10–11mm	

Traverellas are warm-water mayflies and rarely of importance to the fly fisher. They are indigenous to the same slow-flowing habitats that support *Ephoron*, and also emerge in the first two weeks of September in western rivers. Their duns hatch in the afternoon and are waxy yellow in body color and have creamish wings. *Traverella* nymphs have well tentacled gills, easily separating from those of related genera (Fig. 79).

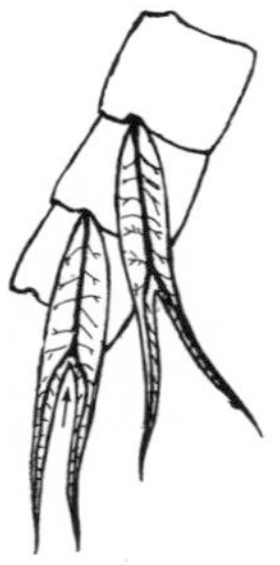

FIG. 74

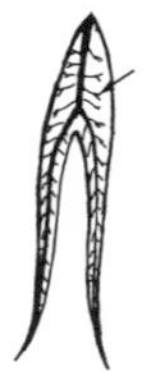

FIG. 75

FIG. 76

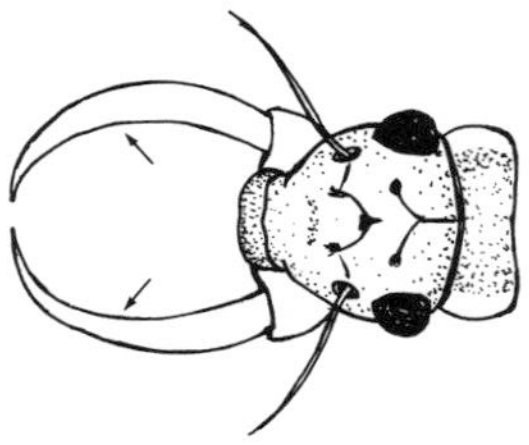

FIG. 77

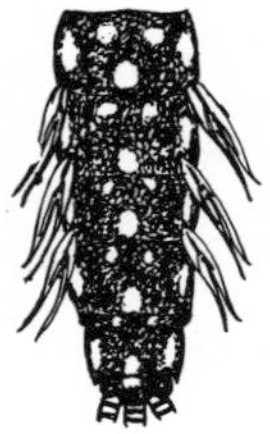

FIG. 78

FIG. 79

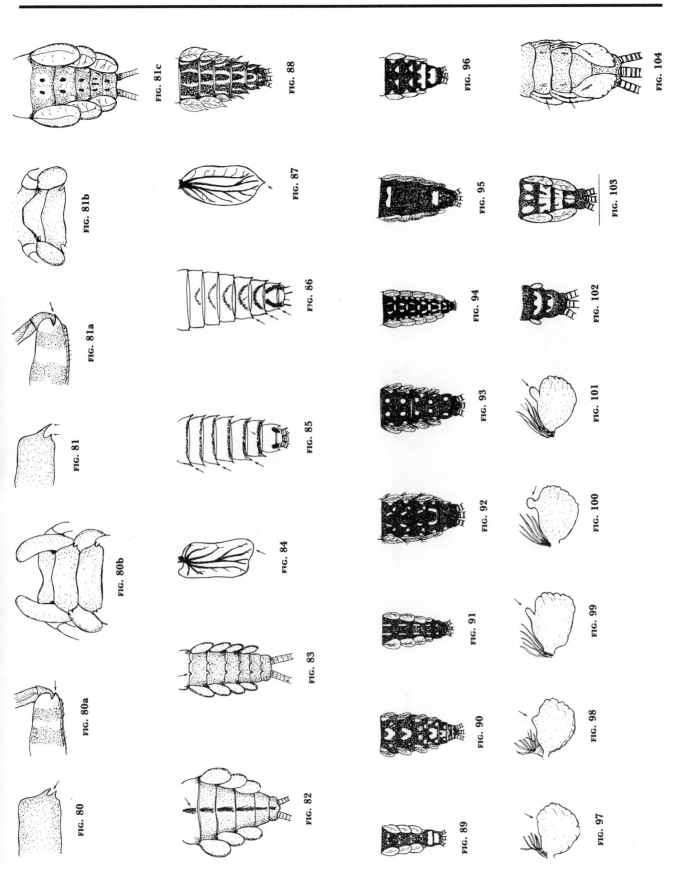

FIG. 81c

FIG. 88

FIG. 96

FIG. 104

FIG. 81b

FIG. 87

FIG. 95

FIG. 103

FIG. 81a

FIG. 86

FIG. 94

FIG. 102

FIG. 81

FIG. 85

FIG. 93

FIG. 101

FIG. 80b

FIG. 84

FIG. 92

FIG. 100

FIG. 80a

FIG. 83

FIG. 91

FIG. 99

FIG. 80

FIG. 82

FIG. 90

FIG. 98

FIG. 89

FIG. 97

FAMILY HEPTAGENIIDAE (NYMPHS)

SPECIES	DIST.	SIZE	POSTERO-LATERAL SPINES (BOTTOM VIEW)	FEMORAL FLANGE	EXTENDED 1ST GILL	GILLS MEET	REMARKS
Genus Epeorus							
E. pleuralis (sg. Iron)	E	9–10mm	subequal length (Fig. 80)	blunt (Fig. 80a)	yes (Fig. 80b)	no	First Epeorus to emerge for the season
E. vitreus	"	E,M	10mm	anterior longer (Fig. 81)	sharp (Fig. 81a)	no (Fig. 81b)	—	Tergites usually with pair of dots (Fig. 81c)
E. punctatus	"	E	8mm	subequal length	blunt	yes	no	Distinctly smaller than E. pleuralis
E. longimanus	"	W	10mm	subequal length	blunt	yes	yes	Dark markings on first segments of leg
E. albertae	"	W	11mm	anterior longer	—	no	—	Follows E. longimanus in emergence
E. deceptivus	"	W	8mm	subequal length	blunt	yes	no	No dark spots on legs; smaller than E. longimanus
E. grandis (sg. Iromopsis)	W	13mm					Tergites with medium row of conspicuous black hairs (Fig. 82)
E. nitidus (sg. Ironodes)	W	10–12mm					Paired abdominal tubercles on tergites; (Fig. 83)

SPECIES	DIST.	SIZE	POSTERO-LATERAL SPINES	DARK POSTERIOR MARGIN ON STERNITES	REMARKS
Genus Stenonema (Fig. 84)					
S. vicarium	E,M	15mm	segments 3–9 (Fig. 85)	yes	Dark orange brown in color; largest Stenonema
S. fuscum	E,M	13mm	segments 3–9	yes	Yellowish brown color; smaller than E. vicarium
S. luteum	E,M	9mm	segments 3–9	yes	Mottled amber in color; smaller than above
S. ithaca	E,M	10mm	segments 7–9 (Fig. 86)	no	Light amber color; fairly common
S. rubrum	E,M	10mm	segments 7–9	no	Color pattern on sternites (Fig. 86)
S. pulchellum	E,M	10mm	segments 7–9	no	Sternites lack markings; late summer species
S. interpunctatum (g. Stenacron)	E,M	10–13mm			This species presently includes four subspecies: S.i. interpunctatum, S.i. canadense, S.i. frontale, and S.i. heterotarsale. The species are practically identical to each other, and all exhibit gills with pointed apex in conjunction with a color pattern (Fig. 88)

SPECIES	DIST.	SIZE	TUFTS ON 7TH GILL	WIDEST POINT OF PRONOTUM	ABDOMINAL SPINES	REMARKS
Genus Heptagenia						
H. aphrodite	E	7mm	no	middle	Segs. 6–8	Abdominal pattern as in figure (Fig. 89)
H. hebe	E,M	6–8mm	no	middle	Segs. 6–8	Abdominal pattern as in figure (Fig. 90)

162

H. diabasia	M	10–14mm	yes	middle	Segs. 6–8	Abdominal pattern as in figure (Fig. 91)
H. juno	E	6–7mm	no	middle	Segs. 6–8	Tergites 1,7–9 partly or entirely white
H. maculipennis	M	6mm	no	middle	—	Tergite 1 entirely pale, 2–9 partly white
H. elegantula	W	8–10mm	yes	front	none	Abdominal pattern (Fig. 92)
H. solitaria	W	9–11mm	yes	—	—	Abdominal pattern (Fig. 93)
H. rosea	W	8–10mm	no	middle	Segs. 6–8	Abdominal pattern (Fig. 94)
H. simplicioides	W	8mm	no	middle	Segs. 6–8	Abdominal pattern (Fig. 95)
H. criddlei	W	8–9mm	no	front	none	Abdominal pattern; striped sternites (Fig. 96)

Genus Rhithrogena

			THUMB-LIKE GILL PROJECTION	COLOR OF ABDOMEN	GILL COLORS	
R. pellucida	E,M	8mm	none (Fig. 97)	reddish brown	dark gray	Emergence May/June; uncommon
R. jejuna	M	10mm	none	pale olive	dark gray	Emergence June/July; uncommon
R. impersonata	M	8–10mm	As in Fig. 98	brownish olive	light gray	Emergence July; uncommon
R. undulata	M	7mm	As in Fig. 99	dark reddish brown	gray	Emergence July; uncommon in Midwest
R. sanguinea	E	—	10mm	bright reddish brown	reddish	Entire nymph red in color
R. morrisoni	W	7–8mm	As in Fig. 101	dark reddish brown	gray	Emergence March/April; abundant
R. robusta	W	10–12mm	none (Fig. 97)	orangish brown	usually red; marked as in Fig. 104	Emergence May/June; fairly common
R. futilis	W	10–12mm	As in Fig. 100	orangish brown	usually red	Emergence June/July; uncommon
R. hageni	W	9.5–11mm	As in Fig. 101	dark reddish brown	gray	Emergence June/July; abundant
R. undulata	W	7mm	As in Fig. 100	dark reddish brown	gray	Emergence July/August; abundant

Genus Cinygmula

			TERGITES 8–10	GENERAL COLOR	
C. subequalis	E	8mm	Tergite 10 pale	brownish olive	Only Cinygmula known in East; fairly common
C. mimus	W	9–10mm	Tergites 8 & 9 pale (Fig. 102)	mottled brown	Emergence May; uncommon
C. ramaleyi	W	7–8mm	Tergites 7 & 8 pale (Fig. 103)	brown	Emergence June/July; fairly common
C. reticulata	W	8mm	unicolorous	lt. reddish brown; gills often red	Emergence August; fairly common

FAMILY EPHEMERELIIDAE (NYMPHS)

SPECIES	DIST.	SIZE	ABDOMINAL SEGMENTS	REMARKS
Subgenus *Ephemerella*				
E. subvaria*	E,M	11mm	black, well-developed tubercles (Fig. 114)	Single band on tibiae (Fig. 114a)
E. rotunda*	E,M	9mm	small, incurved tubercles (Fig. 115)	Double band on tibiae (Fig. 115a)
E. invaria	E,M	8–9mm	minute, incurved tubercles (Fig. 116)	Single band on tibiae (Fig. 116a)
E. excrucians	E,M	7mm	no abdominal tubercles (Fig. 117)	Tails without bands
E. dorothea*	E,M	7–8mm	no abdominal tubercles (Fig. 117)	Tails with bands
E. needhami	E,M	7mm	abdominal tubercles (Fig. 117a)	Usually with pale stripe on head, thorax, and abdomen; late June emerger
E. mollitia	W (California)	11–12mm	no abdominal tubercles	Large *Ephemerella* found in SW
E. inermis*	W	7mm	no abdominal tubercles (Fig. 118)	Often striped along back
E. infrequens	W	8–9mm	no abdominal tubercles (Fig. 119)	Larger in size than E. *inermis*
E. lacustris	W	7–9mm	minute tubercles	Found in Yellowstone Lake, Wy., and in high-altitude lakes of the Gravelly Range of Montana
Subgenus *Drunella*			HEAD PROJECTIONS	
E. cornuta*	E,M	10mm	horns, *sharp* medium projection (Fig. 120)	Much larger than E. *cornutella*
E. longicornis*	N.C., Tenn.	10mm	long distinct horns (Fig. 121)	Appalachian species
E. walkeri*	E,M	9–10mm	head with frontal shelf (Fig. 122)	All legs with tubercles on anterior margins
E. cornutella*	E,M	7mm	horns, *blunt* medium projection (Fig. 125)	Similar to E. *cornuta*
E. lata*	E,M	7mm	barely discernible horns (Fig. 126)	Often with red dashes on legs
E. grandis*	W	14mm	tubercles on back of head not as pronounced as in Fig. 106	Abd. tubercles 8–9 longer than those on segments 2–7 (Fig. 123)
E. doddsi*	W	13mm	head with incomplete frontal shelf (Fig. 124)	Disk-shaped row or hairs on sternites (under abdomen)
E. flavilinea*	W	10–11mm	none	Rounded abdominal tubercles (Fig. 104)
E. coloradensis*	W	11–12mm	none	Pointed abdominal tubercles (Fig. 105)
E. spinifera*	W	10–11mm	long, sharp tubercles on back of head (Fig. 106)	Abd. tubercles 8–9 longer than those on segments 2–7 (Fig. 107)
Subgenus *Attenella*			ABDOMINAL SEGMENTS	
E. attenuata*	E	7mm	barely developed tubercles (Fig. 108)	All segments unicolorous
E. margarita*	W	7mm	small, incurved tubercles (Fig. 109)	Segments 4, 5, & 8 pale
Subgenus *Serratella*			ABDOMINAL SEGMENTS	
E. deficiens*	E,M	6mm	no abdominal tubercles (Fig. 110)	Segments 1–5 usually pale
E. serrata	E,M	6mm	small, round tubercles	All segments dark brown
E. tibialis*	W	8mm	small, round tubercles (Fig. 111)	Complete nymph usually striped
Subgenus *Caudatella*: western genus				
E. heterocaudata	W	7–8mm	blunt, finger-like tubercles (Fig. 112)	Striped sternites (Fig. 112a)
E. hystrix	W	8–11mm	long, sharp tubercles (Fig. 113)	Chevron-like markings (Fig. 113a)

Subgenus *Eurylophella*: only E. *funeralis* found.
Subgenus *Danella*: only one species in genus, E. *simplex*.
Subgenus *Timpanoga*: only one species in genus; divided into subspecies, E. *hecuba*.

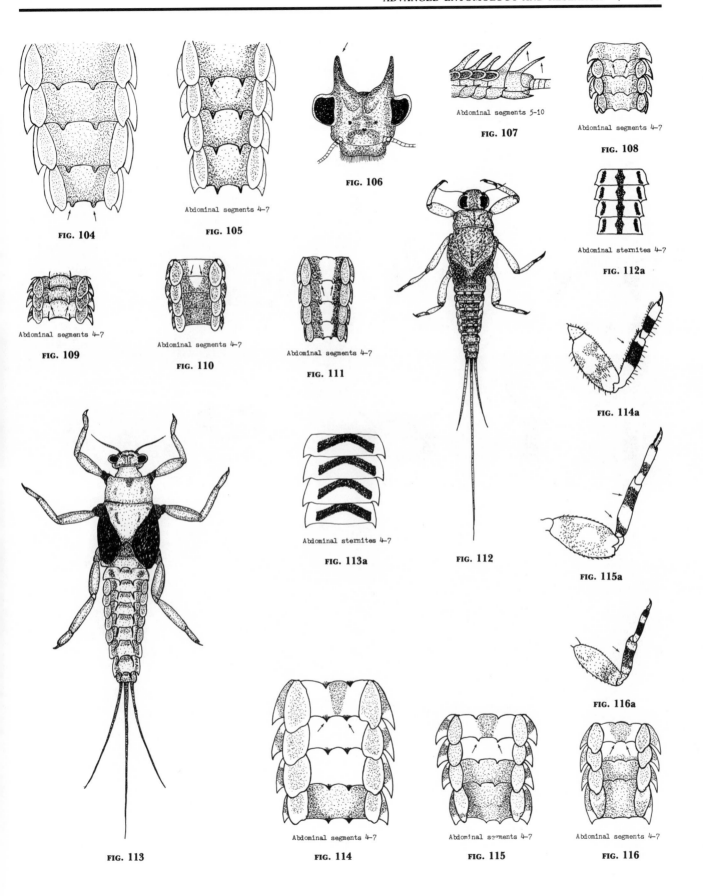

FIG. 104

FIG. 105
Abdominal segments 4-7

FIG. 106

Abdominal segments 5-10
FIG. 107

FIG. 108
Abdominal segments 4-7

FIG. 109
Abdominal segments 4-7

FIG. 110
Abdominal segments 4-7

FIG. 111
Abdominal segments 4-7

FIG. 112a
Abdominal sternites 4-7

FIG. 114a

FIG. 113a
Abdominal sternites 4-7

FIG. 112

FIG. 115a

FIG. 116a

FIG. 113

FIG. 114
Abdominal segments 4-7

FIG. 115
Abdominal segments 4-7

FIG. 116
Abdominal segments 4-7

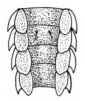

Abdominal segments 4-7

FIG. 117

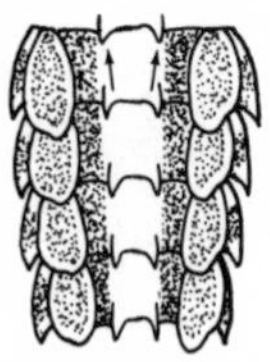

Abdominal segments 4-7

FIG. 117a

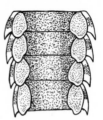

Abdominal segments 4-7

FIG. 118

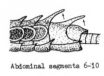

Abdominal segments 6-10

FIG. 123

Abdominal segments 4-7

FIG. 119

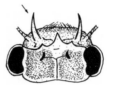

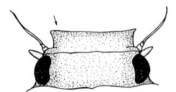

FIG. 120

FIG. 121

FIG. 122

FIG. 124

FIG. 125

FIG. 126

DUN (SUBIMAGO) AND SPINNER (IMAGO) IDENTIFICATION

The species of duns and spinners is ascertained by identifying certain physical characteristics. The following keys will suffice for the determination of family and generic classification. Certain features are not detectable in specimens not yet in the spinner stage, consequently the diagram below is useful for the determination of a dun *only* to the family level; on the other hand, a spinner can be identified as to its family *and* genus if used together with the Key to Adults that follows.

IDENTIFYING FEATURES

FIG. 127

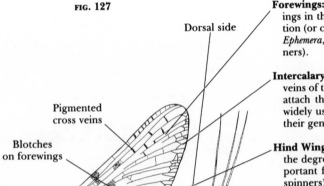

Dorsal side

Pigmented
cross veins

Blotches
on forewings

Angulation
on fore margin
of hind wing

Ventral side

Forewings: General shape is useful for identification. The markings in the form of blotches or cross veins exhibiting pigmentation (or color) is a telltale feature of duns and spinners of genera *Ephemera, Stenonema,* and *Heptagenia* (visible on duns and spinners).

Intercalary veins: These are small veinlets *between* the principal veins of the forewing. The fact that they attach (shown) or do not attach the main veins to the rear margin of the forewing is a widely used characteristic for the separation of the families and their genera (only visible in spinners).

Hind Wing: Its presence or absence, relative size to forewing and the degree of the angulation or bend on its fore margin are important features for generic determination (visible in duns and spinners).

Tails: Fastest way to narrow identification to either the four two- or three-tailed family types. Moreover two genera of mayflies exhibit a shorter tail than the outer ones, and members of a subgenus of Family *Ephemerellidae* all have distinctive longer middle tails than outer ones (visible in duns and spinners).

Male genitalia: A principal identification feature only pronounced and distinctive in *male* mayflies. It is the most exacting feature for precise identification of the species. It is only fully developed in the spinner stage, thus making it the most suitable for exact species determination (fully developed and most noticeable only in spinners).

Tarsi: The amount of segments consisting the tarsi section of either the foreleg or rear leg serves to separate families, namely *Siphlonuridae* from *Heptageniidae*. Genera of the latter family are determined by the relative length of the first and second segments of the foreleg tarsi (visible only in spinners or duns about to become spinners).

MALE GENITALIA

Penis lobes of mayflies take a variety of forms and sizes. Those of the principal species covered in this work are included in the spinner section of this Appendix. The small, terminal segment of the claspers is a useful feature for the separation of certain genera of Families *Ephemerellidae* and *Leptophlebiidae*.

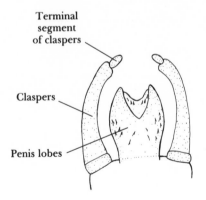

Terminal
segment
of claspers

Claspers

Penis lobes

3 TAILS:
KEY TO ADULTS

Families Tricorythidae and Caenidae

(No hind wings; size 3–6mm)

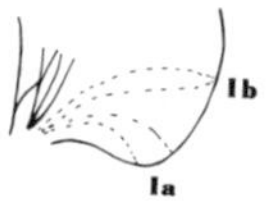

FIG. 128a

FIG. 128b

Vein CuP recurved (fig. Ia); thorax blackish gray . . . genus *Tricorythodes*

Vein CuP not curved (fig. Ib); thorax brown . . . g. *Caenis* and *Brachycersus*

Family Leptophlebiidae

(No costal angulation; attached intercalary veins)

FIG. 129

Middle tail shorter than outer ones . . . g. *Leptophlebia*

All three tails equal in length, brown or pale in color . . . g. *Paraleptophlebia*

Family Ephemerellidae
(Discernible costal angulation; detached intercalary veins)

FIG. 130

Terminal segment of claspers 6X as long as broad . . . sg. *Attenella*
Terminal segment of claspers 2X as long as broad . . . sg. *Drunella*
All other subgenera, see family keys to spinners

Family Ephemeridae (in part)
(Base of two wing veins, MP2 & CuA, distinctly curved unlike the others)

FIG. 131b

FIG. 131a

Wings with patterns of dark markings (shown) . . . g. *Ephemera*
Middle tail shorter than outer; no dark patterns on wings; . . . g. *Potamanthus**
Margin of wing with dense network of intercalaries (Fig. 131b) . . . g. *Ephoron*

This chart was constructed specifically for the determination of the family and generic classification of a mayfly spinner (or imago). Duns can be classified only to their family level, since wing venation used extensively here for the determination of a specimen as to its genus is not visible in the wing of a subimago.

*Belong to families *Polymitarcyidae* and *Potamanthidae*, placed in Family *Ephemeridae* in this work for reasons given in the Foreword.

**Excepting one species, *B. propinquus*, see key to *Baetis* spinners.

2 TAILS:
KEY TO ADULTS

Family Ephemeridae (in part)
(See 3-tailed Ephemeridae, facing page)

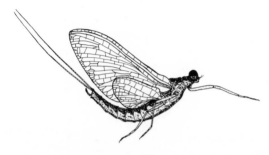

FIG. 132

Largest mayfly found in North American trout waters, usually over 18mm long; dark in coloration . . . g. *Hexagenia*

Family Heptageniidae
(Hind tarsi 5-segmented; CuA *not* connected to rear margin of forewing by series of veinlets)

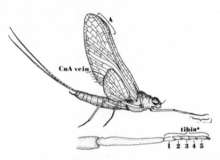

FIG. 133

Stigmatic area of forewing crisscrossed with fine veinlets (point A) . . . g. *Rhithrogena*
First segment of fore tarsi equal to length of segment 2 (as shown) . . . g. *Epeorus*
First segment between ½ and ⅚ length of segment 2 . . . g. *Cinygmula*
First segment less than ½ length of segment 2; penis lobes L-shaped . . . g. *Stenonema*
Similar to *Stenonema*; penis lobes are round . . . g. *Heptagenia*

Family Baetiscidae
(One genus)

FIG. 136

Hind wing with numerous unattached long intercalary veins; robust configuration . . . uncommon . . . g. *Baetisca*

Family Siphlonuridae
(Hind tarsi 4-segmented; series of veinlets connects vein CuA to margin)

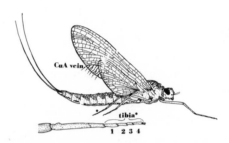

FIG. 134

Forelegs dark, the middle and hind legs contrastingly pale . . . g. *Isonychia*
Round costal angulation (as in illustration) . . . g. *Siphlonurus*
Foremargin of hind wing with sharp or pointed angulation . . . g. *Ameletus*

Family Baetidae
(Short, single, or double detached intercalary veins (A); eyes of male on stalks)

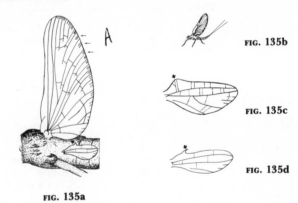

FIG. 135b

FIG. 135c

FIG. 135d

FIG. 135a

Hind Wings Present (Fig. 135b)

Hind wing with an obtuse costal angulation and numerous crossveins (Fig. 135b) . . . g. *Callibaetis*
Hind wing exhibiting a pointed costal angulation (Fig. 135a); double intercalary veins (Fig. 135a) . . . g. *Baetis*
Hind wing exhibiting a hooked costal angulation (Fig. 135d); single intercalary veins . . . g. *Centroptilum*

Hind Wings Absent (Fig. 135b)
Double intercalary veins . . . g. *Pseudocloeon*

Single intercalary veins . . . g. *Cloeon*

KEY TO SPECIES: DUNS

The duns of mayflies cannot be identified as to species with the same amount of accuracy as nymphs and spinners can. However, since there is a limited amount of mayfly species indigenous to trout streams which exhibit different colorations, it is possible to make reasonable "guesses" as to their classification. The verification tables below have proved very useful to me over the years and have been correct 90% of the time after double checking tentative identifications by raising the duns to the spinner stage and mounting their genitalia. The numbers in parentheses are approximate body lengths. They are given in millimeters, the metric system being the most useful for the measurement of insects of a small size. The only families in which males and females differ in general size and coloration are *Ephemerellidae* and *Tricorythidae*, in which case the descriptions and sizes given apply to the males. Most common species and those the reader, in all likelihood, will encounter most of the time are followed by an asterisk.

SPECIES	DIST.	BODY COLOR	COLOR OF WINGS	SEASONAL EMERGENCE
Families Tricorythidae and Caenidae (3 tails; no hind wings) (Fig. 128b)				
Tricorythodes stygiatus	E,M	grayish	clear	June–August
Caenis simulans	E,M,W	cream	clear	June
*Tricorythodes minutus**	E,W	grayish	clear	July–September
Family Leptophlebiidae (3 tails; no pronounced angle on fore margin of hind wings) (Fig. 129)				
Leptophlebia cupida	E,M,W	black (12)	brownish gray	April–May
*Paraleptophlebia adoptiva**	E,M	dark reddish brown (8)	brownish gray	April 20–May 20
P. mollis	E,M	grayish brown (7)	medium gray	June–July
P. debilis	E,M	dark reddish brown (8)	brownish gray	August–Sept.
*P. heteronea**	W	dark reddish brown (8)	brownish gray	June–Aug. 10
P. memorialis	W	dark reddish brown (7)	medium gray	July
*P. debilis**	W	dark reddish brown (8)	brownish gray	Sept.
P. bicornuta	W	blackish brown (11)	dark gray	Sept.–Oct.
Family Ephemerellidae (3 tails; pronounced angle on fore margin of hind wings) (Fig. 130)				
*Ephemerella subvaria**	E,M	medium reddish brown (11)	medium gray	May 1–20
E. needhami	E,M	medium reddish brown (8)	medium gray	June 15–30
*E. deficiens**	E,M	dark reddish brown (6)	dark gray	June 15–July 15
*E. rotunda**	E,M	light brown (9)	creamish slate	May 15–30
*E. dorothea**	E,M	beige (8)	creamish slate	June 1–20
*E. cornuta**	E,M	olive (10)	bluish gray	June 1–20
*E. simplex**	E,M	olive (7)	bluish gray	June 20–July 20
*E. cornutella**	E	olive (7)	bluish gray	June 20–July 20
*E. lata**	E,M	olive (7)	bluish gray	July 1–Aug. 15
E. hecuba	W	dark reddish brown (15)	dark gray	July 1–Aug. 30
*E. tibialis**	W	dark reddish brown (8)	dark gray	Aug. 1–Sept. 15
E. mollitia	W (Cal.)	cream (olive cast) (11)	light gray	June 1–30
*E. infrequens**	W	cream (olive cast) (9)	light gray	June 1–25
*E. inermis**	W	cream (olive cast) (7)	light gray	July 10–Sept.
E. lacustris	W (lakes)	cream (olive cast) (8)	light gray	June 1–Aug. 30
*E. grandis**	W	dark olive (15)	medium gray	June 20–July 15
E. doddsi	W	dark olive (13)	medium gray	July 10–30
E. coloradensis	W	dark olive (11)	medium gray	July 20–Aug. 10
*E. flavilinea**	W	dark olive (10)	medium gray	July 20–Aug. 10
E. heterocaudata	W	medium olive (8)	medium gray	July 15–Aug.
E. margarita	W	medium olive (6)	medium gray	Aug. 1–Sept. 10

KEY TO SPECIES: DUNS (continued)

SPECIES	DIST.	BODY COLOR	COLOR OF WINGS	SEASONAL EMERGENCE
Family Ephemeridae (3 tails; blotches or pigmented crossveins on wings of most species) (Fig. 131a)				
Ephemera guttulata*	E	olive (17–20)	greenish with blackish markings on all wings	June 1–20
Ephemera simulans	E,M,W	brownish (17–20)	brown with blackish markings on all wings	June 20–July 15
Ephemera varia*	E,M	yellow (13–14)	yellowish with dark brown markings only in forewings	July–Aug.
Potamanthus distinctus	E	yellow (14)	yellowish with pigmented crossveins on wings	July–Aug.
Ephoron leukon & album	E,M,W	whitish (11–13)	whitish	Sept. 1–15
Family Ephemeridae (2 tails; extremely large; only one genus) (Fig. 132)				
Hexagenia limbata	E,M,W	dark brown tergites (22–35) with lighter sternites	dark gray to black	May 20–July 30
Family Heptageniidae (2 tails and large hind wings; feature given in adult key for the separation of members of this family from those of Siphlonuridae—a five-segmented hind tarsi is visible on the large duns of family Heptageniidae)				
Epeorus pleuralis*	E	grayish brown (10)	medium gray	April 20–May 20
Cinygmula subequalis	E	grayish brown (9)	medium gray	May 20–June 10
Epeorus vitreus	E,M	yellowish abdomen, orangish thorax (9)	light gray	June 1–July 30
Stenonema vicarium*	E,M	reddish brown (15) with black markings	medium gray, reddish crossveins	May 25–June 10
Stenonema fuscum*	E,M	yellowish brown (12) with black markings	light gray, reddish crossveins	June 1–30
Stenacron heterotarsale	E,M	yellowish brown (10)	yellowish, light brown crossveins	July
Stenonema pulchellum	E,M	whitish (8)	whitish, barely pigmented crossveins	August
Heptagenia hebe	E,M	yellowish (7)	yellowish, light brown crossveins	July 15–Sept.
Rhithrogena morrisoni	W	blackish (9)	dark gray	April–May
Rhithrogena hageni*	W	blackish (9)	dark gray	June–July 20
Rhithrogena undulata*	W	light reddish brown (7)	medium gray, light reddish crossveins	July 10–Aug. 30
Epeorus longimanus	W	gray (10)	medium gray	July 10–30
Epeorus albertae	W	gray (10)	medium gray	July 20–Aug. 20
Epeorus deceptivus	W	light gray (8)	light gray	August 10–30
Heptagenia elegantula	W	orangish (11)	light gray	June 20–July 30
Heptagenia simplicoides*	W	pale cream (10–11)	beige	July 15–Sept. 15
Heptagenia criddlei	W	reddish brown (8) with chevron marks	medium gray	June 15–July 15
Cinygmula ramaleyi	W	dark olive brown (6)	dark gray	June 20–Aug. 10
Cinygmula reticulata	W	orangish (7)	yellow	June 20–Aug. 10
Family Siphlonuridae (2 tails and large hind wings; four-segmented hind tarsi and a series of veinlets connecting CuA vein and rear margin of forewing) (Fig. 134)				
Isonychia sadleri*	E,M	reddish brown, middle and rear legs pale (16)	dark slate	May–Aug.
Isonychia bicolor	E,M	dark brown, middle and rear legs pale (14)	dark slate	May–June
Isonychia harperi*	E,M	reddish brown, middle and rear legs pale (15–16)	dark slate	Sept.–Oct.

KEY TO SPECIES: DUNS (continued)

SPECIES	DIST.	BODY COLOR	COLOR OF WINGS	SEASONAL EMERGENCE
Family Siphlonuridae (cont.)				
Isonychia velma	W	blackish gray (18)	dark gray	Sept.–Oct.
Isonychia sicca campetris	W	dark reddish brown (16)	dark slate	June–July
Siphlonurus occidentalis *	W	gray (15)	medium gray	June 20–Sept. 20

Family Baetidae (2 tails with either no hind wings or minute, often barely discernible ones) (Fig. 135b)

SPECIES	DIST.	BODY COLOR	COLOR OF WINGS	SEASONAL EMERGENCE
Baetis vagans *	E,M	light brown olive (7)	light bluish gray	April–May
Baetis intercalaris *	E,M	dark olive brown (6)	dark gray	May–June
Pseudocloeon carolina *	E	medium olive brown (5)	dark slate	May–June
Pseudocloeon anoka *	M	olive brown (5)	light slate	June–July 30
Pseudocloeon dubium	E,M	light olive brown (4)	light slate	June–July 20
Baetis hiemalis	M	dark olive brown (9)	dark slate	Sept.–Oct.
Baetis parvus *	W	light olive brown (6)	light slate	June–July/Sept.–Oct.
Pseudocloeon edmundsi *	W	bright olive (5)	clear	June–July/Sept.–Oct.
Baetis tricaudatus *	W	medium olive brown (8)	medium slate	Oct. 15–Nov./Feb.–March

*signifies species is illustrated in this book.

KEY TO SPECIES: SPINNERS

At first glance, the following illustrations may appear as Egyptian hieroglyphics, in reality they are of the *male* genitalia of the mayfly species covered in this book. Every male mayfly spinner possesses a genitalia composed of two parts, the claspers and penis lobes, the latter feature being the most distinctive and unique among the species. The genitalia is found attached to the last or apical segment of the abdomen of a male spinner, and since it is visible with the naked eye, it is the quickest way to make the distinction of a male from a female spinner at streamside. The top side or dorsal view is that which exhibits the most features, like spines, etc., and thus that which is shown here.

The great majority of mayflies, unfortunately, approximate 10mm in size and consequently the genitalic *characteristics* for exact species determination are not visible with the naked eye; however, a hand lens of 20 power will make some pronounced features discernible. A microscope of 40–60 power is the most suitable tool for working with spinners, though requiring appreciatively more expense than the reader may care to invest. For such reason, the nymph key in this section is a more practical alternative, since most mayfly nymphs can be determined as to their species classification with only a 15 power hand lens of a high quality.

SPECIES	DIST.	WING SIZE	THORAX	ABDOMEN	REMARKS
Families Caenidae and Tricorythidae (3 tails; no hind wings)					
Tricorythodes stygiatus	E,M	3.5–4mm	black	dark gray	—
Tricorythodes minutus	E,W	3.2–5.2mm	blackish	blackish	genitalia (Fig. 1)
Caenis simulans	E,M,W	3–4mm	bronze brown	cream	genitalia (Fig. 2)
Brachycersus prudens	M,W	4–5.5mm	dark brown	dark brown	genitalia (Fig. 3)

Family Leptophlebiidae (3 tails; no angulation on foremargin of hind wing; attached intercalary veins; 3-jointed claspers)

		BODY LENGTH			
Paraleptophlebia adoptiva	E,M	8mm		dark brown	genitalia (Fig. 4)
P. mollis	E,M	7mm		whitish	penis lobes (Fig. 5)
P. debilis	E,M,W	9mm		light brown	penis lobes (Fig. 6)
P. heteronea	W	8mm		light brown	penis lobes (Fig. 7)
P. memorialis	W	7mm		whitish	penis lobes (Fig. 8)
P. bicornuta	W	10–11mm		dark reddish brown	penis lobes (Fig. 9)
Leptophlebia cupida	E,M,W	11mm		dark mahogany brown	genitalia (Fig. 10)

Family Ephemerellidae (3 tails; angulation on foremargin of hind wing; detached intercalary veins; 2-jointed claspers)

SPECIES	DIST.	WING SIZE	THORAX	ABDOMEN	REMARKS
Ephemerella subvaria	E,M	11mm	dark brown	brown	penis lobes (Fig. 11)
E. rotunda	E,M	9mm	reddish brown	light brown	penis lobes (Fig. 12)
E. invaria	E,M	8mm	light brown	light brown	penis lobes (Fig. 13)
E. dorothea	E,M	8mm	pinkish	whitish	penis lobes (Fig. 14)
E. cornuta	E,M	10mm	blackish olive	blackish olive	genitalia (Fig. 15)[1]
E. walkeri	E,M	9mm	blackish olive	blackish olive	penis lobes (Fig. 16)[1]
E. cornutella	E	7mm	blackish olive	blackish olive	penis lobes (Fig. 17)[1]
E. lata	E,M	7mm	blackish olive	blackish olive	penis lobes (Fig. 18)[1]
E. simplex	E,M	7mm	blackish olive	blackish olive	genitalia (Fig. 19)
E. attenuata	E,M	6mm	blackish olive	medium brown	genitalia (Fig. 20)[2]
E. deficiens	E,M	6mm	dark brown	dark brown	penis lobes (Fig. 21)
E. serrata	E,M	5mm	dark brown	brown	penis lobes (Fig. 22)
E. needhami	E,M	8mm	brown	light brown	penis lobes (Fig. 23)
E. funeralis	E,M	9mm	brown	light brown	penis lobes (Fig. 24)
E. mollitia	W (Cal.)	11mm	dark brown	light brown	penis lobes identical to Fig. 12
E. infrequens	W	9mm	dark brown	light brown	genitalia (Fig. 25)
E. inermis	W	7–8mm	dark brown	light brown	penis lobes (Fig. 26)
E. lacustris	W (lakes nr. YNP)	8mm	brown	grayish brown	—

KEY TO SPECIES: SPINNERS (continued)

SPECIES	DIST.	BODY LENGTH	THORAX	ABDOMEN	WINGS	REMARKS
Family Ephemerellidae (cont.)						
E. grandis	W	15mm	blackish brown	mottled brown		penis lobes (Fig. 27)[1]
E. doddsi	W	13mm	blackish brown	mottled brown		penis lobes (Fig. 28)[1]
E. coloradensis	W	11mm	chocolate brown	grayish olive		penis lobes (Fig. 29)[1]
E. flavilinea	W	10mm	dark reddish brown	reddish brown		genitalia (Fig. 30)[1]
E. spinifera	W (NW)	10mm	dark reddish brown	reddish brown		—
E. margarita	W	6mm	blackish olive	whitish		genitalia (Fig. 31)[2]
E. heterocaudata[3]	W	8mm	light brown	cream, chevroned		genitalia (Fig. 32)[3]
E. hystrix[3]	W	9–11mm	dark reddish brown	dark reddish brown		—[3]
E. hecuba	W	15mm	dark reddish brown	dark reddish brown		—
E. tibialis	W	8mm	dark reddish brown	dark reddish brown		genitalia (Fig. 34)

Family Ephemeridae (3 tails; base of CuA and MP$_2$ veins strongly divergent or curved; all three genera of three tails belonging to this family exhibit distinctive features or coloration, either exhibiting blotches or pigmented crossveins, whitish abdomen or a shorter middle tail)

Ephemera guttulata	E	17–20mm	blackish	whitish	blotches on hind and fore wings	penis lobes (Fig. 35)
E. simulans	E,M,W	17–20mm	dark brown	bottom light brown	blotches on hind and fore wings	penis lobes (Fig. 36)
E. varia	E,M	13–14mm	yellowish	cream	blotches only on fore wings	penis lobes (Fig. 37)
Potamanthus distinctus	E,M	14–15mm	yellowish	white	barely discernible crossveins; middle tail shorter	—
P. myops	M	16mm	yellowish	white	no markings; middle tail shorter	penis lobes (Fig. 38)
Ephoron album and leukon	E,M,W	11–13mm	light brown	white	no markings	penis lobes of E. leukon (Fig. 39)

Family Ephemeridae (2 tails; only one genus)

Hexagenia limbata	E,M,W	22–35mm	dark reddish brown	with triangular markings	with well marked crossveins	penis lobes (Fig. 40)

Family Heptageniidae (2 tails and large hind wings; 5-segmented hind tarsi)

Epeorus pleuralis	E	10–11mm	dark brown	brown	brown venation	penis lobes (Fig. 41)
E. suffusus	E	13–14mm	dark reddish brown	reddish brown	dark venation	penis lobes (Fig. 42)
E. punctatus	E	9–10mm	light brown	light gray	—	—
E. vitreus	E,M	9–11mm	orangish	light grayish brown	—	similar to Fig. 42
E. fragilis	E	7–8mm	orangish	whitish	—	penis lobes (Fig. 43)
Stenonema vicarium	E,M	15mm	dark reddish brown	reddish brown	dark venation	penis lobes (Fig. 44)
S. fuscum	E,M	12mm	reddish brown	light brown	light brown venation	penis lobes (Fig. 45)
Stenacron interpunctatum (sbs. frontale)	E,M	10mm	orangish	whitish	yellow; reddish venation	penis lobes (Fig. 46)
Stenonema rubrum	E,M	10mm	yellowish	cream	dark reddish venation	penis lobes (Fig. 47)
Heptagenia hebe	E,M	8mm	dark brown	brown	dark reddish venation	penis lobes (Fig. 48)
Cinygmula subequalis	E	8–9mm	dark brown	light gray	light brown venation	genitalia (Fig. 49)

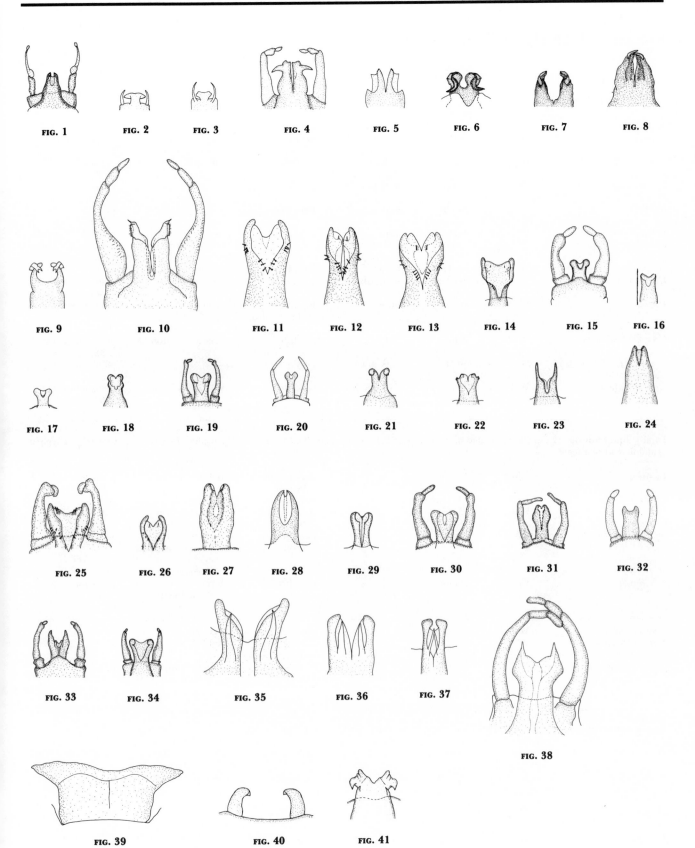

FIG. 1   FIG. 2   FIG. 3   FIG. 4   FIG. 5   FIG. 6   FIG. 7   FIG. 8

FIG. 9   FIG. 10   FIG. 11   FIG. 12   FIG. 13   FIG. 14   FIG. 15   FIG. 16

FIG. 17   FIG. 18   FIG. 19   FIG. 20   FIG. 21   FIG. 22   FIG. 23   FIG. 24

FIG. 25   FIG. 26   FIG. 27   FIG. 28   FIG. 29   FIG. 30   FIG. 31   FIG. 32

FIG. 33   FIG. 34   FIG. 35   FIG. 36   FIG. 37

FIG. 38

FIG. 39   FIG. 40   FIG. 41

KEY TO SPECIES: SPINNERS (continued)

SPECIES	DIST.	BODY LENGTH	EYES	THORAX	ABDOMEN	REMARKS
Family Heptageniidae (cont.)						
Rhithrogena morrisoni	W	8–9mm	blackish	dark gray	clear	—
R. hageni	W	9–10mm	dark brown	brown	light brown venation	penis lobes (Fig. 50)
R. undulata	W	7–8mm	reddish	reddish	light brown venation	penis lobes (Fig. 51)
Epeorus longimanus	W	10mm	dark gray	grayish	—	penis lobes (Fig. 52)
E. albertae	W	10mm	gray	light gray	—	penis lobes (Fig. 53)
E. deceptivus	W	8mm	gray	light gray	—	genitalia (Fig. 54)
Heptagenia elegantula	W	11mm	crimson to orangish	light brown	reddish brown venation	penis lobes (Fig. 55)
H. solitaria	W	11–13mm	brown	light brown	brown venation	—
H. simplicoides	W	9–10mm	orangish or yellowish	whitish	clear in males	penis lobes (Fig. 56)
H. criddlei	W	8mm	brown	light brown, chevron-like markings	clear	penis lobes (Fig. 57)
Cinygmula reticulata	W	7mm	reddish	reddish	yellow venation	penis lobes (Fig. 58)
C. ramaleyi	W	6mm	dark gray	gray	—	penis lobes (Fig. 59)
Heptagenia rosea	W (Pacific Coast)	7mm	dark reddish brown	reddish	yellow venation	penis lobes (Fig. 60)

Family Siphlonuridae (2 tails; 4-segmented hind tarsi; series of veinlets between CuA and rear margin of forewing); (all *Isonychias* have pale middle and rear legs)

SPECIES	DIST.	BODY LENGTH	EYES	THORAX	ABDOMEN	REMARKS
Isonychia sadleri	E,M	15–16mm		dark reddish brown	reddish brown	penis lobes (Fig. 61)
I. bicolor	E,M	13–14mm		dark brown	dark brown	—
I. harperi	E,M	15–17mm		dark reddish brown	reddish brown	Fall emerger
Siphlonurus alternatus	E,M	13mm		dark grayish brown	dark grayish brown; u-shaped markings on sternites	—
S. quebencis	E,M	15mm		dark brown	brown; no u-shaped markings on sternites	penis lobes (Fig. 62)
Isonychia velma	W	18–21mm		blackish gray	dark gray	—
I. sicca campetris	W	15–17mm		dark reddish brown	reddish brown	—
Siphlonurus occidentalis	W	14–16mm		dark grayish brown	grayish brown; u-shaped markings on sternites	penis lobes (Fig. 63)

Family Baetidae (2 tails; detached intercalary veins; reduced or entirely absent hind wings)

SPECIES	DIST.	BODY LENGTH	EYES	THORAX	ABDOMEN	REMARKS
Baetis vagans	E,M	7mm	orange brown	dark brown	2–6 pale brown; 7–10 light brown	hind wing (Fig. 64)
B. intercalaris	E,M	5–6mm	usually reddish	dark brown	2–6 white; 7–10 brown	hind wing (Fig. 65); genitalia (Fig. 66)
B. brunneicolor	M	7mm	—	dark brown	2–6 dk. brown; 7–10 dk. brown	hind wing (Fig. 65)
B. hiemalis	M	9mm	—	blackish brown	2–6 white; 7–10 dk. brown	Fall emerger in Midwest

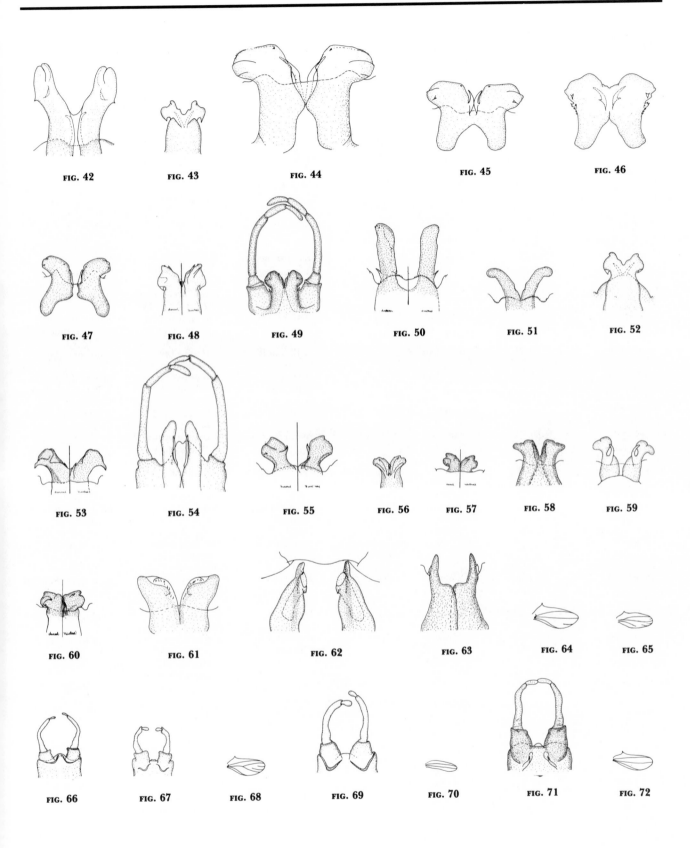

FIG. 42 FIG. 43 FIG. 44 FIG. 45 FIG. 46

FIG. 47 FIG. 48 FIG. 49 FIG. 50 FIG. 51 FIG. 52

FIG. 53 FIG. 54 FIG. 55 FIG. 56 FIG. 57 FIG. 58 FIG. 59

FIG. 60 FIG. 61 FIG. 62 FIG. 63 FIG. 64 FIG. 65

FIG. 66 FIG. 67 FIG. 68 FIG. 69 FIG. 70 FIG. 71 FIG. 72

KEY TO SPECIES: SPINNERS (continued)

Family Baetidae (cont.)

Pseudocloeon carolina	E	5mm	brown	dark olive brown	2–6 light brown; 7–10 dark brown	genitalia (Fig. 67)
P. dubium	E,M	4mm	reddish	light brown	2–6 whitish; 7–10 yell. brown	—
P. anoka	M	4–5mm	orange	brown olive	2–6 white; 7–10 lt. olive brown	—
Baetis parvus	W	5–5.5mm	—	blackish	2–6 white; 7–10 dark brown	hind wing (Fig. 68); genitalia (Fig. 69)
B. propinquus	W,E	4.5–5.5mm	—	blackish brown	2–6 white; 7–10 dark brown	hind wing (Fig. 70); genitalia (Fig. 71)
B. insignificans	W	5.5–6mm	—	dark brown	2–6 lt. olive brown; 7–10 light olive	hind wing (Fig. 70)
B. bicaudatus	W	6–6.5mm	—	dark brown	2–6 light brown; 7–10 brown	hind wing (Fig. 72); genitalia (Fig. 73)
B. intermedius	W	6–6.5mm	—	dark reddish brown	2–6 olive brown; 7–10 light brown	hind wing (Fig. 74)
B. tricaudatu	W	7.5–8mm	—	dark reddish brown	2–6 grayish brown sternites; 7–10 cream	hind wing (Fig. 75); fall and sp. emerger
Pseudocloeon edmundsi	W	5mm	—	reddish brown	2–6 white; 7–10 brown	genitalia (Fig. 76)
P. turbidum	SW	5mm	—	blackish brown	2–6 olive brown; 7–10 dk. olive brown	—
Centroptilum elsa	NW	5mm	orange brown	reddish brown	2–6 olive brown; 7–10 yell. brown	hind wing (Fig. 77); genitalia (Fig. 78)
C. asperatum	NW, SW	5–6mm	yellowish brown	olive brown	2–6 yellowish brown; 7–10 olive brown	hind wing as in Fig. 77
C. bifurcatum	NW	6–6.5mm	dark olive brown	dark olive brown	2–6 yellowish brown; 7–10 brown	hind wing (Fig. 79)
C. selanderorum	NW, SW	5.5mm	orange brown	light brown	2–6 white; 7–8 light brown; 9–10 pale cream	hind wing (Fig. 80)
C. convexum	SW	5.5–6mm	blackish brown	black	2–6 white; 7–10 dark brown	hind wing (Fig. 81)
C. venosum	NW, SW	6.5mm	orange	dark reddish brown	2–6 white, banded at posterior edges; 7–10 lt. reddish brown	hind wing (Fig. 82)
*Callibaetis nigritus**	W	8–10mm	caramel brown	light grayish brown	—	genitalia (Fig. 83)

Family Baetiscidae (2 tails; hind wing with long unattached intercalary veins; uncommon)

			WINGS			
Baetisca obesa	E	9–11mm	hyaline		brownish	genitalia (Fig. 84)

1=apical segment of claspers 2X as long as broad
2=6X as long as broad
3=middle tail longer

*No reliable characteristics were found to separate the species of *Callibaetis*; however, *C. nigritus* prove to be the most widespread and abundant in western trout waters.

FIG. 73   **FIG. 74**   **FIG. 75**   **FIG. 76**   **FIG. 77**   **FIG. 78**   **FIG. 79**

FIG. 80   **FIG. 81**   **FIG. 82**

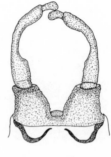

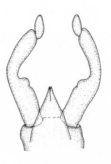

FIG. 83   **FIG. 84**

Selected Bibliography

The research for this book included the study of numerous scientific and angling publications. Without them, accuracy and thoroughness would have been impossible, yet space limitations precluded their citation in the text. The following were of the greatest value in the compilation of this work.

ALLEN, R. K., and EDMUNDS, G. F., Jr., Revisions. "The Subgenus Ephemerella in North America." *Miscellaneous Publications, Entomological Society of America*; 4: 243–282 (1965). "The Subgenus Attenuatella." *Journal of Kansas Entomological Society*; 34: 161–173 (1961). "The Subgenus Drunella in North America." *Miscellaneous Publications, Entomological Society of America*; 3: 147–179

————. "The Rocky Mountain Species of Epeorus." *Journal of Kansas Entomological Society*; 34: 275–288 (1964)

BERNER, L., *The Mayflies of Florida*; University of Florida Studies on Biological Science, Series 4: 1–267 (1950)

BRITT, N. W., "The Biology of Two Species of Lake Erie Mayflies." *Ohio Biological Survey, New Series*; 1: 1–70 (1962)

BURKS, B. D., *The Mayflies, or Ephemeroptera of Illinois*; Bulletin of Illinois Natural History Survey, Vol. 26 (1953)

CAUCCI, A., and NASTASI, R., *Hatches*; Comparahatch (1975)

DAY, W. C., "Ephemeroptera," in *Aquatic Insects of California*; University of California Press, Berkeley (1956)

EDMUNDS, G. F., Jr., "Biogeography and Evolution of Ephemeroptera." *Annals of Revisional Entomology*; 17: 21–43 (1972)

EDMUNDS, G. F., Jr., JENSEN, S. L., and BERNER, L., *The Mayflies of North and Central America*; University of Minnesota Press, Minneapolis (1978)

ELLIOT, J. M., "The Daily Activity Patterns of Mayfly Nymphs." *Journal of Zoology*; 155: 201–221 (1968)

FREMLING, C. R., "Biology of a Large Mayfly, *Hexagenia bilineata*; of the upper Mississippi River." *Bulletin of Iowa State University*; 483: 856–879 (1960)

HILSENHOFF, W. C., "A Key to Genera of Wisconsin Ephemeroptera Nymphs" (Heptageniidae). *Wisconsin Department of Natural Resources, Research Department*; 67: 19–37 (1970)

HYNE, H. B. N., *The Ecology of Running Waters*; University of Toronto Press, Toronto (1970)

JENSEN, S. L., "The Mayflies of Idaho"; University of Utah, Utah (unpublished thesis)

LEONARD, J. W., and LEONARD, F. A., *Mayflies of Michigan Trout Streams*; Cransbrook Institute of Science, Bloomfield Hills, Michigan (1962)

LYMAN, E., "Swimming and Burrowing Activities of Mayfly Nymphs of the genus Hexagenia." *Annals of Entomological Society of America*; 36: 250–256 (1943)

————. "Seasonal Distributions and Life Cycles of Ephemeroptera." *Annals of Entomological Society of America*; 48: 380–391

MECK, CHARLES, *Meeting and Fishing the Hatches*; Winchester Press (1977)

MERRITTS, R. W., and CUMMINS, K. W., *An Introduction to the Aquatic Insects of North America*; Kendall/Hunt Publishing Company, Dubuque, Iowa (1978)

MUTTKOWSKI, R. A., and SMITH, G. M., "The Food of Trout Stream Insects in Yellowstone National Park." *Roosevelt Wildlife Annals*; 2: 241–263 (1929)

NEEDHAM, J. G., TRAVER, J. R., and HSU, Y., *The Biology of Mayflies*; Comstock Publication Company, Ithaca, New York (1935)

NEEDHAM, P. R., *Trout Streams*; Winchester Press (1970)

SPIETH, H. T., "Studies on the Biology of Ephemeroptera, I. Coloration and Its Relationship to seasonal Emergence." *Canadian Entomologist*; 70: 210–218 (1938)

————. "Taxonomic Studies on the Ephemeroptera, IV. The genus Stenonema. *Annals of Entomological Society of America*; 40: 87–122 (1947)

SCHWIEBERT, ERNEST, *Matching the Hatch*; Macmillan (1955)

————. *Nymphs*; Winchester Press (1973)

SWISHER, DOUG, and RICHARDS, CARL, *Selective Trout*; Crown (1971)

TRAVER, J. R., "Mayflies of North Carolina." *Journal of Elisha Mitchell Scientific Society*; 47: 85–236, 48: 141–206 (1932–1933)

Index

(Page numbers in boldface type indicate detailed coverage in text)